/3. 00

THE
LOGIC
DESIGN
OF
TRANSISTOR
DIGITAL
COMPUTERS

THE
LOGIC
DESIGN
OF
TRANSISTOR
DIGITAL
COMPUTERS

PRENTICE-HALL, INC.

GERALD A. MALEY

Adjunct Professor, Syracuse University
Manager, Exploratory Logic Group, IBM

JOHN EARLE

Manager, Exploratory System Logic Group

ENGLEWOOD CLIFFS, N.J. 1963

THE LOGIC DESIGN OF TRANSISTOR DIGITAL COMPUTERS

Gerald A. Maley   and   John Earle

Library of Congress Catalog Card Number 62-19494

Printed in the United States of America

54005–C

PRENTICE-HALL INTERNATIONAL SERIES IN ELECTRICAL
ENGINEERING

William L. Everitt, editor

PRENTICE-HALL, INC.
PRENTICE-HALL INTERNATIONAL, INC., UNITED KINGDOM AND EIRE
PRENTICE-HALL OF CANADA, LTD., CANADA

BLACKWELL AND KOTZEBUE *Semiconductor-Diode Parametric Amplifiers*
BOISVERT, ROBICHAUD, AND ROBERT *Signal Flow Graphs and Applications*
CHANG *Energy Conversion*
MALEY AND EARLE *The Logic Design of Transistor Digital Computers*
NUSSBAUM *Semiconductor Device Physics*

PRENTICE-HALL INTERNATIONAL, INC. *London*
PRENTICE-HALL OF AUSTRALIA, PTY., LTD. *Sydney*
PRENTICE-HALL OF CANADA, LTD. *Toronto*
PRENTICE-HALL FRANCE, S.A.R.L. *Paris*
PRENTICE-HALL OF JAPAN, INC. *Tokyo*
PRENTICE-HALL DE MEXICO, S.A. *Mexico City*

PREFACE

This book presents the practical knowledge, circuits, and techniques needed for the design of the switching logic in a modern digital computer, or any digital network. All the subjects necessary are developed in this book with no special previous knowledge required. The criterion used for selecting and developing the subjects has been "usability" in a practical design situation today. The mathematical foundations and theoretical developments are included in making the material "usable" so that depth is not sacrificed for artifice. The problems at the end of the chapters are chosen to bring this out.

Some of the unique features of this book are: development throughout directly in NOR-type logic circuits, the most important digital circuits in modern computers—a complete chapter devoted to the techniques for using NOR logic developed by the authors, unavailable anywhere else— in this book, for the first time asynchronous sequential circuit theory is developed for electronic circuits, accompanied by many practical design hints—a handbook chapter of worked examples derives optimal solutions to the most used sequential circuits—and many others.

The material has been chosen and written so that the book may be valuable both in learning the subject of logic design and continuing later as a reference manual.

G. MALEY

J. EARLE

CONTENTS

TO

SPEEDY
CI-CI
and
IBM

TRANSISTORS AND CIRCUITS

1

Introduction

Present day digital computers are designed around the transistor and junction rectifier as basic switching elements. From these two components many different circuit configurations may be formed by incorporating various resistors and capacitors. Recently, however, a rather quiet revolution has been taking place in the circuit configurations selected for use in a computer. Mass fabrication has substantially lowered the cost of some simple circuits while ruling out the use of rather complex circuitry. Mass production of computers also requires that computers must be constructed from as few different types of circuits as possible. For these reasons, the use of simple universal circuit configurations has been increasing. A universal circuit is one of which any entire logic network may be constructed without introducing any other circuit configuration. Most of the circuits given in this book are of this type but it should not be implied that an entire computer may be constructed from this limited selection. Computers are required to drive some form of output equipment and in areas such as this, specially-designed circuits will be required. It is understood, therefore, that the circuits given in this book are for use in the main arithmetic and logical units of the machine.

Before proceeding to the logic circuits, one must first understand that all information within a computer is coded in binary form. All information lines within a computer must therefore be at one of two nominal voltage levels. The reason for the choice of but two levels is centered chiefly around the reliability required from many thousands of components. If, for example, plus six volts is used as one level and ground as the other, we may allow excursions of almost three volts on either signal and yet retain the desired information. The choice of what nominal levels to use is strictly governed by the devices to be used and may vary from computer to computer. For reasons of simplicity, the two nominal voltage levels selected are given symbolic values, namely "0" and "1". It is customary to assign the symbol "1" to the most positive of the two levels and "0" to the lower level. When this type of assignment is used, the logic is referred to as "positive logic". However, some computers have been built using the opposite assignment. When this is done, the logic is referred to as "negative logic". Actually there is no advantage gained in choosing either type of assignment over the other. Positive logic, highest voltage level equals "1", was chosen for this book because it is the most commonly used.

Diode Logic

The semiconductor junction diode is essentially a two terminal rectifying element. It is a passive component which means it has no signal amplification ability. It must, therefore, be used in conjunction with some active component when considered for use as a building block for a computer.

The semiconductor diode allows current to flow through it freely in one direction but restricts the flow of current in the opposite direction. This rectifying action occurs at the boundary of the two types of material; "*P*" type and "*N*" type, used in the construction of the device. If the "*P*" type material is biased slightly more positive than the "*N*" type, a large current will be allowed to flow through the device. If biased in the opposite direction the device will allow only a very small current flow. The junction diode with its symbolic representation is shown in Figure 1.1. If two diodes and one resistor are connected together as shown in Figure 1.2, a useful

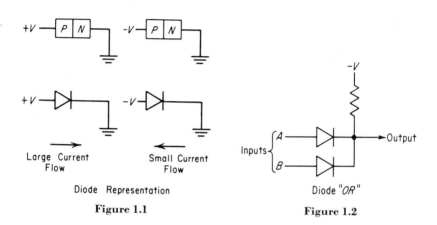

Large Current Flow	Small Current Flow
Diode Representation	Diode "*OR*"
Figure 1.1	**Figure 1.2**

computer circuit called an *OR* is obtained. In this figure, +12 volts is called "1", while ground is called "0". From the circuit configuration, it is clear that the output voltage will be equal to the most positive voltage applied to either input. Therefore if input *A* equals "1", or input *B* equals "1", the output will be a "1". If both inputs are "1", the output will again be "1". Using symbolic nomenclature, a table of all possible input conditions with their respective output conditions is shown in Figure 1.3. The number of inputs to the circuit may be increased by connecting more diodes to the resistor. (Figure 1.4.) The number of diodes that may be connected in this fashion is governed by the back resistance of the diodes. A ten input *OR* circuit is not uncommon.

Another useful computer circuit is obtained by connecting diodes and a resistor in the manner shown in Figure 1.5. This circuit configuration is called an *AND* circuit. The output of this circuit is always equal to the most negative of any of the inputs. The output will be a "1" only if *A* and *B* and *C* are equal to "1". As with diode *OR* circuits, the number of inputs may vary from two to above ten. The upper limit will again depend on the characteristics of the diodes being used.

Input A B	Output
0 0	0
0 1	1
1 0	1
1 1	1

Table of Combinations 2 Input "*OR*"

Figure 1.3

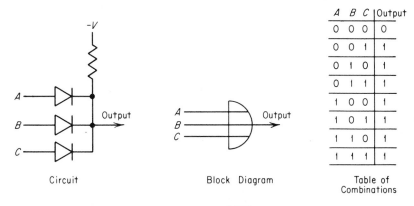

A	B	C	Output
0	0	0	0
0	0	1	1
0	1	0	1
0	1	1	1
1	0	0	1
1	0	1	1
1	1	0	1
1	1	1	1

Circuit   Block Diagram   Table of Combinations

Three Input "ON"

Figure 1.4

Transistor Inverter

If a second junction is added to the diode, making a N-P-N structure or a P-N-P structure, a device capable of amplification is formed. This device is called a transistor. In many respects the N-P-N transistor is similar to a vacuum tube, yet their methods of operation are not actually analogous. The base region is comparable to the grid of a tube in its control of current flow. The collector may be thought of as corresponding to the plate of a

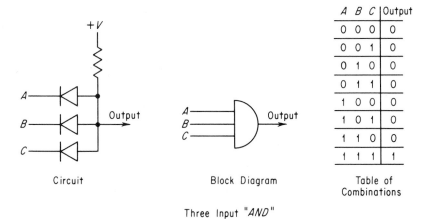

A	B	C	Output
0	0	0	0
0	0	1	0
0	1	0	0
0	1	1	0
1	0	0	0
1	0	1	0
1	1	0	0
1	1	1	1

Circuit   Block Diagram   Table of Combinations

Three Input "AND"

Figure 1.5

Plate

Grid

Cathode

Tube

Collector

Base

Emitter

NPN Transistor

NPN Transistor Symbol

Figure 1.6

tube while the emitter corresponds to the cathode. If the base of the transistor in Figure 1.6 is made slightly more positive than the emitter, the emitter junction will pass current easily. Current will not, however, flow from the collector to the base because of the back biasing on the upper junction. Current does flow, however, from the collector to the emitter, as a result of diffusion of a large number of electrons from the emitter through the thin base and into the collector. As the base is made more positive, more electrons are pulled out of the emitter and are made available for diffusion into the collector, thus increasing the collector current. As the collector current increases, more current is drawn through the load resistor, lowering the collector voltage. As the base is made less positive, less collector current will flow and the voltage at the collector will increase. Since very little voltage change is required to control the base-emitter current, a voltage dividing network may be affixed to the base to establish the correct biasing. (Figure 1.7.) If the input voltage is at ground, the tran-

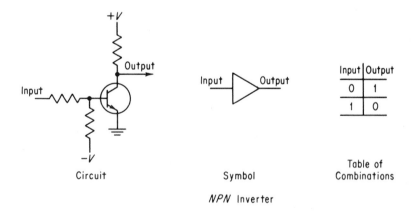

Input	Output
0	1
1	0

Circuit

Symbol

Table of Combinations

NPN Inverter

Figure 1.7

sistor will be fully cut off and the output voltage will be +12. If the input is at +12 volts, the transistor will be fully on (saturation) and the output will be at ground. Thus, a transistor connected in this type of configuration is called an "Inverter". A symbolic "1" passed into an inverter will emerge as a "0" and a "0" input will emerge as a "1". This circuit is sometimes called a *NOT* circuit.

The *P-N-P* transistor inverter performs in a similar manner as the *N-P-N* inverter, with the exceptions of a reversal of polarities on power supplies and current flow. (Figure 1.8.) Using the above circuit and retaining positive logic, the "1" signal will be "ground" and a "0" will be −12 volts. The device will convert a "1" to a "0" and a "0" to a "1". Generally the logician need not concern himself with the fact that a *N-P-N* or a *P-N-P* transistor is being used as long as all blocks are compatible and the function of the block is completely defined. In the past, modifications have been made to the inverter circuit to increase its speed or driving ability. A speed up capacitor is sometimes placed across the upper resistor in the biasing network and a clamping diode added to the output line. These circuit changes will be discussed more fully in the next section.

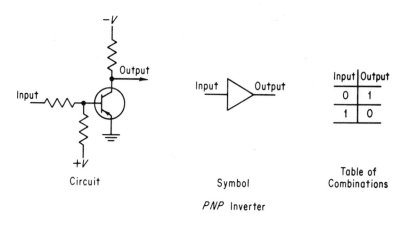

Input	Output
0	1
1	0

Circuit   Symbol   Table of Combinations

PNP Inverter

Figure 1.8

Kirchoff Adders

It is possible to build rather inexpensive *AND* and *OR* circuits from resistors if the source impedance of the signals is low. As an example, the output of two inverters may be *ANDed* together by using three resistors connected as in Figure 1.9. Resistors R_1, R_2, and R_3 may be chosen so that the output will go above ground only when both inputs are at ground. If either, or both inputs are at -12, the output will be below ground level. The output of this circuit is ideally suited as the input to another transistor. (Figure 1.10.) This circuit is sometimes called a $NAND$ since it may be thought of as a $NOT\text{-}AND$ circuit. In other words, looking into the circuit from the output, one would see an inverter circuit preceded by an AND circuit. The number of inputs to this circuit may be increased somewhat depending on the transistor specifications and tolerances on the resistor and power supplies. A typical computer circuit with a fan in of three (maximum number of inputs equals three) is shown in Figure 1.11. This circuit is completely compatible with itself; it will drive like devices and accept input from like devices.

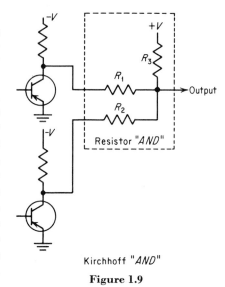

Kirchhoff "AND"

Figure 1.9

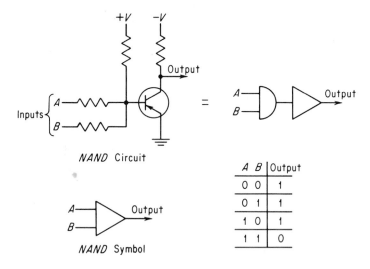

NAND Circuit

NAND Symbol

A	B	Output
0	0	1
0	1	1
1	0	1
1	1	0

Figure 1.10

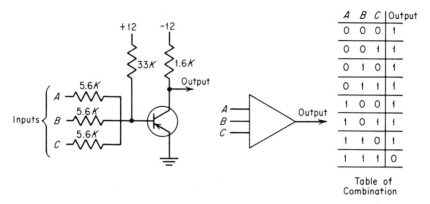

A	B	C	Output
0	0	0	1
0	0	1	1
0	1	0	1
0	1	1	1
1	0	0	1
1	0	1	1
1	1	0	1
1	1	1	0

Table of Combination

Three Input "NAND"

Figure 1.11

A Kirchoff adder may be designated as an *OR* circuit and used in conjunction with the *N-P-N* inverter. (Figure 1.12.) With this circuit, the signal levels will be $+12$ volts for a "1" and ground for a "0". The resistor values are chosen so that the base of the transistor will be above ground if any one or more of the inputs is at $+12$ volts. With the base of the transistor biased above ground, the transistor will pass current and lower the output voltage to ground. The circuit may be thought of as an inverter

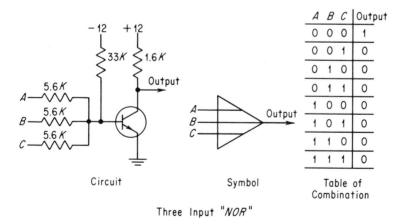

A	B	C	Output
0	0	0	1
0	0	1	0
0	1	0	0
0	1	1	0
1	0	0	0
1	0	1	0
1	1	0	0
1	1	1	0

Circuit　　　　Symbol　　　　Table of Combination

Three Input "NOR"

Figure 1.12

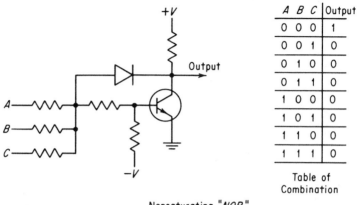

A	B	C	Output
0	0	0	1
0	0	1	0
0	1	0	0
0	1	1	0
1	0	0	0
1	0	1	0
1	1	0	0
1	1	1	0

Table of
Combination

Nonsaturating "*NOR*"

Figure 1.13

preceded by an *OR* circuit. This "Inverter-Or" combination has lead to the naming of this circuit, *NOR*, implying *NOT-OR*.

Increasing the speed of resistor-transistor logic: It is possible to increase the speed of the previous resistor transistor circuits by several methods. A diode may be used in a feedback circuit to prevent the transistor from being driven too deeply into saturation. (Figure 1.13.) This circuit has been referred to as diode feedback. A clamping diode on the collector may also be used for preventing deep saturation and its associated delay. Newer

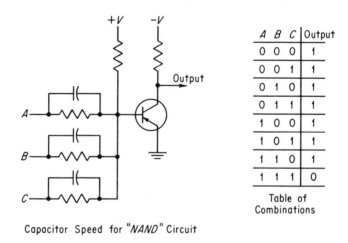

A	B	C	Output
0	0	0	1
0	0	1	1
0	1	0	1
0	1	1	1
1	0	0	1
1	0	1	1
1	1	0	1
1	1	1	0

Table of
Combinations

Capacitor Speed for "*NAND*" Circuit

Figure 1.14

transistors (double diffused mesas) do not suffer a turn off delay after being driven into saturation and therefore do not require the previous precautions.

Speed up capacitors are sometimes used to shunt the input resistor as a means of increasing the response time. (Figure 1.14.) These capacitors, unfortunately, aggravate the crosstalk between inputs. A signal applied to input A will appear as a noise pulse on input lines B and C. If these lines are connected to inputs of other similar circuits, a malfunction may result. If speed up capacitors are used on any of the input lines, it may be necessary to apply further restrictions to the connections made between blocks.

Paralleled Collector Circuits

If two P-N-P transistor inverters are connected with their collectors in parallel, the $NAND$ function is obtained. (Figure 1.15.) The output of this circuit will be nominally ground (a logical "1") if either or both of the inputs are at -12 (logical "0"). This circuit may be thought of as a logic connective in its own right or the principle may be used to extend the number of inputs on a $NAND$ resistor-transistor circuit. If the collectors of two $NAND$ circuits are connected together, the same function is retained but the number of allowable inputs has doubled. (Figure 1.16.) The number of collectors that may be connected together in this manner is usually rather large regardless of the use of a Kirchoff adder on the inputs. The

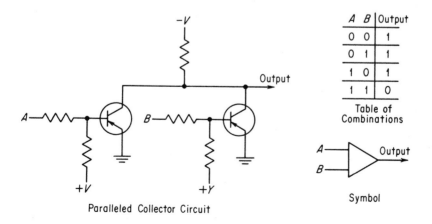

A	B	Output
0	0	1
0	1	1
1	0	1
1	1	0

Table of Combinations

Paralleled Collector Circuit

Symbol

Figure 1.15

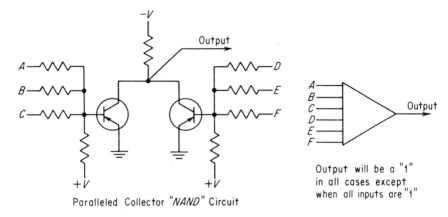

Paralleled Collector "*NAND*" Circuit

Output will be a "1"
in all cases except
when all inputs are "1"

Figure 1.16

Kirchoff adder increases the number of inputs to the logic connective but
at the expense of a reduction in speed.

Direct Coupled Transistor Logic

If silicon transistors are used, it is possible to remove the biasing network
affixed to the base lead of an inverter circuit. The collector of a transistor
may be connected directly to the base of a second transistor. If the common
collector principle of the previous section is used with *N-P-N* transistor
the logic connective formed will be a *NOR*. (Figure 1.17.) If *P-N-P* transistors are used, the *NAND* function will be obtained. Direct Coupled
Transistor Logic offers one other very useful circuit. If the collector of a

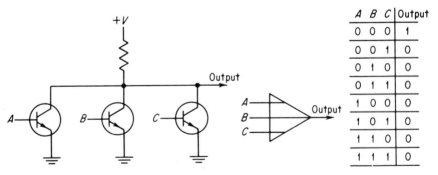

A	B	C	Output
0	0	0	1
0	0	1	0
0	1	0	0
0	1	1	0
1	0	0	0
1	0	1	0
1	1	0	0
1	1	1	0

Direct Coupled Transistor Logic "*NOR*"

Figure 1.17

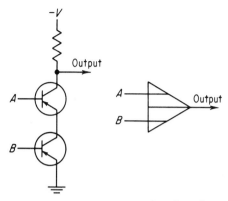

Direct Coupled Transistor Logic "*NOR*"

Figure 1.18

transistor is connected to the emitter of another transistor, the *NAND* or *NOR* function is obtained. (Figure 1.18.) With this circuit configuration, both transistors must be conducting in order to produce a "1" output if *P-N-P* transistors are used. If *N-P-N* transistors are used, the output will be a "1" if either or both transistors are cut off; this will yield the *NOR* function. Circuits of the D.C.T.L. type have relatively fast switching speeds, but require uniform transistor specifications.

Diode Transistor Logic

Diode *AND* circuits and diode *OR* circuits may be combined with transistor inverters to produce both *NAND* and *NOR* functions. Figure 1.19

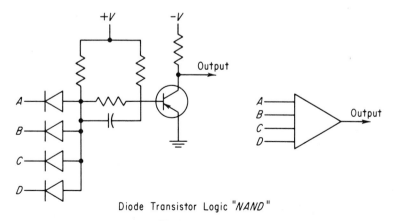

Diode Transistor Logic "*NAND*"

Figure 1.19

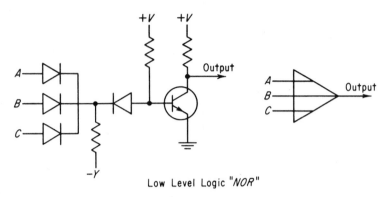

Low Level Logic "*NOR*"

Figure 1.20

illustrates a typical computer circuit which uses a *P-N-P* inverter with a diode *AND*. The diode *OR* may be used with the *N-P-N* inverter. Another form of this same circuitry is sometimes called Low Level Logic. (See Figure 1.20) The diode in the biasing network allows smaller voltage excursions to be used for signals and thus minimizes the effects of stray capacitance and increases switching speeds.

References

DeWitt, D. and A. L. Rossoff, *Transistor Electronics*. New York: McGraw-Hill Book Co., 1957.

Hunter, Lloyd P., *Handbook of Semiconductor Electronics*. New York: McGraw-Hill Book Co., 1956.

Lo, A. W. et al, *Transistor Electronics*. Englewood Cliffs: Prentice-Hall, Inc., 1955.

Pressman, Abraham, *Design of Transistorized Circuits for Digital Computers*. New York: John F. Rider Publisher, Inc., 1959.

NUMBER SYSTEMS
AND
CODES

2

Introduction

From early childhood most individuals are trained to represent quantities in the decimal number system. The decimal system is quite adequate for individuals possessing the ability to remember ten distinct symbols, but nature has not been so generous in the electronics field. Most devices available to the electronic computer designer have but two stable conditions. The designer may therefore decide to construct devices having ten stable conditions from the bi-stable devices provided or may elect to work in a binary system. Both methods have been used in the past, but the most economical procedure for the design of a high speed computer dictates some form of binary representation of quantities.

Binary Number System

The binary system is not too different from the decimal system with the exception of only two symbols, zero and one, in place of the usual ten. When counting in the decimal system, one merely starts by listing all available symbols in their proper order until the list is exhausted. The same procedure holds in binary, but the list is exhausted in two steps, namely 0, 1. The decimal system now dictates a procedure invented by the Hindus called "carrying". In this procedure, we list the first non-zero symbol to the left of the first symbol position and proceed to repeat the listing of all symbols. Following the same procedure for binary we arrive at:

binary		decimal
0	=	0
1	=	1
10	=	2
11	=	3
100	=	4
101	=	5
110	=	6
111	=	7
1000	=	8

The above procedure may be explained mathematically by examining the radix of both the decimal and binary system. A decimal number $(d_3 d_2 d_1 d_0)$ may be written mathematically as $d_3 R^3 + d_2 R^2 + d_1 R^1 + d_0 R^0$ where R is equal to the number of digit symbols employed in the system. R is called the radix and is equal to ten in the decimal number system. A decimal number such as 256 would appear as $2 \times 10^2 + 5 \times 10^1 + 6 \times 10^0$. When the number is written as 256, the powers of ten are implied by positional location of the digits. The same method is applied to binary but in this case the radix is two and a binary number such as 1010 would appear mathematically as $1 \times 2^3 + 0 \times 2^2 + 1 \times 2^1 + 0 \times 2^0$. This may be written as $1 \times 8 + 0 \times 4 + 1 \times 2 + 0 \times 1$, which equals ten in decimal.

Decimal to Binary Conversion

The binary representation of a decimal number may be obtained by repeatedly dividing the decimal number by two. After each successive division, the remainder (which will be a zero or a one) is recorded. The process is continued until the decimal number is exhausted. The binary representation of the original decimal number is a listing of the remainders.

Example: Obtain binary representation of the decimal number 13.

```
              remainders
    2 |13
    2 |6     1      (2 goes into 13, six times with a remainder of 1)
    2 |3     01
    2 |1     101
      0      1101
```

decimal 13 = 1101 binary

Example: Obtain binary representation of the decimal number 125.

```
    2 |125
    2 |62    1
    2 |31    01
    2 |15    101
    2 |7     1101
    2 |3     11101
    2 |1     111101
      0      1111101
```

Decimal 125 = 1111101 binary

Decimal Fraction Conversion

If the decimal number being covered is a fraction, then the number is repeatedly multiplied by two and the carries are recorded.

Example: Convert .75 to binary

```
                  .75
      Carries   ×2
        .1       .50
                ×2
        .11      00     .75 decimal equals .11 binary
```

A fraction may not have an exact representation in the binary system and a round-off procedure must be used.

Example: Find binary equivalent to .34

```
                .34
                ×2
.0              .68
                ×2
.01             .36
                ×2
.010            .72
                ×2
.0101           .44
                ×2
.01010          .88
                ×2
.010101         .76
                ×2
.01010111       .04    .34 Decimal equals approximately .01010111
```

When a number contains both an integer part and a fractional part, both halves are worked out independently and the answers joined together.

Example: Find 96.625 representation in binary

```
2 |96                        .625
2 |48     0                  ×2
                      1     .250
2 |24     00                 ×2
2 |12     000        10     .500
2 |6      0000               ×2
                     101    000
2 |3      00000
2 |1      100000
   0      1100000     96.625 = 1100000.101
```

Trial and Error Conversion

The binary representation of a decimal number may also be obtained by a trial and error procedure of subtraction. The first subtraction is performed by using the highest power of two that will not leave a negative remainder. The same procedure is then applied to the remainder. The highest power of two that will not result in a negative remainder is subtracted from the old remainder. The process is continued until the number is exhausted.

Each power of two that was selected for the subtraction operations is recorded and used to locate the "ones" in the binary number.

Example: Convert 91 to binary

$$
\begin{array}{r}
91 \\
- 64 = 2^6 \\
\hline
27 \\
- 16 = 2^4 \\
\hline
11 \\
- 8 = 2^3 \\
\hline
3 \\
- 2 = 2^1 \\
\hline
1 \\
- 1 = 2^0 \\
\hline
0
\end{array}
$$

$$2^6 2^5 2^4 2^3 2^2 2^1 2^0$$
$$1\ 0\ 1\ 1\ 0\ 1\ 1$$

Decimal 91 = 1011011 binary

Binary to Decimal Conversion

The conversion of a binary number to its decimal form is rather a simple procedure since each bit position has a corresponding decimal weight. The first bit (bit = binary digit) position to the left of the binary point has the decimal weight of 2^0. The next bit position to the left is 2^1 and the next 2^2 and so on out to the left. The first bit position to the right of the binary point is 2^{-1}, the next 2^{-2} and so on. These weights are then multiplied by the bit in their corresponding position and a summation of products will yield the decimal number.

Example: Convert 11001.01 to decimal

$$
\begin{array}{ccccccccc}
1 & 1 & 0 & 0 & 1 & . & 0 & 1 \\
\times 16 & \times 8 & \times 4 & \times 2 & \times 1 & & \times .5 & \times .25 \\
\hline
16 + & 8 + & 0 + & 0 + & 1 & . & + 0 + & .25 = 25.25
\end{array}
$$

Octal Number System

Individuals find it difficult to discuss and even remember long strings of intermingled zeroes and ones as encountered in the binary system. The octal system offers a short hand method of recording binary numbers. It is to this use that individuals have put the octal system. If a binary computer were to print out the binary number 101111011, the operator would read this off as 573 octal. This octal number may be arrived at by grouping the binary number into groups of 3 bits, starting from the right (101/111/011). Each of these groups is then converted to a decimal number. It should be noted that it is impossible to obtain an eight or a nine. If one were to count in octal the next number after 7 would be 10. To convert from decimal to octal, one may first convert to binary and then convert the binary number to octal. A much more straightforward method is obtained by repeatedly dividing by eight and recording the remainders.

Example: Convert 24 decimal to octal

$$8 \lfloor\underline{24}$$
$$8 \lfloor\underline{3} \qquad 0$$
$$0 \qquad 30$$
$$24_{(10)} = 30_{(8)} \ *$$

Conversion from octal to decimal is performed in the same manner as is used to convert binary to decimal. Each octal bit is multiplied by the appropriate power of eight and a summation of the products will yield the decimal number.

Convert 347 octal to decimal

$$\begin{array}{ccc} 3 & 4 & 7 \\ \times 8^2 & \times 8^1 & \times 8^0 \\ \hline 192 + & 32 + & 7 \end{array} = 231 \qquad 347_{(8)} = 231_{(10)}$$

The general equation for converting from one number system to another is given by the following statement. Divide the number to be converted by the power of the base of the new number system. The division is carried on in the number system of the original number.

Floating Point

When working on scientific problems, very large and very small numbers are often encountered. Most present day computers do not have the digit capacity to handle such numbers in the straight binary system. Therefore, scientific computers have available a system called "Floating Point."

---

* The small number in the brackets below the line indicates the base of the number system being used.

With this system, all numbers are represented as fractions multiplied by a power of the radix. In the decimal number system this method would appear as illustrated below. (Exponent is called "characteristic.")

$$decimal$$
$$+576 \ = +.576 \times 10^3 \ = +3 + .576$$
$$+.042 = +.42 \times 10^{-1} = -1 + .42$$
$$-17.92 = -.1792 \times 10^2 = +2 - .1792$$

To avoid the use of a sign with the characteristic, a constant may be added to that portion of the number, equal to one-half of the capacity of the portion of the number set aside for the characteristic. If three decimal digits are set aside for the characteristic then the constant would probably be 500. The numbers listed above would then be listed as:

$$+3 + .576 \ = 503 + .576 \qquad \text{moving the} \qquad +503.576$$
$$-1 + .42 \ = 499 + .42 \qquad \text{sign to the} \qquad +499.42$$
$$+2 - .1792 = 502 - .1792 \qquad \text{left} \qquad -502.1792$$

Inside the computer this operation would have been carried on in the binary system $12 = 1100 = .11 \times 2^4 = .11 \times 2^{100} = 100.11$ adding constant to exponent = 1000100.11. After some arithmetic operations, a zero may appear to the right of the binary point. The removing of such zeroes and the associated updating of the characteristic is usually referred to as normalizing.

A computer designed to handle floating point numbers will require additional hardware since the characteristic and the fraction must be handled differently in such operations as multiply. Some operations on floating point numbers will normally require more computer time. Addition as an example, requires that the numbers be shifted to equalize the characteristics before addition can take place. The characteristic also occupies part of the digit capacity of the machine thereby reducing the number of available significant digits. Despite these obvious disadvantages most scientific computers are being operated in the floating point mode. Floating point offers the advantage of handling very large and very small numbers without the programmer having to concern himself with the location of the binary point.

Binary Coded Decimal

To ease the communication problem between man and machine, a compromise code has been devised which is somewhat favorable to both sides. This B.C.D. coding (Binary Coded Decimal) is arrived at by taking each digit of a decimal number and coding it separately into binary. This implies that each decimal digit will require four bits for coding.

Example: Find the B.C.D. equivalent of 7051

$$\begin{array}{cccc} 7 & 0 & 5 & 1 \\ 0111 & 0000 & 0101 & 0001 \end{array}$$

$$7051_{10} = 0111000001010001_{(\text{BCD})}$$

Since four binary bits have the capability of representing quantities zero through fifteen and they are being used for quantities zero through nine, this method is somewhat wasteful of digit capacity. Despite this disadvantage, most computers designed to handle business problems are using some form of this coding.

Many other methods for coding a single decimal digit have been devised using four or more bits to code each digit.

Excess Three Code

This code is very similar to the B.C.D. code with the exception that three is added to each digit before coding:

zero	0011	five	1000
one	0100	six	1001
two	0101	seven	1010
three	0110	eight	1011
four	0111	nine	1100

This code is called a non-weighted code since bit positions cannot be assigned decimal values. Encoding and decoding is usually obtained by a table look up procedure using the table listed above. For decoding, it is possible to subtract three from each of the decimal representations and then use a binary conversion technique on the four binary bits.

Example: Convert 921 decimal to Excess Three Code

$$\begin{array}{ccc} 9 & 2 & 1 \\ 1100 & 0101 & 0100 \end{array}$$

$$921_{(10)} = 110001010100 \;_{(\text{Excess 3})}$$

One advantage of such a code is the fact that it is self-complementing. If all zeroes in a number are changed to ones and all ones are changed to zeroes, the nines complement of the number is obtained. In some instances, this ability to obtain the nines complement will reduce the required hardware to perform subtraction. The Excess Three Code has an added advantage. All decimal representations have at least one "1" in their Excess Three Coding. This makes possible the distinction of zero from no information which is of prime importance in many applications.

Weighted Four Bit Decimal Codes

The B.C.D. code previously discussed is probably the most frequently used weighted decimal code. Two other such codes are shown below and are referred to by their weights. That is, the 4, 2, 2, 1 code and the 5, 4, 2, 1.

	4221	5421
zero	0000	0000
one	0001	0001
two	0010	0010
three	0011	0011
four	1000	0100
five	0111	1000
six	1100	1001
seven	1101	1010
eight	1110	1011
nine	1111	1100

The 4, 2, 2, 1 code is self-complementing as are all codes whose weights add up to nine. $4 + 2 + 2 + 1 = 9$

For purely educational reasons, some of the other possible four bit weight decimal codes are listed below:

5221	5321	531(−1)*
6331	7321	522(−1)
5211	4421	732(−1)
6321	6421	621(−1)

The last column in the above listing illustrates only four of the possible codes which employ negative weights. These codes are interesting but to the author's knowledge no machine has ever been designed using them.

---

* R. K. Richards, *Arithmetic Operations in Digital Computers* (New York: D. Van Nostrand Co., Inc., 1955).

Five Bit Weighted Decimal Codes

Several machines have been designed using five bit codes. The 74210 is such a code and has the advantage that all digits contain two and only two "ones".

zero	11000	five	01010
one	00011	six	01100
two	00101	seven	10001
three	00110	eight	10010
four	01001	nine	10100

The two "one" bits in each digit make possible the detection of single errors in each digit. Each digit with no 1 bits, one 1 bit and more than two 1 bits can register in the machine as an error. This constant two bit arrangement also eases the circuit design criterion on some functional devices, such as memory, since the designer is assured a constant number of devices will be switching at one time. Assigning "zero" the value of 11000 actually rules this code out of the weighted class but by so doing, the constant two bit arrangement is retained.

Biquinary Code

At least one mass-produced computer has been designed using a seven bit weighted code, known as the biquinary code. (IBM 650). One weighting system for a biquinary code is 5043210.

	50	43210
zero	01	00001
one	01	00010
two	01	00100
three	01	01000
four	01	10000
five	10	00001
six	10	00010
seven	10	00100
eight	10	01000
nine	10	10000

The left hand two bits are used to indicate whether the number is over four or under five. The code given has the constant two bit loading feature and is suitable for single error detection in the left hand two bits or the right hand five bits. Arithmetic operations are rather easy to perform with this particular biquinary code and this accounts for some of its usage.

Gray Codes

All Gray Codes have one basic characteristic in common. As the code is advanced from any number to the next, only one bit of the code will change at a time. Analog measuring devices used to feed information to a digital system must first have their outputs digitalized by a converter. Such converters normally have a Gray Code output. The reason for this is clear when we examine a non-Gray Code such as straight Binary. When the Binary code is advanced from 3 to 4 (0011 to 0100) three bits of the code must change, but it is almost impossible to design a mechanical device such as a set of switches that will change the voltage on several lines simultaneously. Therefore, the output of the instrument might go from 0011 to 0100 in the following fashion: $0011 \rightarrow 0010 \rightarrow 0110 \rightarrow 0100$. These false outputs will last but a short time, but it must be remembered that some digital computers will recognize a voltage change that lasts for only a few milli-microseconds.

The Gray Codes are also useful when designing electronic sequential circuitry for the same reasons as given above.

The most commonly known Gray Code is given below (called "The Gray Code"):

zero	= 0000	five	= 0111	ten	= 1111
one	= 0001	six	= 0101	eleven	= 1110
two	= 0011	seven	= 0100	twelve	= 1010
three	= 0010	eight	= 1100	thirteen	= 1011
four	= 0110	nine	= 1101	fourteen	= 1001

A decimal number may be encoded into Gray Code by first converting to Binary. Each bit of the Binary Code is then added sum modulo two with the next higher binary bit. (Output of a sum modulo two device will be a one only when both inputs are not alike.)

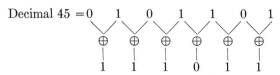

Decimal 45 = 111011 Gray Code

Converting from Gray Code to decimal is usually accomplished by first converting to binary. The conversion proceeds from the high order bit of the Gray Code progressing to the lowest bit. The high order bits are recorded unchanged until the first "1" bit is passed. From there on, the bits being recorded will be "1's" until another "1" bit is encountered in the Gray Code. When this "1" bit is encountered, a zero will be recorded and the recording of "0's" will continue until the next "1" bit is encountered. This will be recorded as a "1" and the recording of "1's" will continue until another "1" is encountered and so on. The procedure is continued until the Gray Code work is exhausted.

Convert 001001011 in Gray Code to binary:

001001011 Gray Code

001	Record all bits until the first "1" is passed.
00111	Record "1's" until next "1" is encountered.
0011100	Record "0's" until next "1" is encountered.
00111001	Record "1's" until next "1" is encountered.
001110010	Record "0's" until next "1" is encountered (word exhausted).
001001011	in Gray Code is equivalent to 001110010 binary

This particular code is a Reflected Binary Code. A code is said to be "reflecting" when it is symmetrical, with the exception of the high order bit, about the mid-point of a complete ascending listing of the code. Most Gray Codes that are not reflecting are usually expensive to decode.

Since there exists a great many Gray Codes of various cycle length, they may be referred to by their cycle length and a series of decimal numbers when a small number of bits is involved.

Cycle length refers to the number of different binary configurations that are going to be arrived at before the code repeats itself. The Gray Code used in the first example would be referred to as Gray Code Length 16 (1, 2, 1, 3, 1, 2, 1, 4, 1, 2, 1, 3, 1, 2, 1, 4). The highest number in the parentheses indicates how many bits are in the code and the entire series of numbers indicates which bit position changes as the code is advanced. The code may be started at, in this example, any four bit number. A Gray Code such as Length 6 (1, 2, 1, 3, 2, 3) will appear different when started at different binary numbers.

Start at 000	Starting at 111
000	111
001	110
011	100
010	101
110	001
100	011
000	111

It is therefore advisable to indicate a starting point to avoid any misunderstanding. A listing of some of the possible Gray Codes are given below. There exists but one Gray Code of cycle length four.

Gray Codes

Length 4	(1,2,1,2)
Length 6	(1,2,1,3,2,3)
	(1,2,3,1,2,3)
Length 8	(1,2,1,3,1,2,1,3)
	(1,2,3,4,1,4,3,2)
Length 10	(1,2,1,3,4,3,1,2,1,4)
	(1,2,1,3,4,1,2,1,3,4)

The chief disadvantage of Gray Codes is the complicated circuitry that is required to perform such simple operations as adding. This difficulty has been the chief reason for their limited use.

Walking or Creeping Code

A five bit Gray Code of cycle length ten is being used in present machines to perform simple counting operations. The Gray Code is (1, 2, 3, 4, 5, 1, 2, 3, 4, 5) and the starting point is 00000.

$$
\begin{aligned}
\text{zero} &= 00000 \leftarrow \text{starting point} \\
\text{one} &= 00001 \leftarrow \text{first bit changed} \\
\text{two} &= 00011 \leftarrow \text{second bit changed} \\
\text{three} &= 00111 \leftarrow \text{third bit changed} \\
\text{four} &= 01111 \\
\text{five} &= 11111 \\
\text{six} &= 11110 \\
\text{seven} &= 11100 \\
\text{eight} &= 11000 \\
\text{nine} &= 10000
\end{aligned}
$$

The reason for the use of this code lies in the simple hardware required to produce a counter to operate in this mode. To advance the count by one, all that is necessary is to move all bits one position to the left while inverting the last bit and placing it in the first position. Any number except zero and five may be detected by a two input *AND* connected with one leg through an Inverter to two adjacent bits.

Error Detecting Codes

When information is transferred from one section of a computer to another, it is not too uncommon for an error to occur. These errors occur for a great many reasons and cannot be completely eliminated regardless of how carefully the circuit designer works. The reason for this lies in the thousands of components used in a computer, each with a certain probability of failure. It is merely a question of time before one or more components will fail in any given computer. The logic designer may predict some of these failures and design error detecting circuitry or error correcting circuitry to cope with them. The value of such circuitry has been argued many times and the issue remains still unresolved.

Single error detection, in the transmission of a binary word (where a word refers to any series of binary bits), may be accomplished by including one extra or redundant bit. This extra bit is normally referred to as a check bit or a parity bit and is used to obtain a total even number of one bits in each word or a total odd number of one bits in each word. The table below illustrates the use of an even check bit with B.C.D. code where each four information bits is a word.

	8	4	2	1	C		8	4	2	1	C
zero	0	0	0	0	0	zero	0	1	0	1	0
one	0	0	0	1	1	six	0	1	1	0	0
two	0	0	1	0	1	seven	0	1	1	1	1
three	0	0	1	1	0	eight	1	0	0	0	1
four	0	1	0	0	1	nine	1	0	0	1	0

When a section of a computer is receiving information, it simply counts the bits in each incoming word and rejects those words which have (in our example) an odd number of bits. What the machine should do when this occurs is usually left to the discretion of the programmer or the operator.

An odd parity would have been a better choice in this example since zero would then contain one "1" bit, making possible the distinction of zero from no information.

One form of single error correction may be obtained by using a check bit with each word and then a check word after each group of words.

Example: Use odd parity bits

	8	4	2	1	C
$2 =$	0	0	1	0	0
$6 =$	0	1	1	0	1
$5 =$	0	1	0	1	1
check word	1	1	1	0	1

Each bit in the check word should be such that the column it is contained in has an odd number of "1" bits. An error in any bit will cause an error to occur in both a row and a column. The bit in error may be located by the intersection of the row in error with the column in error. The check bit in the check word does not always agree vertically and horizontally, therefore no error correction is obtained in the check bits.

Hamming Codes

Of increasing interest to the logic designer is the use of "error correcting codes". Any error correcting code makes possible the detection and correction of an error caused by the machine. To be single error correcting, a code must be such that at least three changes in the bit configuration are made when changing from one number to any other number. A seven bit B.C.D. self-correcting code is shown below. This code is single error correcting.

	8	4	2	1	A	B	C
zero	0	0	0	0	1	1	1
one	0	0	0	1	0	0	0
two	0	0	1	0	0	0	1
three	0	0	1	1	1	1	0
four	0	1	0	0	0	1	0
five	0	1	0	1	1	0	1
six	0	1	1	0	1	0	0
seven	0	1	1	1	0	1	1
eight	1	0	0	0	1	0	0
nine	1	0	0	1	0	1	1

In this case, the "A" bit is used to obtain an odd number of bits in the 1, 2, 4, A positions. The "B" bit is used to obtain an odd redundancy in the 1, 2, 8, B positions and the "C" bit obtains an odd redundancy in the 1, 4, 8, C positions. When a single error is generated, an illegal combination of ones and zeroes will appear. The correct number may be retrieved by a trial and error procedure. Change the first bit, if a legal combination appears, the first bit is wrong and has been corrected. If an illegal combination still exists, restore the number and change the second bit and so on.

The checking bits and the information bits may be intermixed to ease the problem of determining the location of the error. A full Hamming Code of four information bits and three check bits is shown in the following.

Position	1	2	3	4	5	6	7	
Bit Weights	A	B	8	C	4	2	1	
	0	0	0	0	0	0	0	= zero
	1	1	0	1	0	0	1	= one
	0	1	0	1	0	1	0	= two
	1	0	0	0	0	1	1	= three
	1	0	0	1	1	0	0	= four
	0	1	0	0	1	0	1	= five
	1	1	0	0	1	1	0	= six
	0	0	0	1	1	1	1	= seven
	1	1	1	0	0	0	0	= eight
	0	0	1	1	0	0	1	= nine
	1	0	1	1	0	1	0	= ten
	0	1	1	0	0	1	1	= eleven
	0	1	1	1	1	0	0	= twelve
	1	0	1	0	1	0	1	= thirteen
	0	0	1	0	1	1	0	= fourteen
	1	1	1	1	1	1	1	= fifteen

In this case, the "A" bit is used to obtain an even parity on positions 1, 3, 5, 7. The "B" bit is used to produce an even parity on positions 2, 3, 6, 7 while C is used as an even parity for 4, 5, 6, 7.

If, for example, the decimal number six (1100110) is transmitted and as a result of an error is received as 1100010, we may determine and correct the error in the following manner:

Positions

	1	2	3	4	5	6	7
Message with error	1	1	0	0	0	1	0

Parity check positions 4, 5, 6, 7 odd parity = 1

Parity check positions 2, 3, 6, 7 even parity = 0——0 = 101 = 5

Parity check positions 1, 3, 5, 7 odd parity = 1

This combination of parity checks produces a binary number (five in this case) which indicates that the fifth position is wrong. If the number had been received correctly, the combination of the parity checks would have been zero (000). This particular code may be extended to any number of information bits as long as more check bits are added according to the following table:

Information Bits	Check Bits Required
4	3
11	4
26	5
57	6

The general equation for the number of check bits "k" required to encode "n" information bits is:

$$2^k = n + k + 1$$

Alpha Numeric Coding

A great many machines being built today are designed to handle business type problems. Such machines must handle alphabetic as well as numerical information. A code that will handle both alphabetic and numeric characters is called an alpha-numeric code. The IBM card which is used to feed information into a great many computers, uses a 12 bit Hollerith code. This code uses two "1" bits, or holes in the card for each alphabetic character and one "1" *or* hole for each numeric digit. The card contains eighty columns which makes possible the recording of 80 alpha-numeric characters.

Special characters as well as numeric and alphabetic characters are shown below on an IBM card.

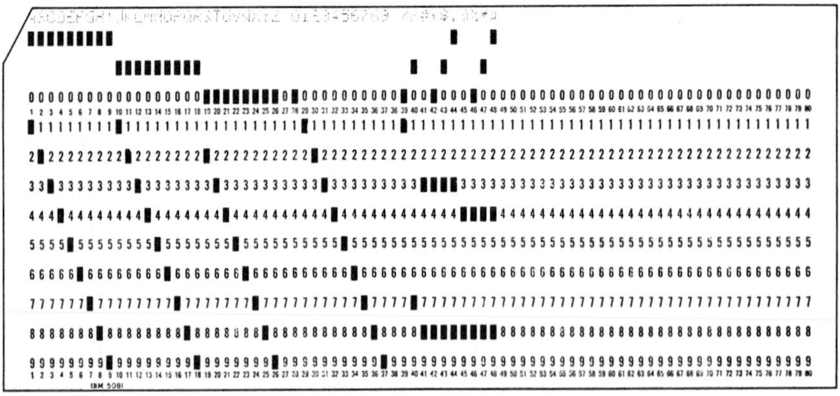

Although the Hollerith code is used on IBM cards, it is not used internally on their large electronic equipment. The 12 bit code is converted to a six bit code which is listed below. The A and B bit positions serve to tell the computer whether the information is numeric or alphabetic. Further, if the character is alphabetic, the A and B bits indicate which third of the alphabet the character is located in.

	BA 8421			BA 8421			BA 8421			BA 8421
0	0 0 0000									
1	0 0 0001	A	1 1 0001	J	1 0 0001				
2	0 0 0010	B	1 1 0010	K	1 0 0010	S	0 1 0010
3	0 0 0011	C	1 1 0011	L	1 0 0011	T	0 1 0011
4	0 0 0100	D	1 1 0100	M	1 0 0100	U	0 1 0100
5	0 0 0101	E	1 1 0101	N	1 0 0101	V	0 1 0101
6	0 0 0110	F	1 1 0110	O	1 0 0110	W	0 1 0110
7	0 0 0111	G	1 1 0111	P	1 0 0111	X	0 1 0111
8	0 0 1000	H	1 1 1000	Q	1 0 1000	Y	0 1 1000
9	0 0 1001	I	1 1 1001	R	1 0 1001	Z	0 1 1000

There are, of course, many ways in which an alpha-numeric coding may be constructed, but one important feature should remain throughout all such codes. The alphabetic characters should be assigned binary numbers in such an order that alphabetic sorting is possible. It should be remembered that the arrangement of information in alphabetical order is rather important in many business problems.

Questions

1. Convert $23.5625_{(10)}$ to binary.
2. Convert binary 10110.11101 to decimal.
3. Convert $318_{(10)}$ to octal.
4. Convert $1426_{(8)}$ to decimal.
5. Convert $143_{(10)}$ to the "Gray Code."
6. Convert 101101 in the "Gray Code" to decimal.
7. Convert $95761_{(10)}$ to B.C.D.
8. Convert $21945_{(10)}$ to Excess Three Code.
9. Devise a Gray Code of cycle length ten that is not given in the book.
10. If we wish to devise a full Hamming Code of eleven information bits where would the four check bits be placed so that an error could be located by these bits?

References

Peterson, W. Wesley, *Error-Correcting Codes*. New York: John Wiley & Sons, Inc., 1961.

Phister, Montgomery, *Logical Design of Digital Computers*. New York: John Wiley & Sons, Inc., 1958.

Richards, R. K., *Arithmetic Operations in Digital Computers*. New York: D. Van Nostrand Co., Inc., 1955.

BOOLEAN
ALGEBRA

3

Boolean Algebra, *OR* the Algebra of Logic, manipulates as its elements *NOT* numerical quantities *AND* arithmetic relations, *BUT* rather is a calculus dealing with truth values *AND* connectives.

And what are "connectives"? The capitalized italic words in the above paragraph *connect* the parts of the sentence together— the remaining words give the meaning, the connectives give the structure: $(U \; OR \; V) \; (NOT \; W \; AND \; X) \; BUT$ $(Y \; AND \; Z)$. The connectives can be grammatical connectives linking phrases as above, or they can be the mechanical linkages connecting gears and springs in a typewriter or adding machine. The connectives may be those discovered between enzymes in a bio-chemistry experiment, or the neural connections in the cerebral cortex of the human brain. Or they may be electronic circuits connecting or mixing electrical signals in a digital network. The whole physical world, insofar as its parts are connected, is a logical world.

And what are its non-numerical values? Boolean Algebra is a *calculus* of truth value, a *grammar* of validity. The logical statement of the first paragraph above may be *true* or *false*, a typewriter key linkage may hold a spring *taut* or *relaxed*, an enzyme *may accelerate* a reaction *or inhibit* it, a neuron *may "fire"* or *not "fire"*, and a voltage may be *positive* or *negative*.

All these examples may be considered as *statements* about the linkage, the enzyme, the neuron, and the voltage. These statements may be *true* or *false*. The variables of Boolean Algebra are not numbers, but statements, and their values are not numerical but the truth or falsity of compound, connected statements.

As an Algebra of Switching Circuits, the variables stand for statements about the voltages on a wire. For example:

Let "A" be the proposition

$$\text{``}A\text{''} = \text{``Wire } A \text{ is at } +12 \text{ volts.''}$$

and "Not A" be the proposition

$$\text{``Not } A\text{''} = \text{``Wire } A \text{ is not at } +12 \text{ volts.''}$$

"A" may be a true statement (with truth value 1), or "Not A" may be true in which case "A" is false (has truth value 0).

This is expressed in circuits by allowing only one of two voltages on a wire, say -12 volts and $+12$ volts. A statement in Boolean Algebra that the variable $A = 1$ or 0 means that "Wire A is at $+12$ volts" is true (1) or false (0). $+12$ volts (in this example) becomes logical 1 and -12 volts becomes logical zero.

Note that 1 and 0 are used in a non-numerical sense here. This is to be distinguished from the use of 1 and 0 to denote numerical values in the binary number system.

In switching applications, Boolean Algebra is used for the description and design of economical switching networks. These networks may add two numbers together, may decode a binary number to a decimal one, signal sequential control circuits when to change state, etc. Such circuits, operating in accordance with Boolean Algebra and including feedback circuits, form the bulk of today's computers and data processors.

The Axiomatic Basis

Studying axioms and proving theorems is dull for many people, but a student should be at least exposed to the foundations and structure if he is ever to use the discipline with sophistication. It is here the novice realizes that high school algebra is alien to this subject where one plus one equals one.

After the simpler theorems have been wrestled with in algebraic proofs, the text switches for the more important theorems to a method of proof requiring less ingenuity but with greater intuitive appeal (the Karnaugh map). This aids the reader's insight to the nature as well as the validity of the theorems—for most people, insight is blurred rather than developed in the purely algebraic approach.

The subject moves quickly in the early stages to dawdle more over discussions of those theorems of most practical interest.

The following axiom set and the initial theorems follow one of Huntington's[3] developments to a large extent although some of the proofs differ. Serrel's work[5] is the basis for some of the commentary and development of several of the later key theorems. Further, background and more thorough and rigorous developments may be found in the references at the end of the chapter.

Elements of an Axiomatic System

Common to many formal systems of symbols is the use of the binary relation " $=$ " (*equals*). What we mean by this sign is simply that:

1) $A = A$, (something is always equal to itself)

2) if $A = B$ then $B = A$ (there is no difference between sides of the equal sign).

3) if $A = B$ and $B = C$ then $A = C$ (things equal to the same thing are equal to each other).

These do not assign a meaning to "equals" but only the possession of certain properties.

In the same class of symbols are the various *parentheses*: ( ), [ ], { }, etc. Parentheses serve to define the range over which a connective is effective. Sometimes they are left out if the range of the connective is clear:

$$[(\overline{A}) + (B)] \cdot D = [\overline{A} + B] \cdot D \text{ or } (A \cdot B) + C = A \cdot B + C$$

A formal system always has given some *primitive* undefined *elements* such as connectives or functions, uninterpreted symbols about which the propositions of the axioms are to be made.

Also given are *primitive rules* accepted as yielding valid transformations from one proposition of the algebra to another; that is, the rules to be considered valid in proving theorems from the axioms and valid (previously proved) theorems. Here we assume the following two primitive rules:

Primitive Rules

1) Rule of Substitution: If two variables are equal, either may be substituted for all occurrences of the other in an expression. Thus, if $X = Y$ then $f(X, A, B, \ldots) = f(Y, A, B, \ldots)$. Thus are functions built up from the given functions; namely, variables, or $ANDs$, or ORs or $NOTs$. For example, the function $f(A, B, C) = A\overline{B} + C$ is built up from the AND: $A(x, y) = x \cdot y$, OR: $0(x, y) = x + y$, NOT: $N(x) = \overline{x}$, A, B, C; by substituting C for y in $0(x, y)$, $A, N(B)$ for x, y in $A(x, y)$, $A(A, N(B))$, for x in $0(x, y)$.

Function: Thus a function is a variable, a primitive connective, or a phrase built from these by substitution.

2) Rule of Inference: If x is an axiom or a theorem validly derived from the axioms, and x implies theorem y, then y is a valid theorem.

Axioms of Boolean Algebra

Primitive Elements:
   a)   A set K, (In our circuit interpretation K will be the set of two truth values or logical levels of voltage 0 and 1, forming an allowed range of values $K = \{0, 1\}$).
   b)   Variables $A, B, C, \ldots$ (which are statements or names of conducting wires in the circuit interpretation having one of the two truth or voltage values in K) with values in K.
   c)   Two connectives: "$+$", (OR); "$\cdot$", (AND) $(OR$ and AND in the circuit interpretation).

Axioms:
   Ia) $A + B$ $(A\ OR\ B)$ is in K
         If A and B have one of the two truth or voltage values in K, then the connective function $(A + B)$ has one of the values in K also.

   Ib) $A \cdot B$ $(A\ AND\ B)$ is in K
         (Similarly, $(A \cdot B)$ has a value in K.)

IIa)   One of the two truth values, or logical voltage values, 0 in K, has the property that
$$A + 0 = A \quad (A \ OR \ 0 = A)$$

IIb)   One of the values, 1 in K, has the property that
$$A \cdot 1 = A \quad (A \ AND \ 1 = A)$$

IIIa) $A + B = B + A$ ($A \ OR \ B = B \ OR \ A$, Commutativity of "$+$")
(The order of variables with the OR connective is unimportant.)

IIIb) $A \cdot B = B \cdot A$ ($A \ AND \ B = B \ AND \ A$, Commutativity of "$\cdot$")
(The order of variables with the AND connective is unimportant.)

IVa) $A + (B \cdot C) = (A + B) \cdot (A + C)$
$A \ OR \ (B \ AND \ C) = (A \ OR \ B) \ AND \ (A \ OR \ C)$
distributivity of "$+$" over "$\cdot$". The first of the two rules for combining OR and AND.

IVb) $A \cdot (B + C) = A \cdot B + A \cdot C$
$A \ AND \ (B \ OR \ C) = (A \ AND \ B) \ OR \ (A \ AND \ C)$
distributing of "$\cdot$" over "$+$". The second of the two rules for combining OR and AND.

V)   If $0 \neq 1$, in K, then for every variable A, with a value in K, there is a variable $\overline{A}$, ($NOT \ A$), with value in K, such that
$A + \overline{A} = 1$ ($A \ OR \ (NOT \ A) = 1$, is always true)
$A \cdot \overline{A} = 0$ ($A \ AND \ (NOT \ A) = 0$, is always false)
The NOT or complement of a variable has the value opposite, in K, to the value of the variable.

VI) $1 \neq 0$ are in K
Truth and falsity, Positive and Negative are distinct, unequal values.

To make the nature of these axioms clearer, we have interpreted, in the axioms, the values 1 and 0 and the primitive connectives "$+$" and "$\cdot$" as shown in the table of Figure 3.1. Here in the tables we have specified the (binary) value of each functional connective "$+$" and "$\cdot$" for every possible combination of the two-valued variables A, B. Diagrammatically in Fig. 3.1, $(A + B)$ is interpreted to be a black box whose output is 1 if $A \ or \ B$ (or

---

* Note: By convention we shall often drop the dot as in $(A \cdot B)$, writing it simply (AB).

both) equal 1, otherwise 0. $A \cdot B$ is a black box whose output is 1 if A *and* B are both 1, otherwise 0. Thus "$+$" is read: *OR*, "$\cdot$" is read: *AND*.

Axioms Ia, b simply close the system in K so no Boolean function of truth or voltage values in K can have a value not in K. Figure 3.1 clearly satisfies this condition.

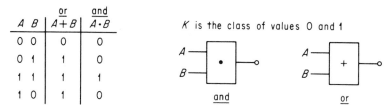

Figure 3.1. A binary interpretation of $+$ and

Axioms IIa, b define 0 and 1 as the identity elements for $+$ and $\cdot$ respectively. This is shown from several viewpoints in Figure 3.2.

Axioms IIa, b tell us we may ignore the order of the variables in addition and multiplication. Thus, we may interchange input wires to these circuits without changing the function.

All the above axioms conform to the rules of high school algebra. IVb also conforms, saying multiplication is distributed over addition. This is familiar. For example, $2 \cdot (3 + 4) = (2 \cdot 3) + (2 \cdot 4)$ in ordinary algebra. But IVa is entirely new; addition is distributive over multiplication. This

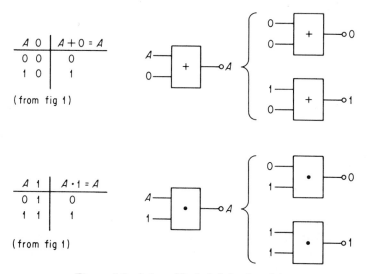

Figure 3.2. Axioms IIa, b defining 0 and 1

is like saying $2 + 3 \cdot 4 = (2 + 3)(2 + 4)$ which illustrates the departure of Boolean Algebra from a numerical algebra. These two axioms give us the rules for factoring second order equations (two levels of gating one of $ANDs$, other of ORs) to higher order equations (more levels), (or the reverse) as we will see later on. That the interpretation of Figure 3.1 satisfies these rules is shown in Figure 3.3 for IVa. Applying the interpretation of Figure 3.1, the table in Figure 3.3 derives the value of each defined sub-function on both sides of the equation. Thus, the value of both functions is built up and shown to be equal. The reader might try duplicating Figure 3.3 for axiom IVb.

IVa $A + BC = (A + B)(A + C)$

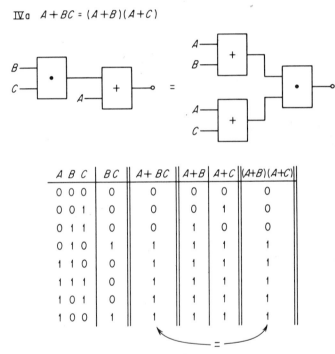

$A\ B\ C$	BC	$A + BC$	$A + B$	$A + C$	$(A + B)(A + C)$
0 0 0	0	0	0	0	0
0 0 1	0	0	0	1	0
0 1 1	0	0	1	0	0
0 1 0	1	1	1	1	1
1 1 0	0	1	1	1	1
1 1 1	0	1	1	1	1
1 0 1	0	1	1	1	1
1 0 0	1	1	1	1	1

Figure 3.3. Consistency of the interpretation of Figure 3.1 with Axiom IVa.

Axiom V introduces the complement of a function (or variable). For our interpretation of Figure 3.1, $\overline{A}$ is called $NOT\ A$. From the definitions of $+$ and $\cdot$ in Figure 3.1 and Axiom V, we can find the table describing $\overline{A}$ as a function of A. $A + \overline{A}$ and $A \cdot \overline{A}$ are plotted in Figure 3.4 and the rows which satisfy V are circled. The rows which satisfy V for both functions are enclosed in a dotted line and define $\overline{A}$ as a function of A as shown in Figure 3.4.

Thus, the complement of 0 is 1 and 1 is 0 as shown in the table of Figure 3.4. The diagrammatic symbol for NOT as used in this text is also shown. The complement is the closest Boolean Algebra comes to a sense of subtraction. Thus, $a + \bar{a} = 1$ might be a definition for $\bar{a} = 1 - a$. This definition has been used at times, but not fruitfully.

Axiom VI is to ensure the algebra does not degenerate to no algebra at all.*

Division as well as subtraction is not defined for Boolean Algebra, but just as the complement performs a job similar to subtraction, so a generalization of the complement (exclusive-or) performs the job of division.

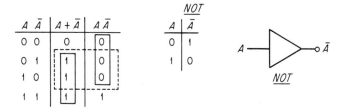

Figure 3.4. Definition of the complement, Axiom V.

Duality: The eight axioms are numbered in pairs, each axiom of the pair is called the dual of the other. The dual of a Boolean expression is found by interchanging all occurrences of $+$ and $\cdot$, and of 1 and 0. The reader should check that all a subscript axioms are duals of the b subscript axioms and vice-versa. Some further examples are:

Function	Dual
$A \cdot 1 + B \cdot 0$	$(A + 0)(B + 1)$
$\bar{A}B + C$	$(\bar{A} + B)C$
$A \cdot (B + \bar{C}) + D$	$(A + B\bar{C})D$
$(\bar{B} + \bar{C})A + BC(AE + F) + G$	$(\bar{B}\bar{C} + A)[B + C + (A + E)F]G$

One must take care with parentheses in taking the dual, particularly of implied parentheses. For example:

Function	Dual
$\bar{A}B + C = (\bar{A}B) + C$	$(\bar{A} + B) \cdot C$

Duality Law: If a theorem is valid, so is its dual. In fact the dual of a proved theorem may be proved by the dual of the proof. This is illustrated in Theo-

---

* Information Theory tells us, in fact, that such a degenerate system with but one (or no) value in K, contains no information at all.

rem 4a. Duality is further discussed following Theorem 13b, (DeMorgan's Theorem).

Theorems, Algebraic Proof

Constructing an algebraic proof in any subject is mostly an art. About the only guiding rule is to try to find an axiom or previously proved theorem which has the same form as one side of the theorem equation, then apply the axiom or theorem. View your progress and the next step with what intuition you can muster and proceed boldly to reduce this to the other side of the theorem equation.

Theorem 1a: 0 is unique

Theorem 1b: 1 is unique

That there exist only one 1 and one 0 with the properties defined in the axioms is a small but necessary property for subsequent theorems. We skip over the proof here as we'll do for other less significant theorems, or theorems that are essentially corollaries.

In the subsequent proofs, the use of IIIa, b will be used implicitly without actually showing them as steps in the proof.

Theorem 2a: $A \cdot A = A$

Theorem 2b: $A + A = A$

Proof: (Note that the right hand side of the equation has the form of IIa.)

$$
\begin{aligned}
A &= A + 0 && \text{IIa} \\
  &= A + A\overline{A} && \text{V} \\
  &= (A + A)(A + \overline{A}) && \text{IVa} \\
  &= (A + A) \cdot 1 && \text{V} \\
  &= A + A \quad q.e.d. && \text{IIb}
\end{aligned}
$$

Figure 3.5 interprets these dual theorems in terms of Figure 3.1.

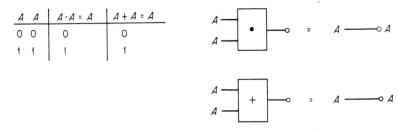

A	A	$A \cdot A = A$	$A + A = A$
0	0	0	0
1	1	1	1

Figure 3.5. Interpretation of Theorem 2a, b.

Theorem 3: $\overline{\overline{A}} = A$

   Proof: $\overline{\overline{A}} = \overline{\overline{A}} \cdot 1$ IIb

            $= \overline{\overline{A}}(A + \overline{A})$ V

            $= \overline{\overline{A}}A + \overline{\overline{A}}\overline{A}$ IVb

            $= \overline{\overline{A}}A + 0$ V (letting $X = \overline{A}$, $\overline{\overline{A}} \cdot \overline{A} = \overline{X} \cdot X = 0$)

            $= \overline{\overline{A}}A + A\overline{A}$ V

            $= A(\overline{\overline{A}} + \overline{A})$ IVb

            $= A \cdot 1$ V (letting $X = \overline{A}$, $\overline{\overline{A}} + \overline{A} = \overline{X} + X = 1$)

            $= A$ *q.e.d.*   IIb

    Figure 3.6 interprets this theorem in terms of Figure 3.4. Note this theorem is its own dual. Functions with this property are called self-dual.

Theorem 4a: $A + 1 = 1$

   1) Proof: $A + 1 = A + A + \overline{A}$ V

   2) $= A + \overline{A}$ 2b

   3) $= 1$ *q.e.d.*   V

To demonstrate the duality law, that the dual of the proof proves the dual of the theorem, we prove the dual of 4a by applying the dual axioms and theorems for each step in the proof of 4a.

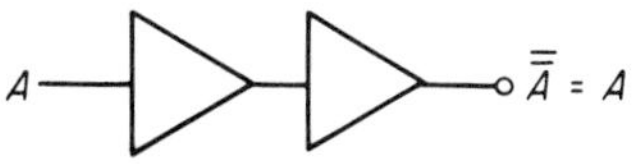

Figure 3.6. Interpretation of Theorem 3.

The dual of 4a is:

Theorem 4b: $A \cdot 0 = 0$

   1) Proof: $A \cdot 0 = AA\overline{A}$ V

   2) $= A\overline{A}$ 2a

   3) $= 0$ V

4b is familiar but 4a is peculiar to Boolean Algebra. This brings us to Boolean arithmetic as described in the next six theorems.

Theorem 5a: $0 + 0 = 0$

Theorem 5b: $1 \cdot 1 = 1$

Theorem 6a: $1 + 0 = 1$

Theorem 6b: $1 \cdot 0 = 0$

Theorem 7a: $\overline{0} = 1$

Theorem 7b: $\overline{1} = 0$

Theorem 8a: $A(A + B) = A$

Theorem 8b: $A + AB = A$

Proof:
$$
\begin{aligned}
A + AB &= A \cdot 1 + AB && \text{IIb} \\
&= A(B + \overline{B}) + AB && \text{V} \\
&= AB + A\overline{B} + AB && \text{IVb} \\
&= AB + A\overline{B} && \text{2b} \\
&= A(B + \overline{B}) && \text{IVb} \\
&= A \cdot 1 && \text{V} \\
&= A \quad q.e.d. && \text{IIb}
\end{aligned}
$$

These are two very important theorems for minimization. Theorem 8b is interpreted in Figure 3.7. In this case, the minimization theorem shows that two electronic circuits $(+, \cdot)$ can be replaced by an equivalent short circuit, a mere piece of wire. All our minimizations of logic circuits will not yield such spectacular economies, however.

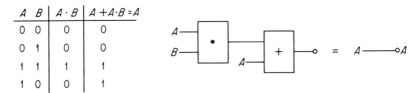

A	B	$A \cdot B$	$A + A \cdot B = A$
0	0	0	0
0	1	0	0
1	1	1	1
1	0	0	1

Figure 3.7. Interpretation of Theorem 8b.

Theorem 9a: $\quad A(\overline{A} + B) = AB$

Theorem 9b: $\quad A + \overline{A}B = A + B$

Proof:
$$
\begin{aligned}
A + \overline{A}B &= (A + \overline{A})(A + B) && \text{IVa} \\
&= 1 \cdot (A + B) && \text{V} \\
&= A + B \quad q.e.d. && \text{IIb}
\end{aligned}
$$

Theorems 9a, b are two other very important minimization theorems.

Theorem 10a: $\quad \overline{A}(A + B) = \overline{A}B$

Theorem 10b: $\quad \overline{A} + AB = \overline{A} + B$

The above two minimization theorems are in the nature of corollaries to 9a, b.

Theorem 11: $\quad (A + B)(\overline{A} + C) = AC + \overline{A}B$

Proof:
$$
\begin{aligned}
(A + B)(\overline{A} + C) &= X(\overline{A} + C) && \text{Letting } X = A + B \\
&= X\overline{A} + XC && \text{IVb} \\
&= (A + B)\overline{A} + (A + B)C && \text{Substitution} \\
&= A\overline{A} + \overline{A}B + AC + BC && \text{IVb} \\
&= \overline{A}B + AC + BC && \text{V, IIa}
\end{aligned}
$$

Now if the theorem is true, BC must be redundant, not necessary. We can hope to apply one of the minimization theorems 8a, b, 9a, b. But to do so requires BC to be expanded in some way. The axioms that could do this are IIb followed by V.

$$BC = 1 \cdot B \cdot C \qquad\qquad\qquad \text{IIb}$$
$$= (A + \bar{A})BC \qquad\qquad \text{V}$$
$$= ABC + \bar{A}BC \qquad\qquad \text{IVb}$$
$$\bar{A}B + AC + BC = \bar{A}B + AC + ABC + \bar{A}BC \text{ by above}$$
$$= x + y + By + xC \qquad \text{Letting } x = \bar{A}B$$
$$y = AC$$
$$= x + y \qquad\qquad\qquad \text{8b (twice)}$$
$$= \bar{A}B + AC \ \ q.e.d. \qquad\qquad \text{Substitution}$$

Notice that this theorem is self-dual.

Rather than develop the algebraic theorems further in the algebra, we shall introduce another interpretation of the axioms (other than Figure 3.1) which will be useful later, and in which theorems and their proofs may be better understood intuitively.

The Karnaugh Map Interpretation of Boolean Algebra

We let the class K be the class of all points in a given square or rectangle. The elements of K are as many sub-rectangles of K as there are variables

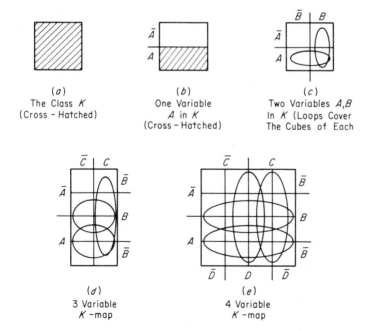

(a)
The Class K
(Cross – Hatched)

(b)
One Variable
A in K
(Cross – Hatched)

(c)
Two Variables A,B
In K (Loops Cover
The Cubes of Each

(d)
3 Variable
K-map

(e)
4 Variable
K-map

Figure 3.8. Karnaugh Maps of zero through four variables.

in the function under discussion, such that all possible overlap of these rectangles are made.

This class is met geometrically by the Karnaugh Maps of one through four variables shown in Figure 3.8. For all possible overlappings of more than four variables, we must go to a three dimensional cube for K (or higher) as we will see later.

The primitive connectives are interpreted as follows: $A + B$ is the area of A together with the area of B (the area of A OR B); $A \cdot B$ is the area common to both A AND B. Figure 3.9 illustrates these.

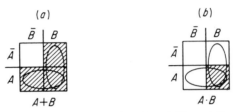

Loops cover the area of each variable and the cross-hatch indicates the area defined by the function

Figure 3.9. Karnaugh Map interpretation of the AND and the OR.

Now we must show this interpretation satisfies the axioms.

In the K-maps below, the loops indicate the cubes included in the set of each variable. Note that if a connective forms a set out of compound sets, the latter are the variables. Cross-hatching indicates the cubes of the new set formed from the variables by the particular connective shown below the map.

Axioms

Ia. $A + B$ is in K, if A, B in K

Ib. $A \cdot B$ is in K, if A, B in K

IIa. $A + 0 = A$

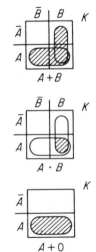

Since 0 is not a primitive element, this axiom is in the way of defining 0 by a property. From the map, it is clear that 0 must be interpreted as the absence of a set, the empty set.

IIb. $A \cdot 1 = A$

Again this defines 1 by this property. The only way to make the axiom reasonable under our interpretation is if 1 is the presence of all sets, namely the K set.

IIIa. $A + B = B + A$

IIIb. $A \cdot B = B \cdot A$

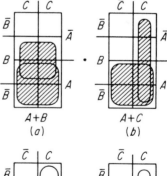

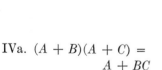

IVa. $(A + B)(A + C) =$
$\quad\quad\quad A + BC$

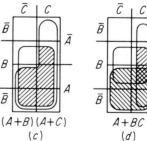

The intersection or area common (c) to the sets $A + B$ (a) and $A + C$ (b) is the same as the set formed by $A + BC$ (d).

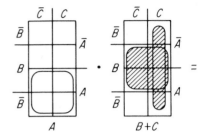

IVb. $A \cdot (B + C) = AB + AC$

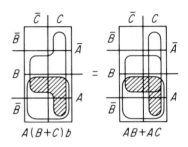

V. $A + \overline{A} = 1$ $A \cdot \overline{A} = 0$

This axiom introduces a new set in reference to a given set ($\overline{A}$ is a function of A) and is defined by these two properties. In the K-map in order for (A + anything) to be 1 (the whole K set), the "anything" or $\overline{A}$ must be *at most* all the area of K, namely equal to 1. But if the intersection $A \cdot \overline{A}$ equals zero, $\overline{A}$ cannot be a part of A. So $\overline{A}$ must be the set of all areas in K not part of set A.

VI. There exists x, y in K such $x \neq y$.

x and y are sets in K, but part of set x (the α cube) is not in set y, and part of set y (the β cube) is not in set x.

The Karnaugh Map in Theorem Proving

Many complex theorems not obvious in the algebra can be seen immediately in a K-map. But further, a better understanding is available by bringing another attribute of intelligence to bear on the algebra, our geometrical intuition.

Theorem 11a: $(A + B)(C + D) = AC + AD + BC + BD$

Theorem 11b: $AB + CD = (A + C)(A + D)(B + C)(B + D)$

This can be proved by drawing the Karnaugh Map of both sides of the equation and noting their identity. Figure 3.10 shows both sides of 11b mapped step by step. These two theorems are a generalization of axioms IVa, b.

Theorem 11b: $AB + CD = (A + C)(A + D)(B + C)(B + D)$

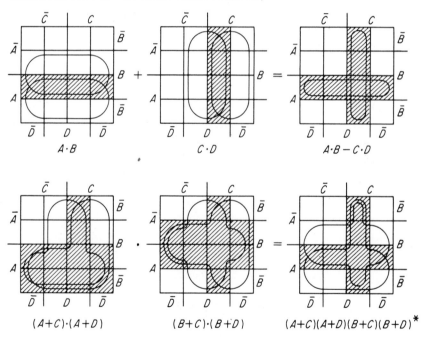

Figure 3.10. Karnaugh Map proof of Theorem 11b.

Theorem 12a: $(A + B)(C + D) = (A + B)C + (A + B)D$

Theorem 12b: $AB + CD = (AB + C)(AB + D)$

These two theorems which follow directly from axioms IVa, b are very useful with the $NAND$ and NOR functions discussed later.

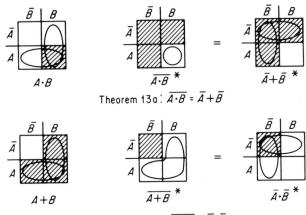

Figure 3.11. K-Map proof of DeMorgan's Theorems.

Theorem 13a: $\overline{AB} = \overline{A} + \overline{B}$

Theorem 13b: $\overline{A + B} = \overline{AB}$

These two theorems are called DeMorgan's theorems and are funda-mental in Boolean Algebra. Karnaugh Map proofs of 13a, b are shown in Figure 3.11. These theorems tell us how to complement any expression in Boolean Algebra. A block diagram interpretation is shown in Figure 3.12. Looked at another way, applying Theorem 18 and Theorem 3 we find:

Theorem 13a': $AB = \overline{\overline{A} + \overline{B}}$

Theorem 13b': $A + B = \overline{\overline{A}\overline{B}}$

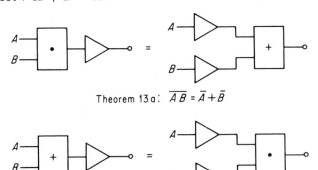

Figure 3.12. Block diagram of DeMorgan's Theorems.

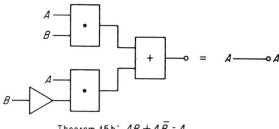

Theorem 15b: $AB + A\overline{B} = A$

Figure 3.13. Block diagram for Minimization Theorem.

These theorems tell us that by interchanging 1's and 0's of the variables and the function (that is, complementing variables and function) we interchange AND and OR. This interchange of AND and OR (as well as 1 and 0) is what we have referred to as duality. Thus, the AND and OR are duals. In general then, another way of getting the dual of a function is to interchange 1's and 0's of the variables and the function.

Theorem 14a: $\overline{AB + CD} = (\overline{A} + \overline{B})(\overline{C} + \overline{D})$

Theorem 14b: $\overline{(A + B)(C + D)} = \overline{AB} + \overline{CD}$

These are generalizations of DeMorgan's theorems.

Theorem 15a: $(A + B)(A + \overline{B}) = A$

Theorem 15b: $AB + A\overline{B} = A$

Theorem 15b is of fundamental importance to most of the minimization techniques discussed later. A block diagram is shown in Figure 3.13 and a K-map proof is shown in Figure 3.14.

Theorem 16a: $A + (B + C) = (A + B) + C \overset{df}{=} A + B + C$
(The latter by definition)

Theorem 16b: $A(BC) = (AB)C = ABC$ (The latter by definition)

These are the associative laws which essentially say we may drop the parentheses as shown in the definitions.

Theorem 15b: $AB + A\overline{B} = A$

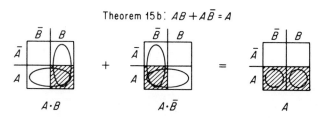

Figure 3.14. K-Map proof of Minimization Theorem.

The following three theorems tell us we can add or multiply both sides of an equation with the same variable (or function) or complement both sides, without changing the equality.

Theorem 17a: if $A = B$ then $A + C = B + C$
Theorem 17b: if $A = B$ then $A \cdot C = B \cdot C$
Theorem 18: if $A = B$ then $\overline{A} = \overline{B}$
Theorem 19a: if $A + B = 0$ then $A = B = 0$
Theorem 19b: if $AB = 1$ then $A = B = 1$

These last two theorems follow directly from Figure 3.1.

Canonical Forms and Expansions

Fundamental to Boolean Algebra is the existence of an algebraic form of any function which explicitly gives the value of the function for every combination of variable values. This is called the canonical form of the function.

Closely associated with the canonical form is the expansion theorem which expands any function in a series about any of its variables. By expanding about all variables of a function, the canonical form results. This form is the essence of synthesis, as we will see. Applying the expansion theorem in reverse is the first major step in minimization. Clearly this is a theorem of some importance since it relates all of the algebraic forms of a function to each other, from the irredundant minimal form to the canonical form.

To allay ambiguity, some definitions are in order.

Def: A *literal* refers either to a variable or its complement, (A or $\overline{A}$).

Def: A *product term* is all literals in a group which are multiplied together, ($A \cdot B \cdot C$).

Def: A *sum term* is all of any group of literals which are summed together, ($A + B + C$).
    If the context is clear or meant to apply to both, just *term* will be used.

Def: A *normal term* is a product or sum term in which no literal appears more than once.

Def: A *canonical term* of a function is a term containing exactly one occurrence of each of the literals of the function, [$f(A, B, C) = A\overline{B}C + \ldots$ shows one canonical product term of an example-function of three variables].

Def: A *normal form* of a function is a normal sum of normal product terms or a normal product of normal sum terms. This will sometimes be referred to as a second order equation or two levels of gating.

Def: A *sum of products form* of a function is one where the product terms are summed $(AB + A\overline{C} + BC$ for instance). We shall abbreviate this S of P.

Def: A *product of sums form* of a function is one where the sum terms are multiplied, $[(A + B)(A + \overline{C})(B + C)$ for example]. We shall abbreviate this P of S.

Def: A *canonical form* of a function is one where all terms are canonical terms appearing only once. The canonical form of a function using *AND*s and *OR*s has two dual forms, P of S and S of P.

The canonical forms of a function are unique within the sense of duality, thus their importance in an algebra with an infinite variety of equivalent function forms. Note that a canonic form is also normal, but a normal form need not be canonic.

Canonical Expansion Theorems:

Theorem 20a: $f(A_1, \ldots, A_n)$
$$= f(A_1, \ldots, A_n) + A_1\overline{A}_1 + A_2\overline{A}_2 + \ldots A_n\overline{A}_n$$
Theorem 20b: $f(A_1, \ldots, A_n)$
$$= f(A_1, \ldots, A_n)(A_1 + \overline{A}_1)(A_2 + \overline{A}_2) \ldots (A_n + \overline{A}_n)$$

Proof: Clearly the function in 20a is merely having 0 added to it while in 20b the function is just being multiplied by 1.

By applying the distributive axiom IVa to a function after expanding with Theorem 20a, the product of sums canonical form will result, taking care to eliminate redundant terms.

By applying the dual distributive axiom IVb to a function after expanding with Theorem 20b, the sum of products canonical form will result, taking care to eliminate redundant terms.

I. *Example of Theorem 20a:* Get the P of S canonical form of this equation:

$f = (A + B)(B + C)$

$\quad = (A + B)(B + C) + A\overline{A} + B\overline{B} + C\overline{C}$ Th. 20a

Let $x = A\overline{A} + B\overline{B} + C\overline{C}$, $y = A + B$, $z = B + C$

$f = yz + x = (y + x)(z + x)$ IVa

$\quad = (A + B + A\overline{A} + B\overline{B} + C\overline{C})(B + C + A\overline{A} + B\overline{B} + C\overline{C})$ Subs.

$\quad = (A + B + C\overline{C})(B + C + A\overline{A})$ Th. 8b

Let $x = A + B$, $y = B + C$

$f = (x + C\overline{C})(y + A\overline{A}) = (x + C)(x + \overline{C})(y + A)(y + \overline{A})$ IVa

$\quad = (A + B + C)(A + B + \overline{C})(A + B + C)(\overline{A} + B + C)$ Subs.

$\quad = (A + B + C)(A + B + \overline{C})(\overline{A} + B + C)$ Th. 2a

II. *Example of Theorem 20b:* Get the S of P canonical form of this equation:

$$f = A\overline{C} + \overline{B}C$$
$$= (A\overline{C} + \overline{B}C)(A + \overline{A})(B + \overline{B})(C + \overline{C}) \qquad \text{Th. 20b}$$
$$= AB\overline{C} + A\overline{B}\overline{C} + A\overline{B}C + \overline{A}\overline{B}C$$

Clearly we need only multiply each term by the variables it is lacking.

Notice that although this application of the canonical expansion yields the canonic form, applied inversely:

$$AB + A\overline{B} = A(B + \overline{B}) = A \cdot 1 = A$$

which is our important minimization theorem of 15b.

A special case is the expansion theorem which expands a function around one of its variables. Applied to every variable of a function it yields a canonic form.

Noting that

$$A \cdot f(A, B, \ldots) = A \cdot f(1, B, \ldots)$$
$$\overline{A} \cdot f(A, B, \ldots) = \overline{A} \cdot f(0, B, \ldots)$$

and

$$f(A_1, \ldots, A_k, \ldots, A_n) = f(A_1, \ldots, A_k, \ldots, A_n) \cdot (A_k + \overline{A}_k)$$
$$= A_k \cdot f(\ldots, A_k, \ldots,) + \overline{A}_k \cdot f(\ldots, A_k, \ldots,)$$

we get the expansion theorems:

Theorem 21a: $f(A_1, \ldots, A_k, \ldots, A_n)$
$$= A_k \cdot f(A_1, \ldots, 1, \ldots, A_n) + \overline{A}_k \cdot f(A_1, \ldots, 0, \ldots, A_n)$$

Theorem 21b: $f(A_1, \ldots, A_k, \ldots, A_n)$
$$= [A_k + f(A_1, . 0, . . , A_n)] \cdot [\overline{A}_k + f(A, \ldots, 1, \ldots, A_n)]$$

III. Example: Expand f about the B variable using theorem 21a.

$$f = \overline{A}\overline{B}\overline{C} + BC + AB + AC$$
$$= B \cdot (\overline{1} \cdot \overline{A}\overline{C} + 1 \cdot C + 1 \cdot A + AC) + \overline{B} \cdot (\overline{0}\overline{A}\overline{C} + 0 \cdot C + 0 \cdot A + AC)$$
$$= B(C + A + AC) + \overline{B}(\overline{A}\overline{C} + AC)$$
$$= B(A + C) + \overline{B}(\overline{A}\overline{C} + AC)$$

Application of this theorem has the effect that when multiplied out the B literal appears in every term.

For insight into the canonical form let us plot both the problem function of Example II above ($A\overline{C} + \overline{B}C$) and the canonical form of the function derived on K-maps. In Figure 3.15 where the canonical form is plotted, note that its map is unique compared to (a) in that the canonical terms loop exactly one square each in the function; this is characteristic of canonical forms. The importance of this for synthesis will be seen in the next chapter.

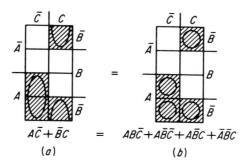

$$A\bar{C} + \bar{B}C \quad = \quad AB\bar{C} + A\bar{B}\bar{C} + A\bar{B}C + \bar{A}\bar{B}C$$
$$(a) \qquad\qquad\qquad (b)$$

Figure 3.15. K-Map of canonical
form of a function, Example II.

Problems

1) Write the dual of the following functions directly:
 a) $\bar{A}BC + B\bar{C} + \bar{A}\bar{B}$
 b) $(A + \bar{B} + \bar{C})(A + \bar{C})(B + C)$
 c) $(A\bar{B} + C)D + (\bar{A} + B)(B + C)E$
 d) $[(B + \bar{C})D + E](\bar{A} + B)C$

2) Prove the following theorems algebraically:
 a) $\bar{A}B\bar{C} + \bar{A}BC + \bar{A}\bar{B}C = \bar{A}B + \bar{A}C$
 b) $B\bar{C} + \bar{A}B + \bar{A}C = B\bar{C} + \bar{A}C$
 c) $A\bar{B} + \bar{A}B = \overline{AB + \bar{A}\bar{B}}$
 d) $AB + BC + AC = (A + B)(B + C)(A + C)$

3) Prove the following theorems with Karnaugh Maps:
 a) $AB + \bar{A}C + BC = AB + \bar{A}C$
 b) $\overline{ABC + A\bar{B}\bar{C} + \bar{A}B\bar{C} + \bar{A}\bar{B}C} = \bar{A}BC + \bar{A}\bar{B}\bar{C} + AB\bar{C} + A\bar{B}C$
 c) if $A\bar{B} + \bar{A}B = C$ then $A\bar{C} + \bar{A}C = B$
 d) if $A = B$ then $A\bar{B} + \bar{A}B = 0$

  (This is the closest Boolean Algebra comes to division.)

4) Expand the following functions about the A variable in their present
 form:
 a) $AB\bar{C} + AD + BC + \bar{A}CD + \bar{A}D$
 b) $BC + C\bar{D} + AC$
 c) $(\bar{A} + B)(\bar{B} + \bar{C})(A + D)(A + B + \bar{D})$
 d) $(C + \bar{D})(B + C + D)(\bar{A} + D)$

5) Expand the following functions to their canonical form P of S or S of P as indicated by their present form:
   a) $AB + \overline{A}C + BC$
   b) $A + B\overline{C}D + CD$
   c) $(A + \overline{B})(\overline{A} + C)B$
   d) $(\overline{A} + B)(A + D)(\overline{B} + \overline{C})$

References

Boole, G., *An Investigation of the Laws of Thought*. New York: Dover Publications, Inc., 1954.

Copi, I. M., *Symbolic Logic*. New York: The Macmillan Co., 1954.

Huntington, E. V., "Sets of Independent Postulates for the Algebra of Logic," Trans. Amer. Math. Soc., **V5**, (1904), pp. 288–309.

Rosenbloom, *Mathematical Logic*. New York: Dover Publications, Inc., 1950.

Serrel, R., "Elements of Boolean Algebra for the Study of Information Handling Systems," Proc. IRE, **V41** (1953), pp. 1366–1379. Corrections: ibid., **V42**, (1954), p. 475.

Shannon, C. E., "Symbolic Analysis of Relay and Switching Circuits," AIEE Trans., **V57**, (1938), pp. 713–723.

Appendix

Theorems of Boolean Algebra:

IIa. $A + 0 = A$

IIb. $A \cdot 1 = A$

IIIa. $A + B = B + A$

IIIb. $A \cdot B = B \cdot A$

IVa. $A + (B \cdot C) = (A + B) \cdot (A + C)$

IVb. $A \cdot (B + C) = A \cdot B + A \cdot C$

V. $A + \overline{A} = 1$

       $A \cdot \overline{A} = 0$

1a.   0 is unique

1b.   1 is unique

2a. $A \cdot A = A$

2b. $A + A = A$

3. $\overline{\overline{A}} = A$

4a. $A + 1 = 1$

4b. $A \cdot 0 = 0$

5a. $0 + 0 = 0$

5b. $1 \cdot 1 = 1$

6a. $1 + 0 = 1$

6b. $1 \cdot 0 = 0$

7a. $\bar{0} = 1$

7b. $\bar{1} = 0$

8a. $A(A + B) = A$

8b. $A + AB = A$

9a. $A(\bar{A} + B) = AB$

9b. $A + \bar{A}B = A + B$

10a. $\bar{A}(A + B) = \bar{A}B$

10b. $\bar{A} + AB = \bar{A} + B$

11. $(A + B)(\bar{A} + C) = AC + \bar{A}B$

11a. $(A + B)(C + D) = AC + AD + BC + BD$

11b. $AB + CD = (A + C)(A + D)(B + C)(B + D)$

12a. $(A + B)(C + D) = (A + B)C + (A + B)D$

12b. $AB + CD = (AB + C)(AB + D)$

13a. $\overline{AB} = \bar{A} + \bar{B}$

13b. $\overline{A + B} = \bar{A}\bar{B}$

13a'. $AB = \overline{\bar{A} + \bar{B}}$

13b'. $A + B = \overline{\bar{A}\bar{B}}$

14a. $AB + CD = (\bar{A} + \bar{B})(\bar{C} + \bar{D})$

14b. $\overline{(A + B)(C + D)} = \bar{A}\bar{B} + \bar{C}\bar{D}$

15a. $(A + B)(A + \bar{B}) = A$

15b. $AB + A\bar{B} = A$

16a. $A + (B + C) = (A + B) + C \stackrel{df}{=} A + B + C$

16b. $A(BC) = (AB)C \stackrel{df}{=} ABC$

17a. if $A = B$ then $A + C = B + C$

17b. if $A = B$ then $A \cdot C = B \cdot C$

18.   if $A = B$ then $\bar{A} = \bar{B}$

19a. if $A + B = 0$ then $A = B = 0$

19b. if $AB = 1$ then $A = B = 1$

20a. $f(A_1, \ldots, A_n) = f(A_1, \ldots, A_n) + A_1\bar{A}_1 + A_2\bar{A}_2 + \ldots A_n\bar{A}_n$

20b. $f(A_1, \ldots, A_n)$
$$= f(A_1, \ldots, A_n)(A_1 + \bar{A}_1)(A_2 + \bar{A}_2) \ldots (A_n + \bar{A}_n)$$

21a. $f(A_1, \ldots, A_k, \ldots, A_n)$
$$= A_k f(A_1, \ldots, 1, \ldots, A_n) + \bar{A}_k f(A_1, \ldots, 0, A_n)$$

21b. $f(A_1, \ldots, A_k, \ldots, A_n)$
$$= [A_k + f(A_1, \ldots, 0, \ldots, A_n)][\bar{A}_k + f(A_1, \ldots, 1, A_n)]$$

LOGIC DESIGN

4

Boolean Functions

There are four dimensions to a Boolean function which a logician uses to characterize a net of switching elements. Each dimension gives him a different way of looking at the function and each has its own context of usefulness. They are:

1) function table
2) algebraic expression
3) block diagram
4) timing chart

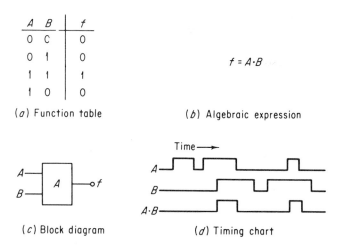

A	B	f
0	C	0
0	1	0
1	1	1
1	0	0

(a) Function table

$f = A \cdot B$

(b) Algebraic expression

(c) Block diagram

Time ⟶

(d) Timing chart

Figure 4.1. The four dimensions of the AND function.

Figure 4.1 shows the AND function of two variables in each of its four dimensions.

Function Table: This is a tabular form of the function giving the function value for each of the possible combinations of the variables. Although the order of the variable values need not be cyclic, this property will be so often used in tabular forms, the Karnaugh map and later in sequential circuits, that it is best to get used to the form. Conventional texts use an ordering corresponding to consecutive binary numbers, but since this form has no advantage at all except a systematic way of writing all the numbers down, the form will not be encouraged. A systematic way of writing a cyclic code is shown in Figure 4.2. In general for n variables, there will be 2^n rows in the table corresponding to all possible arrangements of zero and one among n variables.*

The function table in more than one dimension gives us the Karnaugh map as a special case, practical up to functions of six variables as we will later see. The function table gives us an overall view of the ones and zeros of the function and in the Karnaugh map, patterns can be recognized facil-

---

* Letting zero be implied by the absence of a one, the number of rows may be looked at as the sum of the number of ways $K = 0, 1, 2 \ldots$ up to n ones may be distributed among n variables. This is a summation on K of the number of combinations of n things taken K at a time:

$$\sum_{K=0}^{n} \frac{n!}{(n-k)!K!} = 2^n$$

$K = 0$ is the all zero row, $K = n$ is the all one row, $K = 1$ is all rows with exactly one, 1 and so on.

Cyclic Code:

1. For n variables first write a column of $\frac{1}{2} \cdot 2^n$ zero's followed by $\frac{1}{2} \cdot 2$ ones.
2. To the right, write a column of $\frac{1}{4} \cdot 2^n$ zeros followed by alternating $\frac{1}{2} \cdot 2^n$ zero's and ones except the last group of zeros has only $\frac{1}{4} \cdot 2^n$ zeros.
3. Continue multiplying the figures (2) by $\frac{1}{2}$ each time until equals $\frac{1}{2^n}$

Two variables	Three variables	Four variables
0 0	0 0 0	0 0 0 0
0 1	0 0 1	0 0 0 1
1 1	0 1 1	0 0 1 1
1 0	0 1 0	0 0 1 0
	1 1 0	0 1 1 0
	1 1 1	0 1 1 1
	1 0 1	0 1 0 1
	1 0 0	0 1 0 0
		1 1 0 0
		1 1 0 1
		1 1 1 1
		1 1 1 0
		1 0 1 0
		1 0 1 1
		1 0 0 1
		1 0 0 0

Figure 4.2. A systematic method of generating a cyclic code.

itating the design. Its form is also convenient for the initial specification of a function since the very construction assures us that once completely filled in, the function is completely specified for all possible values of the variables. Further, once an algebraic expression has been reduced to such a table, it is completely analyzed. Thus, the function table forms the starting point of synthesis and the end point of analysis.

The table also has an invariant appeal, for although there is an infinite number of algebraic expressions for the same function, they all have the same function table. This property is useful in proving theorems by perfect induction. If and only if analysis of both sides of an equation yields the same function table for each, the equation is a valid theorem, since both sides have been shown to have the same values for all values of the variables. We used this method earlier in K-map form.

The main drawback of the table is its unwieldy size.

Algebraic Expression: As uniqueness was one of the main attributes of the function table, so a variety of equivalent forms is one of the important features of the algebra.

One algebraic form of a function can be the most concise dimension expressing the function. The algebra can express logical properties of a switching network invariant to the physical form of the network. Another form of the function may be useful for describing the network's construction. And of course algebraic manipulation can be a very useful tool for optimizing the network implementation according to some criteria.

Although the algebra gives us the concision lacking in the tabular form, its disadvantages lie largely in the geometrical insight that was lost in going from tables to algebra. We will later find tabular methods a powerful supplement to algebraic manipulation.

Block Diagram: While the function table and logical expression gave us properties independent of any circuit configuration, the block diagram shows the topology of a particular electronic circuit implementation of the logical function. It is an abstraction from the actual circuit leaving out irrelevancies to the logical function of the network. Since the elements are black boxes and connecting lines, the circuits within might be of any electronic technology.

The block diagram conveys much useful information about the logical circuit unexpressed by the other dimensions. For example the number of levels of gating is explicit, giving a notion of the delay a signal will encounter from inputs to output. Also an expression: $(A \cdot B + C + D)$ $(A \cdot B + E + F)$ does not indicate, as the block diagram of Figure 4.3 does, that the $A \cdot B$ term is generated once and goes to two places. Thus the block diagram is more realistically oriented than the algebra.

Finally, given the circuits for each black box, the block diagram serves as an actual wiring diagram more useful than the circuit diagram since what has been abstracted is exactly the wire connections among the basic circuit-logic elements.

In spite of its closeness to the circuit form, the block diagram contains all the logic information of the function and we will find that it too can often be manipulated, as is the algebra, for optimization.

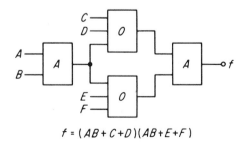

$$f = (AB + C + D)(AB + E + F)$$

Figure 4.3. Block diagram shows explicitly a two output AND while algebra does not.

Timing Chart: This practical dimension is indispensable in the synthesis, analysis, or de-bugging of a complex switching network of more than modest size. Although it is used extensively in computer design it is more for the complications of timing in large systems which will not concern us here. Its purpose is to bring the element of time into Boolean algebra. In any sequential switching network the timed relation between signals is very important and best expressed in a timing chart. In an asynchronous system the signals are all in a timed relation with respect to each other with no time base. We will have use for the timing chart in the latter case in the chapters on asynchronous sequential circuits.

The Number of Functions: The number of significant Boolean functions is of interest. Since, for n variables, each may have one of two values, there are 2^n combinations, or rows in the function table. Since each of the 2^n rows may be a zero or one for a function, there are 2^{2^n} functions of n variables. This number goes up rather dramatically. Values for up to six variables are given in Figure 4.4. Such numbers exceed the tensile strength of imagination. We need a comparative yardstick: Eddington estimated[*] the total number N of "protons and electrons in the universe" is given by $N = 3/2 \times 136 \times 2^{256}$. But note that the number of functions of but 9 variables is $2^{2^9} = 2^{512}$. Thus the number of two valued functions of nine variables is considerably greater than even the estimated number of protons and electrons in the universe. However, many of these functions are equivalent under permutation of the variables. Thus:

$$\overline{A}B \text{ and } A\overline{B}$$

are counted as different functions in the above figures. But if we have a box that will perform the one, it will perform the other by interchanging inputs. Comparison of some of the numbers of these classes of functions, (members of each class being equivalent under a permutation or rearrangement of the variables) is shown in Figure 4.4.

Another less justifiable criterion for reducing the number of functions, that has been used in the past, is to consider classes of functions equivalent under inversions as well as permutations of variables. Under this criterion, not only would the above functions be equivalent but

$$A \cdot B \text{ and } \overline{A} \cdot \overline{B}$$

as well. One can be gotten from the other by inverting some or (in this case) all of the variables. Some of the numbers of classes of functions with this criterion are given for comparison in Figure 4.4.

The Appendix gives a listing of the functions of three variables.

[*] A. S. Eddington, *Fundamental Theory* (New York: Cambridge University Press, 1946), p. 283.

# of Variables n	# of functions of n variables 2^{2^n} *		# of classes of functions of n variables; members of each class equivalent under permutation and/or inversion of variables		# of classes of functions of n variables; members of each class equivalent under permutation of variables (only)
		Approximately		Approximately	
1	4	4	3	3	4
2	16	16	6	6	14
3	256	256	22	22	78
4	65,536	$65\frac{1}{2}$ thous(+)	402	400	3,976
5	4,294,967,296	$4\frac{1}{4}$ billion(+)	1,228,158	$4\frac{1}{4}$ million(+)	—
6	18,446,744,073,709,551,616	2×10^{19}(-)	400,507,806,843,728	4×10^{14}(+)	—

* For higher n note that $2^{2^n} = (2^{2^{n-1}})^2$ thus each additional variable squares the number of functions

Figure 4.4. Table of numbers of functions of n variables.

Analysis

There are three general areas of logical design: analysis, synthesis, and minimization. Analysis is the process of writing the function table from a block diagram or equation; synthesis is the process of deriving equations from a function table; minimization involves manipulation of function tables and equations culminating with implementation in a block diagram with some parameter (s) minimized. We will discuss synthesis and minimization in later sections. Here we are concerned with analysis.

Notice that the canonical form of a function has a one to one correspondence with the function table. Thus for two variables

$$f = \overline{A}\overline{B}f_0 + \overline{A}Bf_1 + ABf_3 + A\overline{B}f_2$$
$$= (A + B + f_0)(A + \overline{B} + f_1)(\overline{A} + \overline{B} + f_3)(\overline{A} + B + f_2)$$

Each term of the canonical form corresponds to a row of the function table. The term $\overline{A}\overline{B}f_0$ means that when $\overline{A}\overline{B} = 1$, $f = f_0$. Since $\overline{A}\overline{B} = 1$ means $A = B = 0$, this term corresponds to the function table row zero-zero with function value f_0. There are 2^n terms in both (dual) forms of the canonical form corresponding to the 2^n rows of the table.

Rules for Analyzing a Block Diagram or Equation:
1) Block diagram: Write the Boolean equation directly from and corresponding to the block diagram.
2) Equations: Apply the necessary theorems to reduce the equations to normal form. The most useful theorems for this will be: DeMorgan's theorems, the distributive laws, $A + AB = A$, $A \cdot A = A$, $A \cdot \overline{A} = 0$, $A + 0 = A$, (and duals).
3) Apply the most appropriate expansion theorem until the equation is in canonical form. (This need not be done explicitly as will be shown but this step is always present in some implicit form.)
4a) Sum of Products form: Assign each term (not multiplied by zero) to its corresponding row in the function table. This means replacing each uncomplemented variable with a 1 and each complemented variable with a 0. (For example $A\overline{B}C$ should be assigned to row 101, $\overline{A}\overline{B}C$ to row 001). In the function column assign a 1 to each row for which there is a term of the function associated, 0 to all others.
4b) Product of Sums form: Assign each term (which is not summed with 1) to its corresponding row in the function table taking care to interchange the sense of ones and zeros in so doing. That is replacing each *complemented* variable with a 1 and each *uncomplemented* variable with a 0. (For example, $(\overline{A} + B + C)$ should be assigned 100, $(\overline{A} + B + \overline{C})$ to 101). In the function column, assign a *zero* to each row for which there is a term of the function associated, *one* to all others.

Example: (Sum of Products) The equation for the block diagram of Figure 4.5 is:

$$f = \overline{(A \cdot B)}A + \overline{(A \cdot B)}B + A$$
$$= (\overline{A} + \overline{B})A + (\overline{A} + \overline{B})B + A \qquad \text{(DeMorgan's th.)}$$
$$= A\overline{B} + \overline{A}B + A \qquad\qquad\quad \text{(Distributivity)}$$
$$= A\overline{B} + \overline{A}B + A\overline{B} + AB \qquad \text{(expansion th.)}$$
$$= A\overline{B} + \overline{A}B + AB \qquad\qquad \text{canonical form}$$

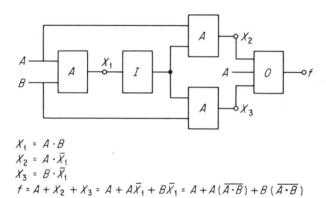

$$X_1 = A \cdot B$$
$$X_2 = A \cdot \overline{X}_1$$
$$X_3 = B \cdot \overline{X}_1$$
$$f = A + X_2 + X_3 = A + A\overline{X}_1 + B\overline{X}_1 = A + A(\overline{A \cdot B}) + B(\overline{A \cdot B})$$

Figure 4.5. Block diagram for analysis.

$f = \overline{A}B + A\overline{B} + AB$
$f:\ 01,\quad 10,\quad 11$

A	B	f
0	0	0
0	1	1
1	1	1
1	0	1

$\overline{A}B$
AB
$A\overline{B}$

Figure 4.6
Tabular analysis.

The completed analysis is shown in Figure 4.6. The function table tells us the output f will be 1 if (and only if) either A or B or both are 1.

Example: (Sum of Products) See Figure 4.7. In this example we show for the P of S form that it is not necessary to apply Rule 3 explicitly in analysis. The expansion can be done in the assignment of terms to the function table rows. Thus for a S of P three variable function, the term $A \cdot B$ would be listed as a 1 for the function in rows ABC and $AB\overline{C}$. One way of writing the binary number of this term (for three variables) is, $AB:11X$ or for four variables, $AB:11XX$. This can be thought of more as putting a 1 in the function at each row in which A and B are both 1. An example of this is shown in the analysis of this example in Figure 4.7 where the equation is reduced to 2nd order, but not to canonical form.

The student should try working the following examples himself before going through the text's solution.

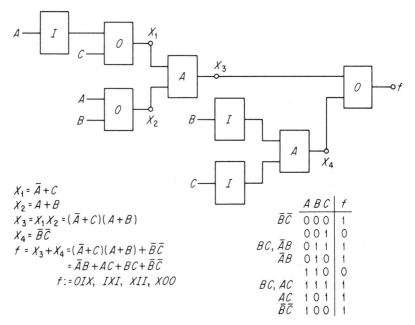

$$X_1 = \bar{A} + C$$
$$X_2 = A + B$$
$$X_3 = X_1 X_2 = (\bar{A} + C)(A + B)$$
$$X_4 = \bar{B}\bar{C}$$
$$f = X_3 + X_4 = (\bar{A} + C)(A + B) + \bar{B}\bar{C}$$
$$= \bar{A}B + AC + BC + \bar{B}\bar{C}$$
$$f := 0IX, \; IXI, \; XII, \; X00$$

	A B C	f
$\bar{B}\bar{C}$	0 0 0	1
	0 0 1	0
$BC, \bar{A}B$	0 1 1	1
$\bar{A}B$	0 1 0	1
	1 1 0	0
BC, AC	1 1 1	1
AC	1 0 1	1
$\bar{B}\bar{C}$	1 0 0	1

Figure 4.7. Analysis without explicit use of the Expansion Theorem.

Example: (product of Sums) See Figure 4.8. Dually, expansion may be performed for the P of S form implicitly in the assignment of terms to the function table rows. Thus for a three variable P of S function, the term $A + B$ would be listed as a 0 for the function in rows $A + B + C$ and $A + B + \bar{C}$. The binary form is similar, for three variables, $A + B:00X$, and for four variables, $A + B:00XX$. Thus we put an 0 for the function in each row in which A and B are both 0. This example problem illustrates this in Figure 4.8.

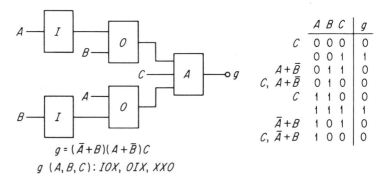

	A B C	g
C	0 0 0	0
	0 0 1	1
$A + \bar{B}$	0 1 1	0
$C, A + \bar{B}$	0 1 0	0
C	1 1 0	0
	1 1 1	1
$\bar{A} + B$	1 0 1	0
$C, \bar{A} + B$	1 0 0	0

$$g = (\bar{A} + B)(A + \bar{B})C$$
$$g \, (A, B, C) : 10X, \; 0IX, \; XX0$$

Figure 4.8. Product of sums analysis.

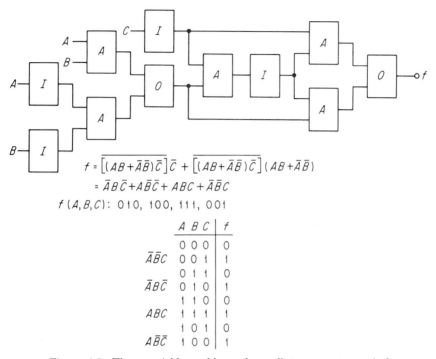

$$f = \overline{\left[(AB+\bar{A}\bar{B})\bar{C}\right]\bar{C}} + \overline{\left[(AB+\bar{A}\bar{B})\bar{C}\right]}(AB+\bar{A}\bar{B})$$
$$= \bar{A}B\bar{C}+A\bar{B}\bar{C}+ABC+\bar{A}\bar{B}C$$
$$f(A,B,C):\ 010,\ 100,\ 111,\ 001$$

	A B C	f
	0 0 0	0
$\bar{A}\bar{B}C$	0 0 1	1
	0 1 1	0
$\bar{A}B\bar{C}$	0 1 0	1
	1 1 0	0
ABC	1 1 1	1
	1 0 1	0
$A\bar{B}\bar{C}$	1 0 0	1

Figure 4.9. Three–variable problem where all terms are canonical.

Example: The analysis of a three variable problem is worked in Figure 4.9. Note that reduction of the function to second order results in the canonical form in this case. It will hereafter be assumed the student can directly write the equation corresponding to a block diagram without resorting to intermediate equations for each block. If not, these problems are a good place to practice.

Example: A four variable problem is worked in Figure 4.10. These problems are also good practice in applying some of the simpler algebraic theorems. Also, writing the function table for 4 variables should be tried before checking with the solution of Figure 4.10.

For analysis up to 6 variables, the Karnaugh map form for the function may be used if desired (5 and 6 variable case is discussed later) but the one dimensional table has the advantage it may be extended to an indefinite number of variables. Notice that in theorem proving with the Karnaugh map, we essentially *analyzed* both sides of the theorem-equation with a Karnaugh map. When analyzing with the map, we apply the expansion theorem only implicitly, but in a faster way than for the table, since we can quickly mark off for a single non-canonical term an area of pattern of ones.

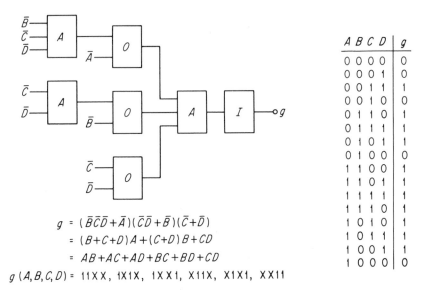

Figure 4.10. A four-variable analysis example.

Marking off loops in the K-map with 1's corresponds to associating a term to more than one row of the table. One of the niceties of the K-map is that by plotting a function on the map, effectively the function is quickly expanded to canonical form.

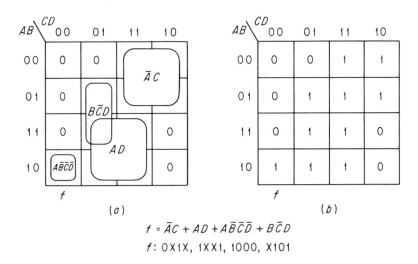

$$f = \bar{A}C + AD + A\bar{B}\bar{C}\bar{D} + B\bar{C}D$$
$$f: 0X1X, 1XX1, 1000, X101$$

Figure 4.11. Karnaugh Map analysis example: sum of products.

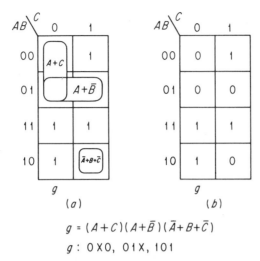

$$g = (A+C)(A+\bar{B})(\bar{A}+B+\bar{C})$$

$$g: 0\,X\,0, \ 0\,1\,X, \ 1\,0\,1$$

Figure 4.12. Karnaugh Map analysis example: product of sums.

Row	A B	f
0	0 0	1
1	0 1	1
3	1 1	1
2	1 0	0

Figure 4.13
Synthesis example.

Example: Analyze the function:

$$f = \bar{A}C + AD + A\bar{B}\bar{C}\bar{D} + B\bar{C}D$$

with a Karnaugh map. Work this first and then check Figure 4.11 for the mapping. Note that since the function is given in 2nd order form we can plot it directly on the map without expanding the algebra to canonical form. Figure 4.11b represents the final form of the analysis. In working this example, before checking the mapping of Figure 4.12, do not multiply out to a sum of product form; for fractions with many terms this can be very time-consuming. A facility with both forms should be developed.

Synthesis

Synthesis is the reverse of analysis; from the function table description we must write (synthesize) a corresponding Boolean equation. Equation manipulation and implementation in a block diagram is not considered here as properly part of synthesis, but rather of minimization and implementation. We first look at synthesis in the sum of products form. Arguing from the function table example of Figure 4.13:

1) f is to be one whenever A and B are both zero (row 0). In order for an

AND to be one all its input variables must be one. Since if $A = 0$ then $\overline{A} = 1$ and if $B = 0$, $\overline{B} = 1$, then $\overline{A} \cdot \overline{B} = 1$ if and only if $A = B = 0$. So the first term of the equation is $\overline{A} \cdot \overline{B}$. That is, the term $\overline{A} \cdot \overline{B} = 1$ if and only if we are in row 0, $A = B = 0$.

Row	A	$\overline{A}$	B	$\overline{B}$	f
0	0	1	0	1	1
1	0	1	1	0	1
3	1	0	1	0	1
2	1	0	0	1	0

Figure 4.14. Expanded table of Figure 4.13.

2) Let us look at the next term in a different way as shown in Figure 4.14, row 1. Here the function table is supplemented to show explicitly the values of the variables and their complements. f_1 should be one, so as inputs to the AND, we choose those literals* which are one, $\overline{A}$, B in row 1. The AND of these two will be one only under the conditions of row 1. Thus, the second term is $\overline{A} \cdot B$.

3) Similar arguments show that $A \cdot B = 1$ if and only if both A, B are one, the condition of row 3.

4) Now we have the unique terms for each of the ones of the function. Since the OR is a one whenever any of its inputs are one, we may OR the product terms together to complete the synthesis:

$$f = \overline{A}\overline{B} + \overline{A}B + AB$$

We may check the result by analysis to see if we obtain the original function table.

Rules for Synthesis of a Function:

1) The function must first be completely specified by completing a function table.

2a) Sum of Products: For each row of the table for which the function is to be *one*, synthesize the product term from the literals that will be one for only the values of the variables in that row. All variables with value *zero* are complemented, all with value *one* are left alone. The resulting literals are multiplied together. (For example the term uniquely one for row 010 is $\overline{A}B\overline{C}$, for row 101 is $A\overline{B}C$). Sum these terms to obtain the logical function.

2b) Product of Sums: For each row of the table for which the function is to be *zero*, synthesize the sum term that will be zero for only the values of the variable in that row. Since the sum of variables is zero, if, and only if all the variables are zero, we choose to sum those literals which are zero in each zero row of the functions. All variables with value *one* are complemented, all with value *zero* are left alone. The resulting literals are summed. (For example the term uniquely zero for row 100 is $(\overline{A} + B + C)$ and for row 110 is $(\overline{A} + \overline{B} + C)$. Multiply these terms together to get the logical function. If the variables have

* A literal refers to either a variable or its complement.

values corresponding to a row for which the function is to be zero, the corresponding sum term will be zero on one input of the output AND forcing the output to zero. If the variables correspond to a row for which the output is to be one, no sum term is zero making all inputs of the output AND a one, and the output function a one.

As a supplement to rules 2a, b, the table of Figure 4.15 shows the product and sum terms corresponding to each row of a two and a three variable function table.

	2 variables				3 variables		
Sum term	Product term	$A\ B$		Sum term	Product term	$A\ B\ C$	
$A+B$	$\bar{A}\ \bar{B}$	0 0		$A+B+C$	$\bar{A}\ \bar{B}\ \bar{C}$	0 0 0	
$A+\bar{B}$	$\bar{A}\ B$	0 1		$A+B+\bar{C}$	$\bar{A}\ \bar{B}\ C$	0 0 1	
$\bar{A}+\bar{B}$	$A\ B$	1 1		$A+\bar{B}+\bar{C}$	$\bar{A}\ B\ C$	0 1 1	
$\bar{A}+B$	$A\ \bar{B}$	1 0		$A+\bar{B}+C$	$\bar{A}\ B\ \bar{C}$	0 1 0	
				$\bar{A}+\bar{B}+C$	$A\ B\ \bar{C}$	1 1 0	
Sum terms = 0 in their rows, 1 in all other				$\bar{A}+\bar{B}+\bar{C}$	$A\ B\ C$	1 1 1	
				$\bar{A}+B+\bar{C}$	$A\ \bar{B}\ C$	1 0 1	
Product terms = 1 in their rows, 0 in all other				$\bar{A}+B+C$	$A\ \bar{B}\ \bar{C}$	1 0 0	

Figure 4.15. Tables of sum and product terms.

Example: Synthesize a sum of products equation and a product of sums equation for the function table of Figure 4.16.

Sum of Products: Row 1 is to be a one so we multiply together those functions of the literals which will each have value one for this (and only this) combination of the variable values; then the product of them will be one. Since $A = B = 0$ we choose their individual literals for complements and with $C = 1$, we take C as is. Multiplying these functions of the literals (001) we get the product term $\bar{A}\bar{B}C$. For rows 2, 6, 4 we find the corresponding terms to be respectively (010) $\bar{A}B\bar{C}$, (110) $AB\bar{C}$ and (100) $A\bar{B}\bar{C}$. Summing the one-terms of the function we synthesize

Row	$A\ B\ C$	f
0	0 0 0	0
1	0 0 1	1
3	0 1 1	0
2	0 1 0	1
6	1 1 0	1
7	1 1 1	0
5	1 0 1	0
4	1 0 0	1

Figure 4.16. Synthesis example: sum of products.

$$f = \bar{A}\bar{B}C + \bar{A}B\bar{C} + AB\bar{C} + A\bar{B}\bar{C}$$

Product of Sums: Row 3 is to be a zero so sum those functions of the variables which will each have value zero for this (and only this) combination of variable values; then the sum of these will be zero. Since $B = C = 1$, we choose their individual complements and with $A = 0$ we take A as is. Summing: row 3 (011) $A + \bar{B} + \bar{C}$. For rows 0, 7, 5, we find their corresponding terms to be respectively (000) $A + B + C$, (111) $\overline{A} + \overline{B} + \overline{C}$, (101) $\overline{A} + B + \overline{C}$, and for the function we synthesize:

$$f = (A + \overline{B} + \overline{C})(A + B + C)(\overline{A} + \overline{B} + \overline{C})(\overline{A} + B + \overline{C})$$

Remember that both expressions for f synthesized above are equal as equating and comparing their function tables will show. They are but different algebraic forms of the same function, illustrating the characterizing quality of variability for the algebra.

Problem-Statement to Function Table: Often the most difficult part of logic design is specifying in a function table what our vague and ambiguous English language formulation of the problem requires. This is even more true for sequential circuits (Chapt. 8). Although this is not a part of switching theory (the latter starts only once the table is written) the propositional calculus can be of some aid. This does not deal with the meaning of sentences, but with the grammatical connectives between propositions. Some of these grammatical connectives can be given fair definitions as logical connectives. So to aid somewhat the translation from English to the language of logic, Table I of Connective Translations is given. In the table, capital letters refer to propositions which are of the form: "The accumulator sign is zero and the instruction is: Branch on Zero"—symbolized: "$A \cdot B$" means: "The accumulator zero wire is positive *and* the Branch zero instruction wire is positive." In the table, for better understanding, we define $A \rightarrow B$ as $\overline{A} + B$ meaning "A *implies* B". That is if the statement "A implies B" is true ($A \rightarrow B = 1$), then whenever $A = 1$, then $B = 1$. Thus, justifying the definition, if $A \rightarrow B = \overline{A} + B = 1$, then whenever $A = 1$, $\overline{A} = 0$ and B must be 1 for $\overline{A} + B$ to be 1.

English	Logical Translation
not A	$\overline{A}$
A	A
$\overline{A}$ and B	$\overline{A} \cdot B$
A or B (inclusive); A or B or both	$A + B$
A or B (exclusive); either A or B but not both	$A \oplus B,\ A\overline{B} + \overline{A}B$
A but B	$A \cdot B$
A although B	$A \cdot B$
A unless B	$A + B,\ A\overline{B} + \overline{A}B$ depending $\overline{A} + \overline{B},\ B \rightarrow \overline{A},\ \overline{A}B$ on context $A\overline{B},\ \overline{A \rightarrow B}$
A on condition that B	$\overline{B} + A,\ B \rightarrow A$
A if B	$\overline{B} + A,\ B \rightarrow A$
if A then B; A implies B	$\overline{A} + B,\ A \rightarrow B$

B only if A	$\overline{A} + B,\ A\,B$
A if and only if B	$\overline{A \oplus B} = AB + \overline{A}\overline{B},\ (A \to B) \cdot (B \to A)$
Not unless A, then B	$\overline{A} + B,\ A \to B$
A provided that B	$\overline{B} + A,\ B \to A$
A as well as B	AB
Not both A and B	$\overline{A} + \overline{B}$
Neither A nor B	$\overline{A}\overline{B}$
A because B	$\overline{B} + A,\ B \to A$

TABLE I

Table of Translations of English Grammer Connectives to Logic Connectives.

Minimization

Synthesis did not turn out to be such a difficult problem but the major problem of design is yet to be dealt with, minimization. Most of the rest of this chapter and the next will be devoted to minimization procedures. The problem is illustrated by the equality of these two expressions:

$$\overline{A}\overline{B}\overline{C} + \overline{A}BC + A\overline{B}C + \overline{A}B\overline{C} + \overline{A}\overline{B}C + ABC = \overline{A} + C$$

The expression form on the left requires six $ANDs$, one OR and a total of 24 inputs to the $ANDs$ and the OR. The completely equivalent function form on the right takes but one OR with two inputs and no $ANDs$. By any reasonable standard of circuit component costs, the right hand side is clearly more economical to implement than that on the left.

The process of reducing the left expression to that of the right is called *minimization*. Since minimality ultimately must refer to the hardware with the problem changing somewhat as the hardware changes, we require an algebraic equivalent to the general nature of minimization for many circuits which will have a fairly close correspondence to most hardware senses of minimality. The key lies partly in the notion of irredundancy. In the following expression:

$$ABC + AB\overline{C}$$

the variable C is redundant or unnecessary because:

$$ABC + AB\overline{C} = AB \qquad \text{Th. 15b}$$

Similarly, in the following expression $ABC + A$, the term ABC is redundant since:

$$ABC + A = A \qquad \text{Th. 8b}$$

Since redundant variables and terms are unnecessary yet cost money in the circuit, the first step of algebraic minimization is to eliminate redundancy to yield an *irredundant* form of the function.

There are in general, many irredundant forms of a function, however. For example:

$$\overline{A}\overline{B}\overline{C} + \overline{A}\overline{B}D + BCD + ABD = \overline{A}\overline{B}\overline{C} + \overline{A}CD + ABD \qquad \text{(eq. 1)}$$

both sides of this equation are irredundant forms of the same function, (there are no superfluous terms or literals in either), but the right hand side requires one less AND than the left. So the second part of algebraic minimization is to select from all the irredundant expressions of a function that which satisfies some criteria of minimality. For most logic circuits, minimizing the number of terms (gates) and the number of literals (inputs) tends to achieve some sense of minimality). Note, however, we are not with this restrictive definition minimizing the inverters on the inputs; we assume (unjustly in many cases) that they are available, to simplify the problem.

Sometimes there are certain combinations of input conditions which the designer knows won't occur. Also, there may be times when he doesn't really care what value the function may take on. In both of these instances we call such a canonic term, a "don't care" situation. We can take advantage of such conditions in our minimization. Since a "don't care" term means that the function may be chosen either as a 1 or as a 0, we can choose it to take whichever value will yield the most economical circuit. Suppose

$$ABC$$

is a "don't care" condition in the function:

$$\overline{A}BC + A\overline{B}C$$

Then by choosing the don't care as a 1 we can minimize to

$$\overline{A}BC + A\overline{B}C + ABC = AC + BC$$

In our Karnaugh maps, don't cares will be indicated by ϕ, a 0 and a 1 superimposed.

Quine's Minimization Method: We see these two principles for minimization applied in Quine's method which is basic to most other methods. First we get rid of redundant literals in all possible ways by systematically applying the theorem:

$$AB + A\overline{B} = A \qquad \text{Th. 15b}$$

to all pairs of terms in a canonical form of the function.

First, write the canonical terms in a column. Starting with the top term on the list, pair it with every term below it to see if they differ in only one variable; when such a pair is found, put a check mark by each term of the pair and, dropping this redundant literal, write the result of the combined pair of terms in a new column. Even though a term is checked, continue pairing it for possible combinations with the remaining terms. It need only be checked once, however, no matter how many times it combines with other terms. After the top term is compared with all other terms, start with the next term pairing it with all terms below it in the list. Continue until all pairs have been examined. Then repeat the process in the second column checking for pairs which combine, generating a third column. Continue until no further combinations may be made. The terms in all the columns which have not been checked are all of the irredundant terms of the function. We call these the prime implicants.

Reduction Table for f: (Decimal numbers in the brackets show which terms combined to give that particular term.)

$$f = \overline{A}\overline{B}\overline{C}\overline{D} + \overline{A}\overline{B}\overline{C}D + \overline{A}\overline{B}CD + \overline{A}BCD + ABCD + AB\overline{C}D$$

	Canonical Terms		1st Application of Theorem
(0)	$\overline{A}\overline{B}\overline{C}\overline{D}$ ✓	(0, 1)	$\overline{A}\overline{B}\overline{C}$
(1)	$\overline{A}\overline{B}\overline{C}D$ ✓	(1, 3)	$\overline{A}\overline{B}D$
(3)	$\overline{A}\overline{B}CD$ ✓	(3, 7)	$\overline{A}CD$
(7)	$\overline{A}BCD$ ✓	(7, 15)	BCD
(15)	$ABCD$ ✓	(13, 15)	ABD
(13)	$AB\overline{C}D$ ✓		

(Note each term must be compared against *all* other terms below it)

In this case no reductions are possible in the second column and it contains the list of the prime implicants. Although the sum of the prime implicants yields the function, in general this results in redundant terms. So we next select the sum of the fewest number of irredundant terms (prime implicants) that yields the function.

We construct a table with the prime implicants as rows and the canonical terms as columns and check each column for which a prime implicant appears within the canonical term. This is shown in Figure 4.17. We must pick the fewest number of prime implicants such that together they have checks under all the canonical terms. The simplest choice is shown in Figure

Cononical Terms

Prime implicants	$\overline{A}\overline{B}\overline{C}\overline{D}$	$\overline{A}\overline{B}\overline{C}D$	$\overline{A}\overline{B}CD$	$\overline{A}BCD$	$ABCD$	$AB\overline{C}D$
* $\overline{A}\overline{B}\overline{C}$	Ⓧ	Ⓧ				
* $\overline{A}\overline{B}D$		Ⓧ	Ⓧ			
$\overline{A}CD$			X	X		
* BCD				Ⓧ	Ⓧ	
* ABD					Ⓧ	Ⓧ
Column #	1	2	3	4	5	6

Figure 4.17. Table for selecting minimal sum of prime implicants.

4.17 with the pertinent checks circled and the chosen prime implicants starred.

$$f = \overline{ABC} + ABD + \overline{A}CD$$

Notice that this is the same function as equation 1.

The reader should see how the left hand side of equation 1 can be gotten from the table if a wrong choice of prime implicants is made.

A more efficient implementation of Quine's method is given in the next chapter for use with large numbers of variables. Here we are interested in implementing these basic ideas in a topological method which has many advantages for small numbers of variables.

The Karnaugh Map as a Minimization Tool

A New Notation for the Karnaugh Map: We have already shown an interpretation of the axioms in Karnaugh Maps and have shown how theorems may be proved using them such that our understanding of the algebraic relations is enforced by geometric intuition. We now wish to use the Karnaugh Map to *derive* theorems, namely minimality theorems. Thus, we must find true theorems of the form $f(A_1, A_2, \ldots A_n) = g(A_1, A_2, \ldots A_n)$ where f is a given function in non-minimal redundant form and we must find a function of form g which is minimal (in some sense) such that this theorem holds. That is, we must find a functional form g equivalent to the given function f, but irredundant and in some sense minimal.

Since we will need to draw loops, etc. on the map for this, it is convenient to minimize the loopings and cross-hatchings of before and give the map a neater form.

We can define K as any set. Thus we can code the set of the variable A as 1 and the set of $\overline{A}$ as 0, relative to the K set of A. This can be done for all sets. Further, any function formed from sets by the Boolian connectives is also a set. Thus a Boolian function f can be coded a 1 in all of the cubes of the set, and a 0 elsewhere, relative to the K set of f. Thus we translate "sets" into "functions" where 1 and 0 are the "values" of the function or its variables. Each elementary set (now variable) will have its presence, 1, or absence, 0, indicated by one of these values on each row or column instead of looping the set. Rather than cross hatching the cubes of a function-set we shall place a 1 in a cube if it is a member of the resultant function-set and 0 if it is not. Examples for 2, 3, 4 variables are shown in Figure 4.18. Representative functions have been plotted on the map and written algebraically below.

The first step in minimization is to apply the theorem

$$AB + A\overline{B} = A$$

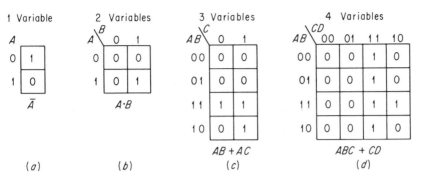

Figure 4.18. Boolean function notation for Karnaugh Map.

to find those canonical terms which differ in but the value of one variable. Now, notice that as we go from each cube in the Karnaugh Map of Figure 4.19, the value of exactly one variable changes. Notice also the end around adjacencies shown between the left and right hand columns and the top and bottom rows. For example the cubes a, b are end around adjacent if we note that $a = 1000$ and $b = 1010$; they differ only in the value of C.

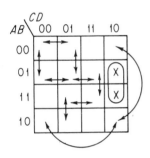

Figure 4.19. Adjacent cells of the Karnaugh Map differ in one variable.

Since each cube of the map with a one in it corresponds to a canonical term, the adjacencies of the Karnaugh Map serve as a useful tool for applying the theorem above to detect the prime implicants. Notice that the two boxes marked x in Figure 4.19 correspond to the two canonical terms.

$$ABC\overline{D} + \overline{A}BC\overline{D}$$

and since adjacent cells can be combined in one term this leaves A redundant as indicated by the loop. This looping says

$$ABC\overline{D} + \overline{A}BC\overline{D} = BC\overline{D}$$

which is the application of our basic minimization theorem. The first column of Quine's reduction table is simply all the loops of one or the canonical terms as shown for a function in Figure 4.20(a). The second column is the loops of two shown in Figure 4.20(b). The third column (if any) corresponds to the loops of four (Figure 4.20(c)). Notice the different kinds of loops of four; especially the four corner ones. The next column is the loops of eight and so on. In this case, there are no loops of eight. The prime implicants are the largest loops each one is contained in. In the case of Figure 4.20, the prime implicants are all the loops of four in (c).

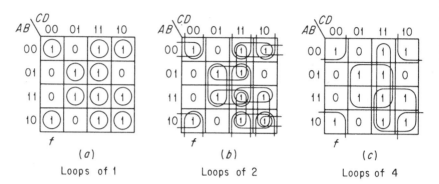

Figure 4.20. All loops of 1, 2, 4 adjacent ones.

To discern the prime implicants on a Karnaugh Map, then, we must learn to recognize patterns of adjacent ones and groups of ones. For familiarization, all basic patterns are shown for three variable maps in Figure 4.21 and for four variables in Figure 4.22.

One of the advantages of the map method is that we can loop the prime implicants immediately by inspection without going through the intermediate steps. We merely make all the largest loops containing only 1's such that each 1 is contained in at least one loop and such that no loop is

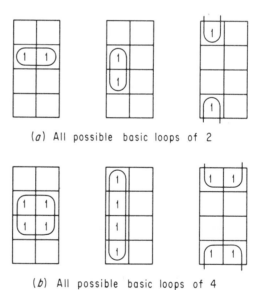

(a) All possible basic loops of 2

(b) All possible basic loops of 4

Figure 4.21. All basic patterns of adjacencies for 3 variables.

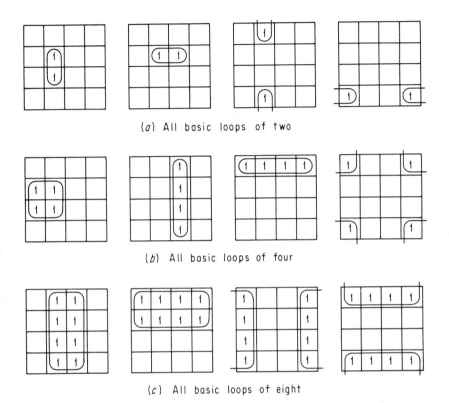

(a) All basic loops of two

(b) All basic loops of four

(c) All basic loops of eight

Figure 4.22. All basic patterns of adjacencies for four variables.

completely covered by other loops. The prime implicants are looped for three different functions in Figure 4.23 (a,b,c).

The second advantage of the map is that the redundancy of some prime implicants relative to a given choice of others is geometrically clear. That is, all ones of the redundant loop are covered by loops of already chosen prime implicants. For example in Figure 4.23(c)

$$f = B\overline{C} + AD + C\overline{D} \qquad \text{(eq. 2)}$$

You will notice that all the 1's are covered with only these prime implicants. This is made clearer in Figure 4.24 where the same function as Figure 4.23(c) is mapped, but cross hatched areas indicate the prime implicants chosen. The looped areas are the prime implicants remaining. Clearly, none of the latter cover 1's of the function not already covered by the chosen prime implicants—they are unnecessary with respect to equation 2 above—redundant terms.

In this last example, observe that the choice made was the only set of irredundant prime implicants possible. (This should be verified.) However,

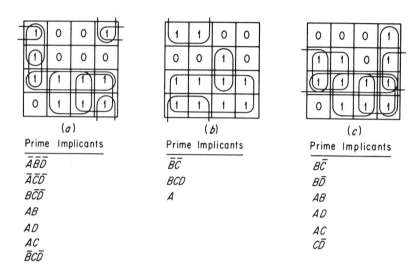

Prime Implicants

$\overline{A}\overline{B}\overline{D}$
$\overline{A}\overline{C}\overline{D}$
$B\overline{C}\overline{D}$
AB
AD
AC
$\overline{B}\overline{C}\overline{D}$

Prime Implicants

$\overline{B}\overline{C}$
BCD
A

Prime Implicants

$B\overline{C}$
$B\overline{D}$
AB
AD
AC
$C\overline{D}$

Figure 4.23. Prime implicants looped for three functions.

Figure 4.24. A set of ir-redundant prime impli-cants chosen from Figure 23(c).

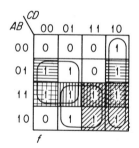

Irredundant Form: $f = B\overline{C} - AD - C\overline{D}$ (looped)
Redundant Terms: $B\overline{D}, AB, AC$ (cross-hatched)

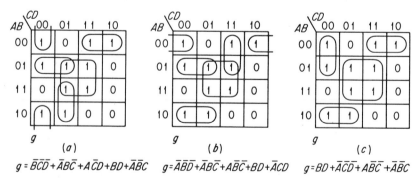

$g = \overline{B}CD + \overline{A}B\overline{C} + A\overline{C}D + BD + \overline{A}\overline{B}C$ $g = \overline{A}\overline{B}\overline{D} + \overline{A}B\overline{C} + A\overline{B}\overline{C} + BD + \overline{A}CD$ $g = BD + \overline{A}\overline{C}D + A\overline{B}\overline{C} + \overline{A}\overline{B}C$

Figure 4.25. A function with a non-unique irredundant form.

the choice is not generally unique. Consider the function of Figure 4.25(a,b,c) which shows three different choices of prime implicants each yielding an irredundant form of the function. A count of terms and literals shows (a) and (b) to be equivalent in cost while (c) costs one less term. By these criteria (a) and (b) are equivalent, but (c) is the minimal form of the function. Figure 4.25 does not exhaust the irredundant forms of the function either. There are, in fact, seven more of them, but none as economical as Figure 4.25(c).

Minimization by Karnaugh map thus requires the designer to recognize patterns of ones on the map; he must choose the fewest number of the largest loops that cover all the function. But, there is yet one pitfall in this pattern minimization. Let us follow the sequence a novice might step through in picking the loops of a function. Figure 4.26(a,b) shows such a sequence; (c) shows the combined result. Clearly in (c) the first choice of $\overline{CD}$ was wrong; it turns out to be redundant. This obvious loop of four is an attractive lure for most people at first glance. The correct choice should have been that of Figure 4.26(b).

But this difficulty can be eliminated. And this is the third major attribute of the Karnaugh map. The first was that prime implicants are immediately recognizable; the second is that the redundancy or irredundancy of a term (relative to a particular choice of terms) is graphically clear. Their third attribute is that all the prime implicants need not be looped and there is an effective procedure for choosing prime implicants such that no redundant ones ever are chosen unknowingly as done in Figure 4.26(c).

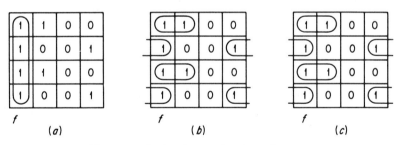

Figure 4.26. Step by step loopings of a map.

Procedure for Selecting an Irredundant Set of Prime Implicants

From the Karnaugh Map:

1) Loop all those 1's that cannot combine with (are not adjacent to) any other 1's.
2) Loop all those 1's that will combine in a loop of two but will not make a loop of four.

3) Loop all those 1's that will make a loop of four but not a loop of eight.
4) etc. Stop when all 1's are covered.

These rules keep us from getting redundant loops since each loop (that might be redundant), smaller than a given loop, has been chosen earlier for reasons which made it the only loop to cover certain 1's.

5) The only thing left is to make sure not to introduce loops of the same size such that one (some) are redundant.

Note that in our novice's problem (Figure 4.26) these rules would have us start at the point in the sequence, and finish, at map (b). There are no loops of one that won't make loops of two, but there are loops of two that won't make loops of four and all 1's are now covered, so we stop.

Example: Minimize

$$f = \overline{A}D + \overline{A}B\overline{C}\overline{D} + B\overline{C}D + A\overline{C}D + \overline{B}D + A\overline{B}\overline{C} + ABC\overline{D}$$

using a Karnaugh map.

First the function is plotted on a Karnaugh map and then all loops of 1 that don't make loops of two are circled (Figure 4.27(a)). Now all loops of two that don't make loops of four are chosen, (b). All loops of four that don't

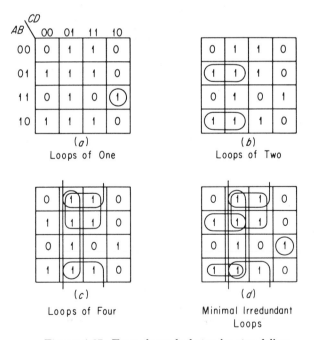

(a) Loops of One

(b) Loops of Two

(c) Loops of Four

(d) Minimal Irredundant Loops

Figure 4.27. Example worked step by step following the rules for selecting an irredundant form.

make loops of eight are shown in (c). All ones have been covered so we have the solution in the composite map (d). We write from (d):

$$f = \overline{A}B\overline{C} + A\overline{B}\overline{C} + \overline{C}D + \overline{A}D + \overline{B}D + ABC\overline{D}$$

Since there were no alternative loopings this is minimal with respect to the number of terms.

Example: Minimize

$$f = \overline{B}\overline{C} + BD + \overline{C}D + A\overline{C} + AB + BC + \overline{A}C\overline{D} + \overline{A}\overline{B}\overline{D}$$

Here as shown in Figure 4.28 there is no unique irredundant form. The (a) map has four 4-loops and one 2-loop. Both (b) and (c) have three 4-loops

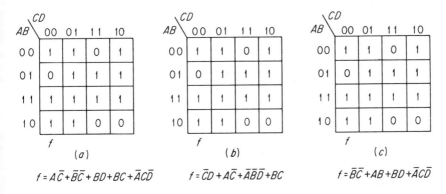

Figure 4.28

and one 2-loop. Maps (b) and (c) are equivalent minimal forms of the function. That they are minimal, however, can only be assured if all irredundant coverings are looked at. It is easy to see that the irredundant coverings not shown in Figure 4.28(d) are all equivalent or more in cost of terms and literals. There are several possible variations. For example, in (a) we could have looped, $\overline{A}\overline{B}\overline{D}$ instead of $\overline{A}C\overline{D}$ and it would not have affected the cost count of terms and literals.

However, equivalent solutions are important and the Karnaugh maps' ability to display equivalent solutions so they may be easily seen is a fourth important property.

The use of equivalent solutions:

1) Some of the gates for one solution may already be available in other parts of the switching circuit.
2) One solution may put less loading on some variables perhaps eliminating the need for a driver.
3) One solution may require fewer inverters on the inputs.

4) One solution may factor to a better circuit than the others. (Factoring is explained later.)

The extent to which one pursues all the avenues of equivalent solutions is determined by how much you want the most minimal circuit and to the extent you will compromise with an approximation. With four variables Karnaugh maps, this is not much of a problem since it is handled so quickly. For larger numbers of variables, the problem requires more decisions of the nature of that above. With only twice as many or eight variables, there are problems where the number of equivalent solutions can range in the hundreds.

When equivalent or even near equivalent solutions arise, this is the time to plug into the problem the details of the circuit restrictions, the components freely available and those that are not available.

Example: Analyze the block diagram of Figure 4.29 and write the minimal second order equation for the function. (The complex factored form of Figure 4.29 is good analysis and algebraic manipulation practice so the student is advised to write the two level equation for it checking this with the K-map of Figure 4.30.)

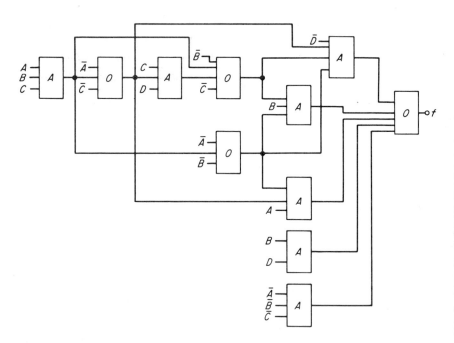

Figure 4.29. Analysis and minimization problem.

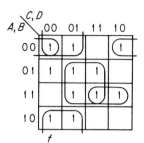

Figure 4.30. *K*-Map and loops for circuit of Figure 4.29.

Figure 4.30 shows the minimal s of P solution for the circuit of Figure 4.29.

Example: Several more maps have been looped as examples in Figure 4.31(d).

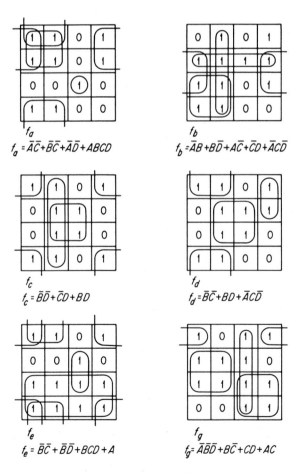

$$f_a = \bar{A}\bar{C} + \bar{B}\bar{C} + \bar{A}\bar{D} + ABCD$$

$$f_b = \bar{A}B + B\bar{D} + A\bar{C} + \bar{C}D + \bar{A}C\bar{D}$$

$$f_c = \bar{B}\bar{D} + \bar{C}D + BD$$

$$f_d = \bar{B}\bar{C} + BD + \bar{A}C\bar{D}$$

$$f_e = \bar{B}\bar{C} + \bar{B}\bar{D} + BCD + A$$

$$f_g = \bar{A}\bar{B}\bar{D} + B\bar{C} + CD + AC$$

Figure 4.31. Several map functions with prime implicants chosen.

Problems

1. Analyze the following Block Diagrams:

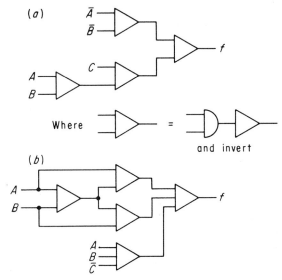

2. Analyze the following equations:

(a) $f = \overline{A}\overline{B} + \overline{A}\overline{C}D + AC + \overline{B}C$

(b) $f = \overline{A}B + \overline{A}D + ABD + BCD$

(c) $f = AB\overline{C} + B\overline{C}D + \overline{A}BD + \overline{A}CD + \overline{A}\overline{B}C$

(d) $f = (A + C)(\overline{B} + C)(\overline{A} + B)(\overline{A} + \overline{C})$

3. Synthesize the following:

(a) Sum of product equation required

(b) Product of sums equation required

4. Minimize the following expressions using Quinne's method:

(a) $\overline{A}\overline{B}C + \overline{A}BC + ABC + AB\overline{C}$

(b) $\overline{A}\overline{B}C + \overline{A}B\overline{C} + AB\overline{C} + \overline{A}BC + ABC + A\overline{B}C$

5. Minimize using K-map.

(a) $f = \overline{A}CD + \overline{A}BD + ACD + ABD$

(b) $f = \overline{A}B\overline{C}\overline{D} + \overline{C}D + AB\overline{D} + \overline{A}BC\overline{D}$

(c) $f = B\overline{C}\overline{D} + AB\overline{C} + \overline{B}CD + \overline{A}BD + BC\overline{D}$

(d) $f = A\overline{B}\overline{C} + A\overline{C}D + BCD + \overline{A}CD + \overline{A}B\overline{D}$

(e) $f = \overline{A}B\overline{C}\overline{D} + A\overline{B}\overline{D} + \overline{B}C\overline{D} + AB\overline{C}D + \overline{A}BD$

MINIMIZATION METHODS

5

Introduction

This chapter covers the more commonly used methods of minimizing the hardware requirements of a digital computer. While extremely helpful, these methods do not provide the complete answer in themselves. There is still a great need for the use of intuition in designing the economical computer.

The Five-Variable Karnaugh Map

When minimizing expressions of five variables, the use of a five-variable map is suggested. This map provides the same information concerning the five-variable expression as the four-variable map provides for the four-variable expression. However, since there are thirty-two combinations of five-variables and their complements, the five-variable map must have twice as many boxes or squares as the four-variable map. It is possible, therefore, to use two four-variable maps in the construction of a five-variable map. While physical drawing of this map may differ among authors, it should show, by adjacencies, all entries that differ by only one variable. For example, this may be accomplished by a three-dimensional drawing of two four-variable maps placed one on top of the other.

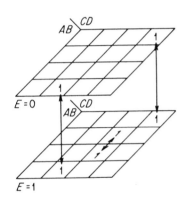

Figure 5.1. Five-variable Karnaugh Map.

Figure 5.1 illustrates the three-dimensional five-variable map. Each of the four-variable maps covers the same four variables while the fifth variable is assigned zero on the upper map and one on the lower map. In addition to the original adjacencies in each of the four-variable maps, there now exist adjacencies in the third dimension. Any square in the upper map is considered adjacent to the square directly below it. For ease of drawing, the two maps are normally displayed side by side, but must be thought of as being one on top of the other. Two examples of the use of five-variable Karnaugh maps to minimize expressions are given:

Example I considers the function $AB\overline{C}\overline{D} + A\overline{B}\overline{C}E + \overline{A}C\overline{D}\overline{E} + AB\overline{C}\overline{D}E + A\overline{B}\overline{C}E$ which is mapped in Figure 5.2. There are no single ones that cannot be combined into at least a loop of two; therefore, there are no five-variable terms in the solution. There is one loop of two that cannot be combined into a loop of at least four; this yields the term $\overline{A}C\overline{D}\overline{E}$. There are two loops of four each that cannot be combined to produce a larger loop and these produce the terms $A\overline{C}\overline{D}$ and $A\overline{B}\overline{C}$. These terms are then OR'ed together to give us the answer: $\overline{A}C\overline{D}\overline{E} + A\overline{C}\overline{D} + A\overline{B}\overline{C}$. It is well to remember that "don't care" conditions play an equally important part in minimizing five-variable expressions as they did in minimizing four-variable expressions. Reading the blank or zero squares from the map with the complements of the variables will, as before, produce the P of S form of the expression. It should be remembered that the P of S form is sometimes cheaper to implement than the S of P form.

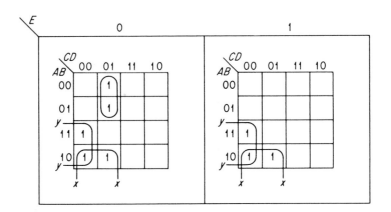

Figure 5.2. Five – variable problem.

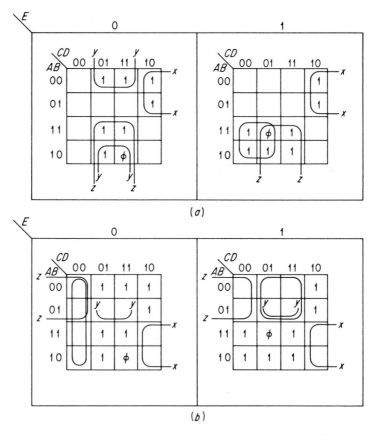

Figure 5.3. Five– variable mapping with "don't cares."

Example II is illustrated in Figure 5.3 and considers the function: $\overline{A}BD\overline{E} + \overline{A}C\overline{D}E + AC\overline{D}E + \overline{A}C\overline{D} + ABD\overline{E} + A\overline{C}DE + ACDE + A\overline{B}\overline{C}E$. Don't cares $= A\overline{B}CD\overline{E} + AB\overline{C}DE$. Mapping the ones gives an answer of $\overline{A}C\overline{D} + BD\overline{E} + A\overline{C}E + AD$; while mapping the blanks we obtain $(\overline{A} + \overline{C} + D)(A + \overline{D} + \overline{E})(A + \overline{B} + \overline{D})(C + D + E)(A + C + D)$.

The Six-Variable Karnaugh Map

Karnaugh mapping may be extended to any number of variables; however, it must be remembered that its usefulness is dependent upon the ability of the individual to recognize patterns of ones displayed on these maps. Six-variable map reading requires much practice to obtain proficiency. A six-variable map is constructed of two five-variable maps as shown in Figure 5.4. This drawing is not accurate in that the upper plane and the lower plane must be thought of as being adjacent. Some of the possible adjacencies are shown in Figure 5.4. For ease of drawing, the four maps are normally redrawn as in Figure 5.5, but the student may find it necessary to use Figure 5.4 until a familiarity with the maps is obtained.

An example of Six-Variable Karnaugh Mapping is given in Figure 5.5, where the following function is considered:

$$\overline{A}B\overline{C}DE\overline{F} + \overline{A}BCE\overline{F} + \overline{A}BC\overline{E}$$
$$+ A\overline{B}\overline{C}\overline{D}E + AC\overline{D}F + \overline{A}\overline{B}CEF$$

From the map we obtain this answer: $\overline{A}B\overline{C}DE\overline{F} + A\overline{B}\overline{C}\overline{D}E + AC\overline{D}F + \overline{A}BC$. "Don't care" conditions may be used with a six-variable map, but this increases the difficulty in reading the map. The P of S solution is, as before, obtainable from any Karnaugh mapping. For complicated six-variable expressions the Quine-McCluskey method is recommended.

Figure 5.4. Six— variable map.

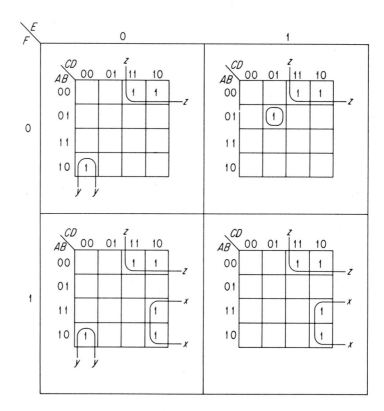

Figure 5.5. Six – variable mapping problem.

The Quine-McClusky Method

This method is actually a procedure for reducing Boolean expressions of any number of variables. It is a better mechanization of the Quine method of the last chapter. Although long, it can be useful when working with expressions of six or more variables. Several individuals have programmed this procedure on large digital computers.

The Boolean expression to be minimized must first be expanded to its canonic sum form. A canonic form, you recall, is that expression obtained by expanding the sum of products (AND to OR) expression until all terms contain one occurrence of all variables or their complements. An expression such as $AB + A\overline{B}\overline{C}$ when expanded to its "standard sum" would appear as $ABC + AB\overline{C} + A\overline{B}\overline{C}$. Now the expression is converted to a "binary form". This is accomplished by assigning binary weights to each of the variables. That is, the binary weights of 1, 2, 4 and 8 are assigned to the variables D, C, B and A respectively. A one is used if the variable is not complemented and a zero is used if the variable is complemented. This, in effect, assigns a binary number to each of the terms. Thus the term, $\overline{A}\overline{B}\overline{C}D$, would be written as 0001 and $A\overline{B}C\overline{D}$ would be 1010 just as it was in the last chapter. After all of the terms have been converted to binary numbers, they are separated into groups, determined by the sum of ones in each. Therefore, binary numbers 0001, 0100 and 1000 would all be in the same group, while 1011, 1101 and 1110 would be in another group. At this point, the binary numbers are converted to decimal form. The decimal numbers are then arranged in ascending order within the groups.

Example:

$$T = \overline{A}\overline{B}\overline{C}D\overline{F} + \overline{A}\overline{B}C\overline{D}E + \overline{A}\overline{B}C\overline{D}\overline{F} + \overline{A}\overline{B}CD\overline{F} + \overline{A}\overline{B}CDE + A\overline{B}C\overline{D}\overline{E}F$$

Expanding to canonic form:

$$T = \overline{A}\overline{B}\overline{C}\overline{D}\overline{E}\overline{F} + \overline{A}\overline{B}\overline{C}D\overline{E}F + \overline{A}\overline{B}C\overline{D}E\overline{F} + \overline{A}\overline{B}C\overline{D}EF + \overline{A}\overline{B}CD\overline{E}\overline{F}$$

$$+ \overline{A}\overline{B}C\overline{D}E\overline{F} + \overline{A}\overline{B}CD\overline{E}\overline{F} + \overline{A}\overline{B}CDE\overline{F} + \overline{A}\overline{B}CDEF + A\overline{B}C\overline{D}\overline{E}F$$

converting to binary form:

$$T = 000000 + 000010 + 000110 + 000111 + 001000$$

$$+ 001010 + 001100 + 001110 + 001111 + 101001$$

Grouping them in proper order (Decimal to binary tables given in appendix):

Column I	Column II
000000	0
000010	2
001000	8
000110	6
001010	10
001100	12
000111	7
001110	14
101001	41
001111	15

The next step involves comparing numbers from adjacent groups in the previous listing. The objective is to determine numbers that differ by powers of two. It should be remembered that one is a power of two.

Beginning with the upper group, the smallest decimal number from this group is compared successively to all numerically greater numbers which appear in the next group. When the two numbers being compared differ by a power of two, the pair is placed in a new column (Column III) along with the value by which they differ. The value by which they differ is placed in brackets. The second number in the first group is then compared with all numerically greater numbers in the second group. This process continues until the first group is exhausted. A line is then placed under the last entry in the new column being formed.

The first number in the second group is then compared with all numerically greater numbers in the third group. This procedure continues until the entire list is exhausted. Any decimal number that fails to combine with any other number is noted for later reference. It would be well at this point to explain what is happening.

This first comparison is seeking out all terms that differ by only the complementing of one variable. They may be thought of as a loop of two in the Karnaugh map. All possible loops of two are being recorded in the new column being formed. All decimal numbers that failed to compare are actually terms or individual ones in the map that cannot be combined into at least a loop of two. A further comparison is now needed to determine what terms can be grouped into loops of four.

Column I	Column II	Column III	Column IV
000000	0 ✓	0, 2 (2) ✓	0, 2, 8, 10 (2, 8)*
————	–	0, 8 (8) ✓	————————
000010	2 ✓	————	2, 6, 10, 14 (4, 8)*
001000	8 ✓	2, 6 (4) ✓	8, 10, 12, 14 (2, 4)*
————	–	2, 10 (8) ✓	————————
000110	6 ✓	8, 10 (2) ✓	6, 7, 14, 15 (1, 8)*
001010	10 ✓	8, 12 (4) ✓	
001100	12 ✓	————	
————	—	6, 7 (1) ✓	
000111	7 ✓	6, 14 (8) ✓	
001110	14 ✓	10, 14 (4) ✓	
101001	41*	12, 14 (2) ✓	
————	—	————	
001111	15 ✓	7, 15 (8) ✓	
		14, 15 (1) ✓	

The second comparison is performed on Column III. This comparison is almost identical with the method used on Column II except that both of the decimal numbers in the brackets must be the same before checking the difference of the first decimal number in each row. This comparison may produce a fourth column which is a listing of all possible loops of four in the Karnaugh map. The same loop may appear more than once, but should be recorded only once in Column IV.

* Indicates terms that did not combine properly with other terms.

Example:

0, 2 (2)	0, 2, 8, 10 (2, 8)	should be listed once as
0, 8 (8)	0, 8, 2, 10 (8, 2)	0, 2, 8, 10 (2, 8)

2, 10 (8)
8, 10 (2)

The order of the digits has no significance.

Again, terms that fail to compare are recorded; these are loops of two that cannot be grouped into loops of four.

A new comparison is now performed on Column IV. Again, all terms in the brackets must be identical before a comparison can be made. Only the first decimal number in each row is actually checked to determine if they differ by a power of two. A new comparison is performed on each column that is generated until further comparisons are impossible.

All terms that failed to combine are now listed vertically. These are the actual loops, prime implicants, used to cover the ones in the Karnaugh map.

	0	2	8	6	10	12	7	14	41	15
41									x	
0, 2, 8, 10 (2, 8)	x	x	x		x					
2, 6, 10, 14 (4, 8)		x		x	x			x		
8, 10, 12, 14 (2, 4)			x		x	x		x		
6, 7, 14, 15 (1, 8)				x			x	x		x

A graphical method is used to eliminate unnecessary prime implicants and to show all possible answers. The horizontal axis of this chart is a listing of all decimal numbers contained in the original expression. The vertical axis consists of all terms that fail to combine. Check marks are now placed in the chart corresponding to the decimal number in the terms located to the left. Numbers in brackets are not included. The object is to select a set of terms that will place at least one check mark under each of the decimal numbers in the original transmission. A column that has but one check mark under it, such as the zero column, indicates that the term that produced that check is needed in the answer. In the chart shown above, the terms 0, 2, 8, 10 (2, 8); 8, 10, 12, 14 (2, 4); 6, 7, 14, 15 (1, 8) and 41 are needed in the answer. The others such as 2, 6, 10, 14 (4,8), for example, are not needed. In many cases, the designer will be faced with the problem of having more than one possible set of terms to check in each column. The designer, in this case, should choose, in most cases, the longest terms since these require the least hardware to implement.

Decoding or reconversion of the answer is the reverse of the original process of coding. The first decimal number in each term is converted to its binary representation. The decimal numbers in the brackets then indicate which bit positions of that term are to be crossed out. The remaining bits are then converted to their alphabetic variables corresponding to previous assigned weight. Therefore, the answer for the example is:

$$T = 0, 2, 8, 10 \ (2, 8) + 8, 10, 12, 14 \ (2, 4) + 6, 7, 14, 15 \ (1, 8) + 41$$

$$= 00\cancel{0}0\cancel{0}0 + 001\cancel{0}\cancel{0}0 + 00\cancel{0}11\cancel{0} + 101001$$

$$= \overline{A} \cdot \overline{B} \cdot \overline{D} \cdot \overline{E} + \overline{A} \cdot \overline{B} \cdot C \cdot \overline{F} + \overline{A} \cdot \overline{B} \cdot D \cdot E + A \cdot \overline{B} \cdot C \cdot \overline{D} \cdot \overline{E} \cdot F$$

$$T = \overline{ABDE} + \overline{ABCF} + \overline{ABDE} + A\overline{B}C\overline{D}\overline{E}F$$

The use of shorthand notation can be helpful when working with longer problems. This notation may be obtained by simply using the first decimal number of the term and all decimal numbers in the brackets. A term such as 0, 2, 8, 10 (2, 8) may therefore be written as 0, (2, 8). Of course, the full set of decimal numbers must be restored for the final charting. This may be accomplished by adding all possible combinations of the numbers in the bracket to the number outside the bracket. A term 8 (2, 4) may be expanded by adding 2 to 8, 4 to 8 and 4 + 2 to 8 to produce the missing numbers 10, 12, 14. The term would therefore be 8, 10, 12, 14 (2, 4).

A method has been devised for showing all possible choices of prime implicants. This method is based on the chart used to select the prime implicants and is accomplished by assigning a variable to each of the terms in the left-hand column.

Example:

var.	3	5	6	7	11	13	14
3, 7(4)	a	x			x			
3, 11(8)	b	x				x		
5, 7(2)	c		x		x			
5, 13(8)	d		x				x	
6, 7(1)	e			x	x			
6, 14(8)	f			x				x

In this example the term 3, 7(4) has been assigned "a" while the term

3, 11 (8) has been assigned "b" and so on. To place a check mark under "3" either the term "a" or "b" will be needed. To place a check mark under "5" the term "c" or "d" will be needed. We may now write an expression that will place a check mark under each of the decimal numbers.

$$(a + b)(c + d)(e + f)(a + c + e)(b)(d)(f)$$

This expression is now multiplied out. Redundant terms are dropped by applying the theorems: $A + AB = A$, $A(A + B) = A$ producing the following expression:

$$(a + c + e)(b)(d)(f)$$

$$abdf + bcdf + bdef$$

From this expression we can see three possible answers. Each of the terms gives us a set of prime implicants which will produce the correct answer. The designer may now choose whichever set he prefers.

The Quine-McCluskey method may be extended to include "don't care" conditions. The "don't care" terms are converted to binary and then to decimal numbers as are all other terms. The decimal numbers for the "don't care" terms are then combined with the list of decimal numbers for the original transmission. This entire list is put through the comparing procedure until further comparisons are no longer possible. The graphical method of eliminating unnecessary terms remains exactly the same as before. Only decimal numbers appearing in the transmission are used on the horizontal axis. "Don't care" terms should not be placed on the horizontal axis. The vertical axis consists of terms that are not combined in the various columns; "don't care" terms (decimal numbers) will appear here. The final solution is read from the chart and converted to the original variables. This solution, if possible, will have used the "don't care" terms to obtain a minimal solution.

The Multiple Output Problem

As larger combinational logic problems are undertaken, the conditions associated with more than one output are soon encountered. These multi-output problems have a Boolean expression associated with each output. The designer may, if he chooses, treat each output as a separate problem and, in some cases, this will produce the least expensive circuitry. In a great many cases a sharing of hardware may result if the multi-output problem is treated in its entirety. Many methods have been proposed for minimizing this type of problem. Most are based on a "cut and try" procedure. "Cut and try" solutions will normally produce a usable answer rapidly, although better solutions may be obtained by a formal method. One "cut and try" method is given below; however, the formal solution presented later in the book is recommended.

Recognizing Common Terms

Minimization of multi-output problems may be obtained by recognizing terms that are common to two or more mappings of the outputs. To aid in this visual recognition, all output expressions are plotted on the same map. For a two-output problem, each square in the map will have two binary digits. The first expression is plotted on the map in the left-hand section of each box and the second expression is placed in the right-hand section.

Example: I (Figure 5.6)

$$T_1 = \overline{A}C + \overline{A}BD + AB\overline{C}D + A\overline{B}\,\overline{C}\,\overline{D}$$
$$T_2 = B\overline{C}D + A\overline{B}\,\overline{C}\,\overline{D} + AC\!D + ABD$$

From the combined map in Figure 5.6 the common terms may be read off immediately by looking at boxes that have two one's in them. The common terms in this example are $A\overline{B}\,\overline{C}\,\overline{D}$ and $B\overline{C}D$. These terms need only be

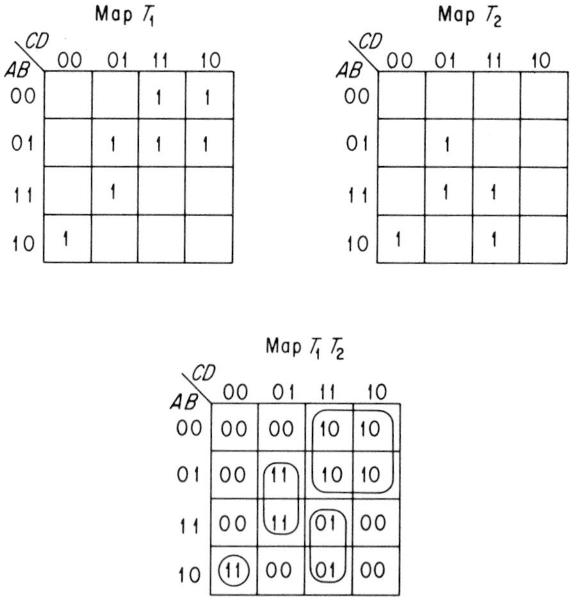

Figure 5.6. Multi-output, Example 1.

generated once and used in both expressions. The answer to the above example would be:

$$T_1 = \overline{A}C + A\overline{B}\overline{C}\overline{D} + B\overline{C}D$$

$$T_2 = ACD + A\overline{B}\overline{C}\overline{D} + B\overline{C}D$$

These expressions may be rewritten to show the use of common terms while Figure 5.7 shows the resulting circuitry.

$$\left.\begin{array}{l} T_1 = \overline{A}C \\ T_2 = ACD \end{array}\right\} + A\overline{B}\overline{C}\overline{D} + B\overline{C}D$$

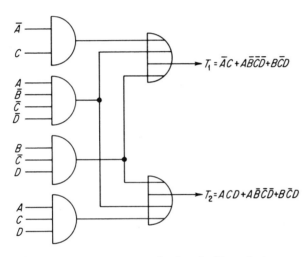

Figure 5.7. Multi-output circuitry for Example 1.

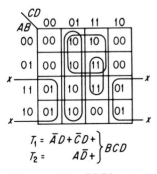

Figure 5.8. Multi-output, Example 2.

The most difficult portion of the above method is in the decision of whether or not to use the common terms. In many cases this decision cannot be made until all solutions have been tried.

Example: II

$$T_1 = \overline{C}D + \overline{A}\overline{B}D + BCD$$

$$T_2 = BCD + AC\overline{D} + A\overline{C}\overline{D}$$

These transmissions are mapped in Figure 5.8. In this problem the designer may choose not to use the common term BCD, in transmission one, since a term with fewer variables, namely BD, will provide the same outputs. In this case the two transmissions would be as follows:

$$T_1 = BD + \overline{A}D + \overline{C}D$$

$$T_2 = A\overline{D} + BCD$$

This solution would require 16 diodes or literals to implement, while using the common term would require only 14 diodes or literals.

$$T_1 = \overline{A}D + \overline{C}D +$$
$$T_2 = \qquad \overline{A}D +$$ $\Big\} BCD$

In this case the decision to use the common term could have been made without working out both possible answers. The designer should have noted that the term BCD would have to be gener-ated for transmission two and therefore could cost nothing to use in transmission one. Figure 5.9 illustrates a case where it does not pay to use the common term.

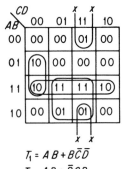

$$T_1 = AB + B\overline{C}\overline{D}$$
$$T_2 = AD + \overline{B}CD$$

Figure 5.9. Multi-output, Example 3.

Example: III

$$T_1 = ABD + B\overline{C}\overline{D} + AB\overline{D}$$
$$T_2 = ABD + \overline{B}CD + A\overline{B}D$$

In this example the common term ABD does not have to be generated for either transmission and the designer is now faced with the problem of generating it or using other terms to produce the correct outputs. In this example the common term should not be generated since the common term will be included in terms required by both expressions.

For two-output four-variable problems the decision to use a common term is not too difficult. But as more outputs are encountered and the number of variables increases, the problem reduces to an exhaustive routine of typing all possible solutions. A three-output five-variable problem is shown to illustrate this point.

Example: IV

$$T_1 = A\overline{B}\overline{C}DE + \overline{A}BD\overline{E} + \overline{A}CDE + \overline{A}BDE$$
$$T_2 = \overline{A}BD + A\overline{B}\overline{C}DE + ACD\overline{E} + A\overline{C}D\overline{E} + \overline{A}CDE$$
$$T_3 = \overline{A}\overline{B}\overline{C}D + \overline{A}BD + ACD\overline{E} + AC\overline{D}\overline{E}$$

The map of these three transmissions is shown in Figure 5.10. From this map many common terms may be found.

The term $\overline{A}BD$ is common to all three transmissions. Terms $ACD\overline{E}$, $\overline{A}C\overline{D}E$, $BCD\overline{E}$, $\overline{A}BCE$ and $A\overline{B}\overline{C}\overline{D}E$ are common to two transmissions. By using a systematic approach to the problem, most of the guesswork can be eliminated. The term $A\overline{B}\overline{C}\overline{D}E$ is a single box and will be needed for transmission one; therefore it may be used in transmission two. The term $\overline{A}C\overline{D}E$ is needed in transmission one and therefore may be used in transmission two. The term $\overline{A}BD$ is needed in transmission one and therefore may be used in transmission two and three. The remainder of the problem is solved by a cut and try method.

$$T_1 = \overline{A}BD + A\overline{B}\overline{C}\overline{D}E + \overline{A}C\overline{D}E$$

$$T_2 = \overline{A}BD + A\overline{B}\overline{C}\overline{D}E + \overline{A}C\overline{D}E + AD\overline{E}$$

$$T_3 = \overline{A}BD + AC\overline{E} + \overline{A}B\overline{C}\overline{D}$$

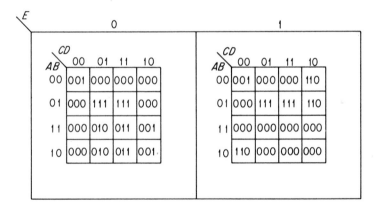

Figure 5.10. Multi-output, Example 4.

Generating and selecting minimal terms: As the complexity of multi-output problems increases, it is necessary to adopt some formal procedure for generating and selecting the minimal set of terms. To minimize a multi-output problem, the terms required will be: all prime implicants of each of the output expressions mapped separately and all prime implicants obtained from all conjunctions of the original expression. For a three output problem, all prime implicants from maps T_1, T_2, T_3, $(T_1)(T_2)$, $(T_1)(T_3)$, $(T_2)(T_3)$ and $(T_1)(T_2)(T_3)$ are needed.

Example: V

$$T_1 = \overline{A}\overline{B} + \overline{A}D$$
$$T_2 = BD + AD$$
$$T_3 = A + BD$$

Seven four-variable maps will be required. (Figure 5.11.)
From the maps we obtain the following terms:

From T_1	$\overline{A}\overline{B},\ \overline{A}D$
From T_2	$BD,\ AD$
From T_3	$A,\ BD$
From $T_1 \cdot T_2$	$\overline{A}BD$
From $T_1 \cdot T_3$	$\overline{A}BD$
From $T_2 \cdot T_3$	$BD,\ AD$
From $T_1 \cdot T_2 \cdot T_3$	$\overline{A}BD$

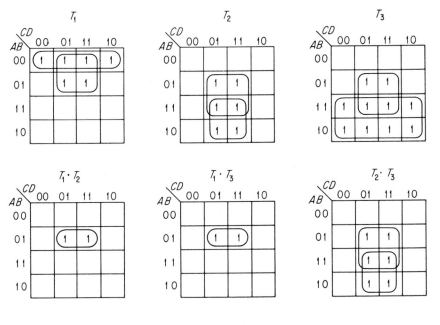

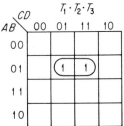

Figure 5.11. Mapping for multi-output, Problem 5.

The problem is now one of selecting which terms to be used with each output. A table very similar to that used with the Quine-McCluskey is used to display all possible choices (Figure 5.12). Across the top of the table is placed all terms of all output expressions written in canonic sum form. The terms obtained from the mappings are arranged vertically on the left side of the table. The identity of the map from which the prime implicant was derived is retained. An "X" is than placed under each term that is contained within the prime implicant located to the left. Prime implicants from map T_1 may place "X's" under only those canonic terms that are in expression T_1. Prime implicants from map $T_1 \cdot T_2$ place "X's" under canonic terms from expression T_1 and expression T_2. All prime implicants have been assigned new symbols as a shorthand procedure. Prime implicants are now chosen so as to place at least one "X" under each of the canonic terms. As in the Quine-McCluskey method, some columns may have only one "X"; and the prime implicants generating these "X's" must be chosen. In our example, prime implicants "a" and "e" are essential. Using the newly assigned symbol, an expression is written, showing all possible choices of remaining prime implicants.

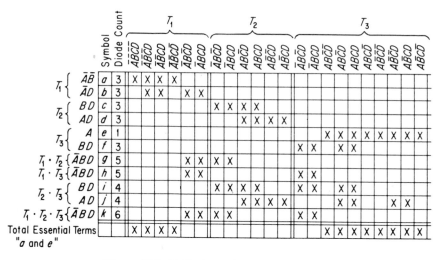

Figure 5.12. Table for multi-output, Example 5.

$$(b + g + h + k)(c + g + i + k)(c + d + i + j)(d + j)(f + h + i + k)$$

Dropping redundant terms and multiplying out

$$bcfd + bcfj + bid + bij + gfd + gfj + ghd + ghj + gid$$
$$+ gij + hcd + hcj + hid + hij + kd + kj$$

Since there are sixteen terms in the above expression, there are sixteen different irredundant circuits that will satisfy the original problem. At this point, some sense of cost must be introduced to enable the designer to choose between the sixteen circuits. In our example we will assume that diode AND and OR circuits are being used and all variables and their complements are available. With this information we may now determine, in diodes, the cost of using each of the prime implicants from the table. Prime implicants such as $\overline{A}\overline{B}$ from map T_1 will require three diodes: two diodes for the AND and one diode for the input to the output OR. Prime implicant BD from map $T_2 \cdot T_3$ will require four diodes: two for the AND and one more for each of the output OR's of T_2 and T_3. From our sixteen possible circuits, we now choose "kd", as this combination has the lowest possible diode count. To the prime implicants "k" and "d" we must now add the essential terms "a" and "e". Our entire choice of terms is therefore:

$$a = \overline{A}\overline{B} \text{ for } T_1$$
$$e = A \text{ for } T_3$$
$$k = \overline{A}BD \text{ for } T_1 \cdot T_2 \cdot T_3$$
$$d = AD \text{ for } T_2$$

The resulting equations are shown below.

$$T_1 = \overline{A}\overline{B} + \overline{A}BD$$
$$T_2 = AD + \overline{A}BD$$
$$T_3 = A + \overline{A}BD$$

The column in the table labeled "diode count" should actually be "cost". It should be clear at this point that within a logic net, some terms may be derived for only the cost of a piece of wire while other terms may require "Inverters" or "Drivers" that are rather expensive. The cost of these terms must be left to the designer since they vary so widely with circuits and other total machine considerations.

Large Multi-Output Problems

When problems of more than six variables are being solved, the Quine-McCluskey method may be used in place of mapping to obtain the required terms. For a four-output problem, the Quine-McCluskey method would be used 15 times. It is advantageous to develop a method whereby all terms may be obtained in one procedure. It is possible to alter the Quine-McCluskey method somewhat to obtain all required terms in one operation.

Example: VI

$$T_a = A\overline{C} + AB$$
$$T_b = \overline{B}C + AC$$

Expanding each equation to canonic sum form and rewriting in decimal number form, we have

$$T_a = 4, 6, 7$$
$$T_b = 1, 5, 7$$

A character is now affixed to each of the decimal numbers to indicate which of the transmissions it belongs to.

$$T_a = 4_a, 6_a, 7_a$$
$$T_b = 1_b, 5_b, 7_b$$

The entire group of decimal numbers is now arranged according to the number of bits contained in their binary representations. This is essentially the same procedure as used for single output expressions. Numbers such as 7_a and 7_b are listed in the same group, one below the other.

$$1_{(b)}$$
$$\underline{4_{(a)}}$$
$$5_{(b)}$$
$$\underline{6_{(a)}}$$
$$7_{(a)}$$
$$7_{(b)}$$

The comparison procedure is now started with the usual restrictions that all numbers (and characters) in the brackets must be alike before a comparison can be made between groups. Furthermore, within each group a comparison of a different type is carried on. This second comparison is used to check for identical numbers outside of the brackets but with unlike characters in the brackets. This situation occurs in our example and the method of recording it is shown below. It should be noticed that the two comparison methods are carried on alternately.

The number $1_{(b)}$ is first compared with all numbers below it in the same group, looking for another $1(-)$. It is then compared with all higher decimal numbers in the next group with the same characters in brackets. A comparison within a group does not place a check mark after either term.

1 (b) ✓	1, 5 (4, b)
4 (a) ✓	4, 6 (2, a)
5 (b) ✓	5, 7 (2, b)
6 (a) ✓	6, 7 (1, a)
7 (a) ✓	7 (a, b)
7 (b) ✓	

No further comparisons are possible in our example. The charting procedure given before is now used to show all possible answers (Figure 5.13).

Terms 4, 6(2a) and 1, 5(4, b) are required since there is but one "X" in columns 1 and 4. An expression is now written showing all possible answers. Our expression is therefore:

$$(W)(V)(Y + Z)(X + Z)$$

	Symbol	Cost in Diodes	T_a			T_b			
			4	6	7	1	5	7	
1,5(4,b)	V	3				X	X		$\bar{B}C$ for T_b
4,6(2,a)	W	3	X	X					$A\bar{C}$ for T_a
5,7(2,b)	X	3					X	X	AC for T_b
6,7(1,a)	Y	3		X	X				AB for T_a
7(a,b)	Z	3			X			X	ABC for $T_a T_b$
Total Essential Terms "a and b"			X	X		X	X		

Figure 5.13. Cost table, Example 6.

Multiplying out

$$WVXY + WVZ$$
$$X = 3 \text{ diodes}$$
$$Y = 3 \text{ diodes}$$
$$Z = 5 \text{ diodes}$$

Our answer will be

$$WVZ = T_a = \bar{A}\bar{C} + ABC$$
$$T_b = \bar{B}\bar{C} + ABC$$

at a total cost of 11 diodes.

A somewhat larger problem is now worked out in detail to show the principles involved—

$$T_a = 5, 7, 13, 15$$
$$T_b = 0, 4, 12, 13, 14, 15$$
$$T_c = 0, 4, 9, 11, 13, 15$$

0 (b) ✓   0 (b, c) ✓   0, 4 (4, b, c) ⊗
0 (c) ✓   0, 4 (4, b) ⊗   13, 15 (2, a, b, c) ⊗
4 (b) ✓   0, 4 (4, c) ⊗
4 (c) ✓   4 (b, c) ✓   5, 7, 13, 15 (2, 8, a) ⊗
5 (a) ✓   4, 12 (8, b) ⊗   9, 11, 13, 15 (2, 4, c) ⊗
9 (c) ✓   5, 7 (2, a) ✓   12, 13, 14, 15 (1, 2, b) ⊗
12 (b) ✓   5, 13 (8, a) ✓   13 (a, b, c) ✓
7 (a) ✓   9, 11 (2, c) ✓   13, 15 (2, a, b) ⊗
11 (c) ✓   9, 13 (4, c) ✓   13, 15 (2, a, c) ⊗
13 (a) ✓   12, 13 (1, b) ✓   13, 15 (2, b, c) ⊗
13 (b) ✓   12, 14 (2, b) ✓   15 (a, b, c) ✓
13 (c) ✓   7, 15 (8, a) ✓
14 (b) ✓   11, 15 (4, c) ✓
15 (a) ✓   13 (a, b) ✓
15 (b) ✓   13 (a, c) ✓
15 (c) ✓   13, 15 (2, a) ✓
           13 (b, c) ✓
           13, 15 (2, b) ✓
           13, 15 (2, c) ✓
           14, 15 (1, b) ✓
           15 (a, b) ✓
           15 (a, c) ✓
           15 (b, c) ✓

Prime Implicants		T_a				T_b						T_c					
		5	7	13	15	0	4	12	13	14	15	0	4	9	11	13	15
0, 4 (4, b)	E					X	X										
0, 4 (4, c)	F											X	X				
4, 12 (8, b)	G						X	X									
0, 4 (4, b, c)	H					X	X					X	X				
* 5, 7, 13, 15 (2, 8, a)	I	X	X	X	X												
* 9, 11, 13, 15 (2, 4, c)	J													X	X	X	X
* 12, 13, 14, 15 (1, 2, b)	K							X	X	X	X						
13, 15 (2, a, b)	L			X	X				X		X						
13, 15 (2, a, c)	M			X	X											X	X
13, 15 (2, b, c)	N								X		X					X	X
13, 15 (2, a, b, c)	O			X	X				X		X					X	X
Terms covered by essential terms		X	X	X	X			X	X	X	X			X	X	X	X

* Essential Terms

Generating all sets of prime implicants

$$IJK(E + H)(E + G + H)(F + H)(F + H)$$
$$IJK(EF + H)$$
$$IJKEF + IJKH$$

$IJKH$ is selected as our answer since it has one less prime implicant than $IJKEF$.

$$I = 5, 7, 13, 15(2, 8, a) = BD \text{ for } T_a$$
$$J = 9, 11, 13, 15(2, 4, c) = AD \text{ for } T_c$$
$$K = 12, 13, 14, 15, (1, 2, b) = AB \text{ for } T_b$$
$$H = 0, 4, (4, b, c) = \overline{A}\,\overline{C}\,\overline{D} \text{ for } T_b \text{ and } T_c$$
$$T_a = BD$$
$$T_b = AB + \overline{A}\,\overline{C}\,\overline{D}$$
$$T_c = AD + \overline{A}\,\overline{C}\,\overline{D}$$

Factoring

The minimum product form or the minimum sum form of a Boolean expression is not always the equation best suited for implementation. Factoring of common terms or variables will in many instances produce an expression that will require less hardware to implement. No general method for factoring applicable to hand manipulation is known. Factoring, at best, is an art based on previous "cut and try" solutions. The problem is made more difficult by the fact that the best factored solution may not start from a minimum two level solution. That is, it may require redundancy. This is unfortunate since no large digital computer could be economically built without a great deal of factoring. Some examples of factoring are obvious as the following problem demonstrates.

$$T = AB\overline{C} + A\overline{B}C + AD$$

Since the variable A is common to all terms it may be factored

$$T = A(B\overline{C} + \overline{B}C + D)$$

This new expression will require only nine diodes to implement as compared with the original eleven diodes. It should be pointed out that factoring will normally increase the number of levels a signal may have to pass through and therefore the response time of the circuit will be increased. Designers encounter little difficulty in performing some kind of factoring from the minimum sum form but they often find it difficult to factor from the minimum product form. This should not be. The designer should remember that an expression such as

$(A + B + CD)(A + \overline{B} + \overline{D})$ may be factored to $A + (B + CD)(\overline{B} + \overline{D})$

In other words common terms or variables inside each bracket may be factored out and *OR*'ed to the expression. The designer should therefore work with both the sum and the product form when attempting factoring. Factoring may be applied to only part of an expression as demonstrated by the following examples.

Example 1. $T = A\bar{B}C + \bar{A}D + \bar{B}CD$
$= \bar{B}C(A + D) + \bar{A}D$

Example 2. $T = (AB + C)(\bar{C} + \bar{D})(AB + \bar{B}C)$
$= [AB + (C)(\bar{B}C)][\bar{C} + \bar{D}]$
$= (AB + \bar{B}C)(\bar{C} + \bar{D})$

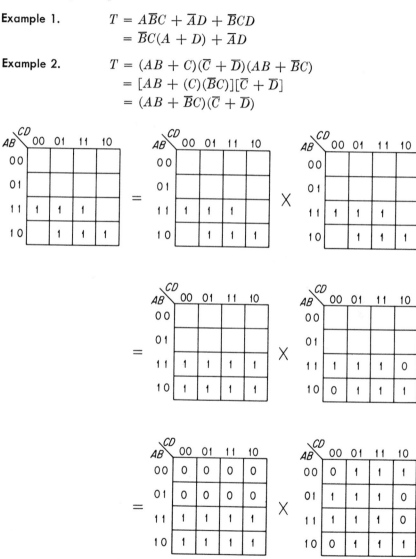

$$T = (A)(D + B\bar{C} + \bar{B}C)$$

Figure 5.14. Factoring $AB\bar{C} + A\bar{B}C + AB$.

Factoring may be performed with the aid of Karnaugh maps as well as a straight algebraic method. One such mapping method is that of assuming we want to express the original transmission as a product of a sum of products. This product of a sum of products may be shown as two Karnaugh maps with their outputs *ANDed* together to product the required expression.

An example, (Figure 5.14), will demonstrate the procedure.

$$T = AB\overline{C} + A\overline{B}C + AD$$

Ones are first placed in both the y and z maps wherever they appear in map x. This is necessary since the outputs of the y and z maps are going to be *ANDed* together to produce the expression in map x. Ones may now be placed anywhere in map y as long as a zero is placed in the z map in the corresponding location and vice-versa. It is impossible to give fixed rules regarding the placing of ones and zeros, however the overall goal is to produce large areas of ones in each map. Another example may serve to illustrate the procedure (Figure 5.15).

Another mapping procedure for factoring, which is sometimes helpful, is that of including some zeros in the first attempt at looping large areas.

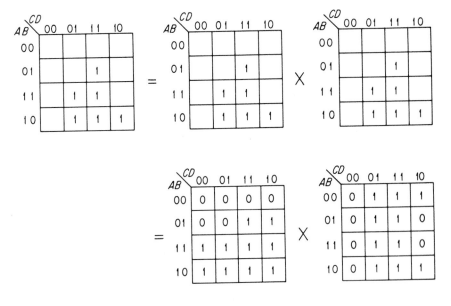

$$AD + BCD + A\overline{B}C = (A + BC)(D + \overline{B}C)$$

Figure 5.15. Factoring $AD + BCD + A\overline{B}C$.

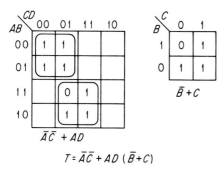

The large areas which contained these zeros are then remapped on a smaller map. The expression from the smaller map is then *AND*ed with the term used to obtain that area. Figure 5.16 demonstrates the principle. The labeling for the small map will be all variables that varied over the area of the term which contains the zero.

$\bar{A}\bar{C} + AD$

$T = \bar{A}\bar{C} + AD\,(\bar{B}+C)$

Figure 5.16. Factoring $\bar{A}C + ACD + A\bar{B}D$.

Figure 5.17 illustrates the principle for

$$T = CD + A\bar{B} + A\overline{C}\overline{D}$$

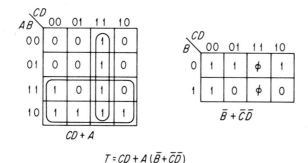

$CD + A$

$\bar{B} + \overline{C}\overline{D}$

$T = CD + A\,(\bar{B}+\overline{C}\overline{D})$

Figure 5.17. Factoring $CD\ A\bar{B}\ A\overline{C}\overline{D}$.

The smaller map in this case has two "don't care" conditions since these two terms are already included in the term CD.

This method, unlike the previous one, will in some case produce a four-level answer. The mapping procedures have one definite advantage over algebraic method. In some cases the addition of a redundant variable or term will allow a very clever factoring but the algebraic methods are based on expressions that have no redundancies. The mapping methods allow a designer to use any terms or variables he may believe are helpful even though they are redundant.

Problems

I. Minimize the following expressions using Karnaugh maps

(a) $CDE + \overline{A}B\overline{C}\overline{E} + \overline{A}BDE + \overline{A}BC\overline{E}$

(b) $\overline{B}D\overline{E} + \overline{A}\overline{C}D\overline{E} + \overline{C}DE + \overline{B}C\overline{D}$

(c) $\overline{B}CD\overline{E} + \overline{A}\overline{B}C\overline{D}\overline{E} + A\overline{C}D\overline{E} + A\overline{B}DE + AB\overline{C}DE$

(d) $\overline{A}\overline{B}C\overline{E} + BD\overline{E} + BCDE + ABDE$

(e) $\overline{A}BD\overline{F} + AB\overline{C}\overline{D}E\overline{F} + \overline{A}BD\overline{E} + A\overline{B}\overline{C}F + \overline{A}BDF + AB\overline{C}\overline{D}E\overline{F}$
$$+ A\overline{B}\overline{C}EF$$

II. Minimize by using Quine-McCluskey method

   (a) $\overline{A}\overline{C}\overline{D}E\overline{F} + ACDEF + AB\overline{C}DF + \overline{A}\overline{C}DE + AB\overline{C}D\overline{E}F$
$$+ AB\overline{C}EF + \overline{A}\overline{C}D\overline{E}F$$

   (b) $\overline{A}\overline{B}EF + CEF + AC\overline{E}F + CDE\overline{F} + ACD\overline{E}F$

III. Minimize the following by using one Karnaugh map

   (a) $T_1 = \overline{A}B\overline{C} + \overline{A}BD + \overline{A}BCD + \overline{A}CD$

   $T_2 = \overline{C}D + ACD$

   (b) $T_1 = AB + \overline{A}B\overline{C}$

   $T_2 = CD + \overline{A}\overline{C}D + \overline{A}D + \overline{B}\overline{C}$

   (c) $T_1 = AD + A\overline{B} + AC$

   $T_2 = B\overline{C} + \overline{A}B + B\overline{D}$

   (d) $T_1 = \overline{A}B + \overline{A}\overline{C} + B\overline{C}$

   $T_2 = C\overline{D} + A\overline{B} + A\overline{C}$

   $T_3 = \overline{A}C + ABCD$

IV. Use as many maps as necessary to minimize the following

   (a) $T_1 = ABD + \overline{A}\overline{C}D$

   $T_2 = \overline{B}\overline{D} + ABD + B\overline{C}D$

   $T_3 = \overline{B}\overline{D} + ABCD + \overline{A}B\overline{C}$

Answer: 22 Diodes

   (b) $T_1 = CD + AD$

   $T_2 = CD + AD + ABC$

   $T_3 = A\overline{C}D + \overline{A}BC\overline{D}$

Answer: 19 Diodes

V. Use Quine-McCluskey to minimize the following

   (a) $T_1 = A\overline{B} + \overline{B}D + B\overline{C}\overline{D}$

   $T_2 = AD + B\overline{D} + BC + \overline{A}BD$

Answer: 18 Diodes

(b) $T_1 = \overline{C}D + \overline{A}D$

$T_2 = \overline{A}B\overline{C} + A\overline{C}D + A\overline{B}C + \overline{B}C\overline{D}$

$T_3 = BC\overline{D} + A\overline{B}D$

Answer: 25 Diodes

VI. Factor the following. Use only diode circuits.

(a) $\overline{C}D + \overline{A}\overline{B}\overline{C} + \overline{A}C\overline{D}$ Answer: 4 Diodes

(b) $\overline{A}\overline{B}\overline{C} + \overline{A}C\overline{D} + BCD + ABD$ Answer: 12 Diodes

(c) $AB + A\overline{D} + \overline{A}CD + \overline{A}\overline{C}D$ Answer: 8 Diodes

References

Caldwell, Samuel H., *Switching Circuits and Logical Design*. New York: John Wiley & Sons, Inc., 1958.

Hurley, Richard B., *Transistor Logic Circuits*. New York: John Wiley & Sons, Inc., 1956.

Phister, Montgomery, *Logical Design of Digital Computers*. New York: John Wiley & Sons, Inc., 1958.

IMPLEMENTING NOR
AND NAND LOGIC

6

Chapter Summary

This chapter discusses the theory and practice of implementing Boolean statements in the *NOR* family of transistor circuits which were surveyed in Chapter I. The logical functions implemented by these circuits, the *NAND* and *NOR*; *AND-NOT* and *OR-NOT*, respectively, are defined and their relationship to the *AND*, *OR*, *NOT* functions of the previous chapters derived. Special techniques for analysis, synthesis, minimization, factoring, etc., analogous to those of Boolean Algebra, are developed taking into consideration the specific properties of these logic (and circuit) connectives.

Practical Importance of NANDS and NORS

The logic-circuit blocks of the *NOR* family of transistor circuits have some ideal characteristics from the designers view. Some of these are: 1) each is a single universal logic block, sets of which can be used to generate any Boolean function, 2) each block has current and voltage gain and level setting ability, 3) each block can drive several other blocks directly, 4) sequential circuit design can be more flexible since amplification need not be inserted in the feedback loops, 5) the number of inputs can be increased by paralleling circuits, commoning collectors in many cases, 6) there are practically no circuit constraints on interconnections other than a maximum number of inputs and loads, 7) the functions exhibit considerable logical power, 8) the functions are available in a whole family of circuits in both speed range and cost, and these can be made circuitwise compatible with each other. For these and many economy and simplicity reasons, this circuit family is achieving wide usage in modern computers.

NOR and NAND Defined

We must take care to distinguish the *NOR* and *NAND* functions at the outset since the mutual duality of the functions and their design techniques can cause confusion.

NAND Function: Interpretation in Boolean Algebra:

$$1 \text{ variable } - \quad \overline{A}$$
$$2 \text{ variables} - \quad \overline{A \cdot B} = \overline{A} + \overline{B} \quad (NOT\text{-}AND)$$
$$3 \text{ variables} - \quad \overline{A \cdot B \cdot C} = \overline{A} + \overline{B} + \overline{C}$$
$$n \text{ variables} - \quad (n \geq 1) -$$
$$\overline{A_1 \cdot A_2 \cdots \cdot A_n} = \overline{A}_1 + \overline{A}_2 \cdots + \overline{A}_n$$

Interpretation in block diagram:

A "black" box with $n (\geq 1)$ inputs and one output which has the value 1 if and only if at least one of the inputs is 0. The block diagram symbol is shown in Figure 6.1(a).

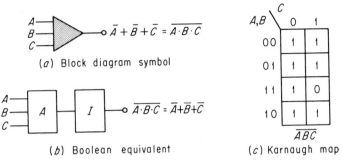

(a) Block diagram symbol

$\bar{A}+\bar{B}+\bar{C} = \overline{A \cdot B \cdot C}$

(b) Boolean equivalent

$\overline{A \cdot B \cdot C} = \bar{A}+\bar{B}+\bar{C}$

A,B \ C	0	1
00	1	1
01	1	1
11	1	0
10	1	1

$\overline{ABC}$

(c) Karnaugh map

Figure 6.1. The $NAND$ function, interpreted.

This is equivalent to a Boolean block diagram of an AND followed by an $INVERTER$. This is illustrated in Figure 6.1(b).

Interpretation in function table:

The Karnaugh map of the function is given in Figure 6.1(c).

NOR Function: Interpretation in Boolean Algebra:

$$\text{1 variable} - \quad \bar{A}$$
$$\text{2 variables} - \quad \overline{A+B} = \bar{A} \cdot \bar{B} \quad (NOT\text{-}OR)$$
$$\text{3 variables} - \quad \overline{A+B+C} = \bar{A}\bar{B}\bar{C}$$
$$\text{n variables} - \quad (n \geq 1) -$$

$$\overline{A_1 + A_2 \cdots + A_n} = \bar{A}_1 \cdot \bar{A}_2 \cdots \cdot \bar{A}_n$$

Interpretation in block diagram:

A "black" box with $n(\geq 1)$ inputs and one output which has the value 1 if and only if *all* the inputs are 0. The block diagram symbol is shown in Figure 6.2(a).

This is equivalent to a Boolean block symbol of OR followed by an $INVERTER$. This is illustrated in Figure 6.2(b).

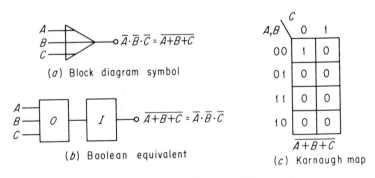

(a) Block diagram symbol

$\bar{A} \cdot \bar{B} \cdot \bar{C} = \overline{A+B+C}$

(b) Boolean equivalent

$\overline{A+B+C} = \bar{A} \cdot \bar{B} \cdot \bar{C}$

A,B \ C	0	1
00	1	0
01	0	0
11	0	0
10	0	0

$\overline{A+B+C}$

(c) Karnaugh map

Figure 6.2. The NOR function, interpreted.

Interpretation in function table:

The Karnaugh map of the function is given in Figure 6.2(c).

Since the $NAND$ and NOR functions are mutually dual, if a statement, theorem, technique is valid for one of the functions, the dual of the statement, theorem, technique is valid for the other function. So for simplicity, the development will be made mostly in terms of the $NAND$ function with occasional examples in the NOR function.

The Transform Method of Design with the NAND and NOR Functions

Properties and Nature of the Transform: The Transform Method of design described in this section makes the logic design of logic-circuits with the $NAND$ block (or NOR) as easy and as rapid as designing circuits of AND, OR, and NOT blocks. Essentially, it allows the designer to work in the familiar and simpler Boolean Algebra, making use of all the tools of Chapters III–V, and during the last step of drawing the block diagram he may apply a simple set of transform rules that map his Boolean equations or diagrams into $NAND$ diagrams (or NOR diagrams).

For this to be practical, the transformations must in some sense be minimality-preserving. For two-levels of gating the minimality preserving transform assures as minimal (irredundant) a circuit as that synthesized in Boolean Algebra. Since minimality assurance for factored forms in any of these algebras is lacking using practical hand methods, no more can be asked than that no sense of minimality be lost in the transform. Thus, for factored forms, the minimality-preserving nature of the transform assures that the same total number of blocks, and the number of inputs to and outputs from each block be unaffected in the transform. Indeed, the identical inter-connection configuration is preserved—all that is changed by the transform is the labeling of the blocks, (with one exception, as we'll see).

To achieve this sense of minimality preservation in the Transform Method requires that a few simple constraints be added to the design done in Boolean Algebra. These effectively are nothing but taking into account that, ultimately, the design must be implemented in the $NAND$, and its special properties must be taken into account during factoring and minimization.

Deriving the Transform from a Terminal Analysis of the NAND and NOR Functions

In Figures 6.3 and 6.4, the logical nets for an equation are shown in a $NAND$ net and an AND-OR net. Looking only at the terminals outside the dotted

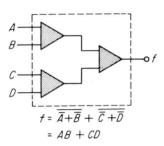

$$f = \overline{\overline{A+B}} + \overline{\overline{C+D}}$$
$$= AB + CD$$

Figure 6.3. Terminal analysis of the $NAND$ net.

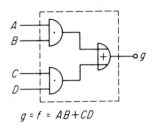

$$g = f = AB + CD$$

Figure 6.4. Terminal equivalent of the $NAND$ net of Fig. 6.25.

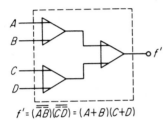

$$f' = (\overline{\overline{AB}})(\overline{\overline{CD}}) = (A+B)(C+D)$$

Figure 6.5. Terminal analysis of a NOR net.

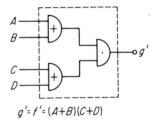

$$g' = f' = (A+B)(C+D)$$

Figure 6.6. Terminal equivalent of the NOR net.

lines of Figures 6.3 and 6.4, their behavior as logical functions is identical.

A similar dual relationship is shown for the NOR function in Figures 6.5 and 6.6. All is not so straightforward, however, as shown in Figure 6.7. Thus, a single variable coming in at the first level of gating must be complemented in the transformation of the circuit to Boolean notation.

More generally, variables entering at odd levels of gating* must be complemented in the transform. This is illustrated in the analysis of Figure 6.8. The third level gate is an odd level, so the variables must be complemented in the Transformation to Boolean notation. Notice that for the $NAND$, three levels, transforms to an OR-AND-OR form with complementing of the odd level variables.

---

* In counting levels in $NAND$ and NOR nets, start with the output gate as level 1 and work backward (and numerically up) until the inputs are reached. We conform, however, to the usual Boolean standard of not counting inverters as levels although the distinction is more difficult with $NAND$ elements. Still, this is a reasonable and useful convention in application. These points are important to remember since counting levels will be an important aspect of Transform synthesis and analysis.

That the third level becomes an *OR* and its variables complemented could be expected. For, if we group the levels into pairs (1, 2), (3, 4) . . . the third level (all odd levels) can be looked at as a first level in its level pair and the terminal analysis of Figures 6.3 and 6.4 hold. Similarly, any fourth level (all even levels) is the second level of the pair and thus transforms to an *AND*. Thus four levels in the *NAND* would yield an *AND-OR-AND-OR* form. Five levels are shown in Figure 6.9.

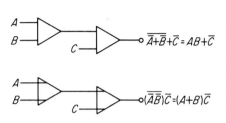

Figure 6.7. Exception in the terminal analysis.

An insight into these Transform rules is afforded if we redraw a *NAND* network from the point of view of *AND-INVERTERS*. The comparison of the terminal analyses of Figures 6.3 and 6.4 and the analysis rules illustrated in Figures 6.8 and 6.9 can be understood by comparing the two diagrams of Figure 6.10(a,b). Both diagram the same function with the level of gating indicated by the number in the block. Looking back into the network from output f to *AND* gate A_2 (Figure 6.10(b)) we see an *AND* followed by two inverters in series, I_2 and I_1. As far as the signal at f is concerned, these inversions cancel and f sees the *AND* A_2 as an *AND*. Similarly, for A_2'.

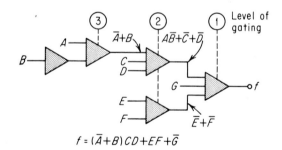

$$f = (\bar{A}+B)CD+EF+\bar{G}$$

Figure 6.8. Odd gating level property of the *NAND* function.

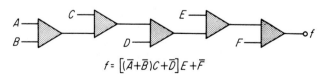

$$f = \left[(\bar{A}+\bar{B})C+\bar{D}\right]E+\bar{F}$$

Figure 6.9. Five-level *NAND* net.

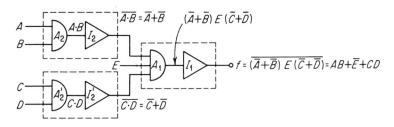

(a) *NAND* network

(b) Equivalent *AND*-inverter circuit

(Numbers in the blocks refer to the level of gating.)

Figure 6.10. Insight into the transform rules by comparing a *NAND* network to its equivalent in *AND*-inverter blocks.

Thus, the second level gates 2 and 2′ of Figure 6.10(a) Transform to *AND*'s A_2 and A_2' of Figure 6.10(b). Looking back from output f to the *AND* A_1 with respect to the first level variable E (Figure 6.10(b)), f sees an *AND* in series with an inverter, thus (with respect to E), gate 1 of Figure 6.10(a) transforms to an *OR* with first level inputs complemented ($E \rightarrow \overline{E}$) by DeMorgan's theorem. A more general case is shown in Figure 6.11. For Figure 6.11(a), looking back to *NAND* gates 2, 2′, 4, f sees (in Figure 6.11(b)) *AND*'s A_2, A_2', A_4 in series with an even number of inverters canceling to transform *NAND*s 2, 2′, 4 to *AND*'s A_2, A_2', A_4. For Figure 6.11(a), looking back to *NAND* gates 1, 3, 3′ with respect to variables entering on these levels, f sees A_1 with respect to H, A_3 with respect to D and $\overline{C}$, A_3' with respect to E and F—all with an odd number of inverters in series which transform these *AND*'s to *OR*'s with variables entering on those levels complemented by DeMorgan's Rule. Note that $\overline{C}$ drives both an even and an odd level of gating becoming $\overline{C}$ and C respectively.

The reader may readily verify that with the *NOR* function, three levels of gating transforms to an *AND-OR-AND*, four levels, *OR-AND-OR-AND* ... and so on. This may be verified by viewing a *NOR* network as *OR-INVERTERS* as done for the *NAND* in Figures 6.10 and 6.11. Note that complementing variables at odd levels holds for both functions in the transform.

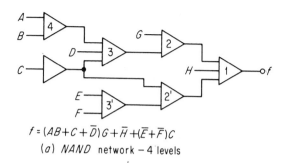

$$f = (AB + C + \bar{D})G + \bar{H} + (\bar{E} + \bar{F})C$$
(a) NAND network – 4 levels

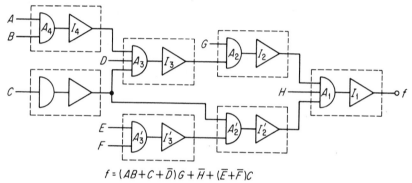

$$f = (AB + C + \bar{D})G + \bar{H} + (\bar{E} + \bar{F})C$$

(b) Equivalent AND-inverter circuit

(Numbers in the blocks refer to the level of gating.)

Figure 6.11. Comparison of NAND with AND-inverter diagrams of same function—four levels.

Inverse Transform Rules for Analysis of NAND or NOR Networks

(The Inverse Transform is from NAND or NOR to Boolean networks.)

NAND Networks:

1) Write an e inside each even level gate and an o inside each odd level gate, ignoring all inverters (single input blocks). If a gate appears both as an even and an odd level, leave it blank* and all gates into it blank as well.

2) Transform all o-gates to OR's. Transform all e gates to AND's. Transform all blank gates split in two as an AND (writing an e in it) driving the odd level loads, and as an OR (putting an o in it) driving the even level loads. Alternatively, treat the blank gates as though the output

---

* This constitutes a special case not derivable by the Transform alone, as we'll see.

drove only odd levels, transform to AND's and insert an inverter in the output driving even levels.

3) Complement all variables entering OR's or o blocks. Any inverters to AND's (e levels) remain the same.

NOR Networks:

1) Same as for $NAND$.
2) Transform all e-gates to OR's and all o-gates to AND's. Transform all blank gates split in two as an OR (putting an e in it) driving the odd level loads, and an AND (putting an o in it) driving the even level loads. Alternatively, treat the blank gates as though the output drove only odd levels, transform to OR's and insert an inverter in the output driving even levels.
3) Complement all variables entering AND's, or o blocks. Any inverters to OR's (e levels) remain the same.

Analysis with these rules is quick and easy with only a little practice.

Example 6.1: Analyze the net of Figure 6.13(a) transforming to a Boolean equation. First label the gates as to their odd or even level, ignoring inverters, as done in the figure. There are no blank gates so all e gates become AND's and all o gates become OR's with inputs complemented. The equivalent Boolean diagram is shown in Figure 6.12.

Example 6.2: Analyze the net of Figure 6.13(b). The levels are labeled on the diagram with three blank gates which split each into an AND driving the odd levels and an OR driving the even levels. Inputs to all OR's are comple-

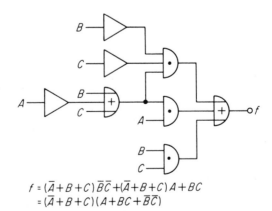

$$f = (\bar{A} + B + C)\,\bar{B}\bar{C} + (\bar{A} + B + C)\,A + BC$$
$$\quad = (\bar{A} + B + C)(A + BC + \bar{B}\bar{C})$$

Figure 6.12. Inverse transform of Fig. 6.13(a).

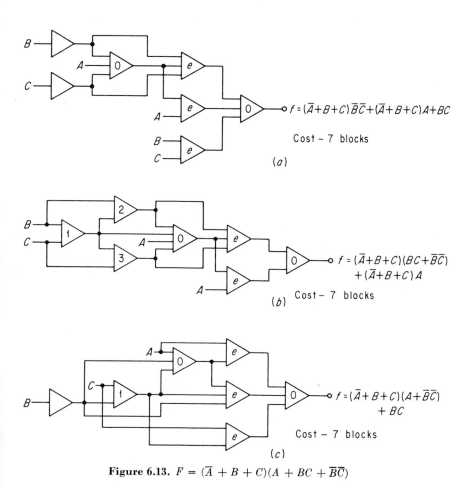

Figure 6.13. $F = (\bar{A} + B + C)(A + BC + \bar{B}\bar{C})$

mented and the transformed circuit is shown in Figure 6.14(a). The blank gate driving two other blank gates and an odd level, splits as shown, AND's driving OR's and OR's driving AND's. Corresponding gates are numbered for reference. Sharing gates among levels is clearly advantageous. In Figure 6.14(b) the alternative method of inserting inverters in blank gates driving even levels is used.

Example 6.3: Assuming the NOR function, analyze Figure 6.13(c). There is one blank gate, all other levels are labeled. Now o gates change to AND's and e's to OR's with all inputs to AND's complemented. The blank gate splits as an AND driving the even levels and an OR driving the odd levels. See Figure 6.15(a). Figure 6.15(b) makes the same analysis but using the alternative of using inverters instead of splitting gates.

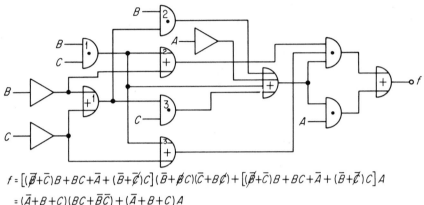

$$f = [(\bar{B}+\bar{C})B+BC+\bar{A}+(\bar{B}+\bar{C})C](\bar{B}+\not{B}C)(\bar{C}+B\not{C})+[(\bar{B}+\bar{C})B+BC+\bar{A}+(\bar{B}+\bar{C})C]A$$

$$= (\bar{A}+B+C)(BC+\bar{B}\bar{C})+(\bar{A}+B+C)A$$

$$= (\bar{A}+B+C)(A+BC+\bar{B}\bar{C})$$

(a)

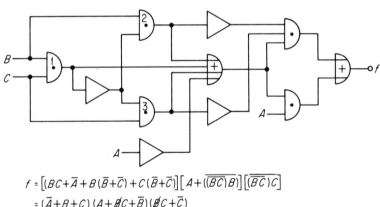

$$f = [(BC+\bar{A}+B(\bar{B}+\bar{C})+C(\bar{B}+\bar{C})][A+(\overline{(\overline{BC})B})][\overline{(\overline{BC})C}]$$

$$= (\bar{A}+B+C)(A+\not{B}C+\bar{B})(\not{B}C+\bar{C})$$

$$= (\bar{A}+B+C)(A+BC+\bar{B}\bar{C})$$

(b)

Figure 6.14. Inverse transforms of Fig. 6.13(b).

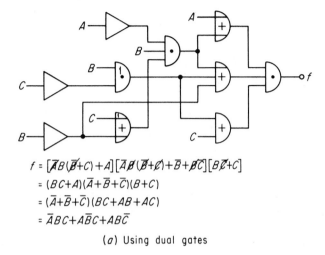

$$f = [\overline{A}B(\overline{B}+C)+A][\overline{A}B(\overline{B}+C)+\overline{B}+\overline{B}C][B\overline{C}+C]$$
$$= (BC+A)(\overline{A}+\overline{B}+\overline{C})(B+C)$$
$$= (\overline{A}+\overline{B}+\overline{C})(BC+AB+AC)$$
$$= \overline{A}BC+A\overline{B}C+AB\overline{C}$$

(*a*) Using dual gates

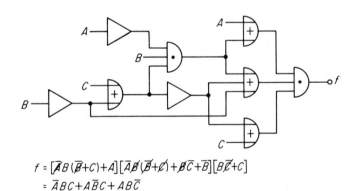

$$f = [\overline{A}B(\overline{B}+C)+A][\overline{A}B(\overline{B}+C)+B\overline{C}+B][B\overline{C}+C]$$
$$= \overline{A}BC+A\overline{B}C+AB\overline{C}$$

(*b*) Using inverters

Figure 6.15. Inverse transforms of Fig. 6.13(c) assuming *NOR* elements.

The Transform Rules (from Boolean Notation to NAND or NOR)

1) a. *NAND*—Factor the Boolean equations to a form where the output
   is an *OR* (*or-and-or*, etc.). Try to get complemented variables on odd
   levels, uncomplemented on even levels.
   b. *NOR*—the same, except factor to a form where the output is an *AND*
   (*and-or-and*), etc.
2)   Lay out the gating from the equations exactly as though they were
     in *AND*'s and *OR*'s instead of *NAND*'s and *NOR*'s, except that both
     NAND and *NOR* variables coming in at odd levels of gating should
     be complemented.

Example 6.4: Exclusive-or, *NAND* function: $A\bar{B} + \bar{A}B$

The function cannot be factored in this form so apply the transform directly to get the circuit of Figure 6.16. This requires five transistors.

Let us try a different form of the equation, the product of sums:

$$A\bar{B} + \bar{A}B = (\bar{A} + \bar{B})(A + B)$$

Now we demonstrate a little trick that can often be usefully applied, *partial
multiplication* (actually a form of the distribute laws). To keep the uncomplemented variables on the second (even) level and move the complemented
ones to the third (odd) level, partially multiply out as follows: $(\bar{A} + \bar{B})$
$(A + B) = (\bar{A} + \bar{B})A + (\bar{A} + \bar{B})B$. Implementing and complementing
third level variables yields the four transistor exclusive-or circuit of Figure
6.17, requiring but four transistors over the previous five. Partial multiplication is useful for forcing complemented variables to odd levels where the
complements will drop off in the Transform, and uncomplemented variables
to even levels where they will not be complemented by the Transform.

Another useful trick which helps in getting the function in the right
form, is the adding or multiplying by a constant. If we are to implement the

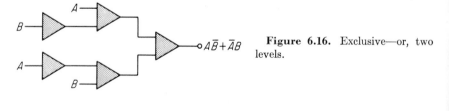

$A\bar{B} + \bar{A}B$ **Figure 6.16.** Exclusive—or, two
levels.

Figure 6.17. Four
transistor exclusive—
or, factored.

$(\bar{A}+\bar{B})A+(\bar{A}+\bar{B})B$
$= A\bar{B}+\bar{A}B$

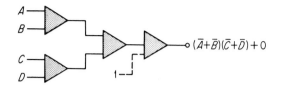

Figure 6.18. Trick of adding a constant.

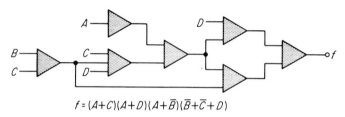

$$f = (A+C)(A+D)(A+\bar{B})(\bar{B}+\bar{C}+D)$$

Figure 6.19. Example function.

function $(\bar{A} + \bar{B})(\bar{C} + \bar{D})$ in the $NAND$, the output gate must be an OR. Instead of refactoring or multiplying out, add a zero to the function, which doesn't affect the function: $(\bar{A} + \bar{B})(\bar{C} + \bar{D}) + 0$. Now the output is an OR as required and we implement as in Figure 6.18, dropping the redundant 1 input transformed from the 0. For the NOR, given a function with an OR output, multiply by the constant 1 and the output will be the required AND.

Example 6.5: Implement this function with the $NAND$:

$$(A + C)(A + D)(A + \bar{B})(\bar{B} + \bar{C} + D)$$

Factoring:

$$(A + \bar{B}CD)(\bar{B} + \bar{C} + D)$$

Here we may illustrate another trick. In the second term the variables B, C are complemented, D is not. It would be desirable to separate the complemented ones from the uncomplemented and put them on odd and even levels of gating respectively. We can do this by associativity followed by partial multiplication.

$$(A + \bar{B}CD)((\bar{B} + \bar{C}) + D) = (A + \bar{B}CD)(\bar{B} + \bar{C}) + (A + \bar{B}CD)D$$

The $\bar{B} + \bar{C}$ term is odd so the complements get dropped, but we still have the complement in $\bar{B}CD$. This can be gotten from an existing term, however:

$$[A + (\bar{B} + \bar{C})CD]\cdot(\bar{B} + \bar{C}) + [A + (\bar{B} + \bar{C})CD]\cdot D$$

This is implemented in Figure 6.19. Actually there is now a redundant term (gate). Can you find it? A more economical solution (five transistors) can be gotten from the sum of products form of the function by similar manipulation if the reader will try it.

Bundling: Another useful trick is bundling, letting a signal be represented by a bundle of wires instead of a single wire. Suppose you have a situation like that in Figure 6.20(a), where a signal f and its complement $\bar{f}$ are both

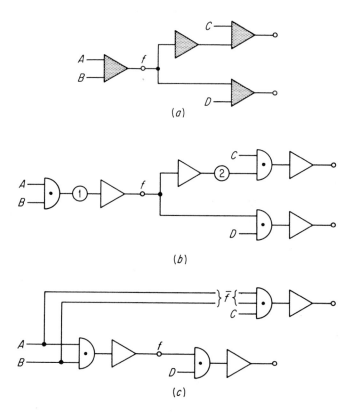

Figure 6.20. Bundling illustrated.

required. Looking at it from an *AND-Inverter* approach (Figure 6.20(b)) we see we require at (2), the signal at (1). But since this can't be tapped, we can take signals A, B as a bundle representing $\bar{f}$ which will be *AND*ed with C to form $\overline{C(A \cdot B)} = \overline{C\bar{f}} = $ Since $f = \overline{A \cdot B}$ as in Figure 6.20(c). Because of the inversion of each block, if a complementary input is needed, and the *NAND* or *NOR* gate it is generated from does not have too many inputs, and we are not going into a gate with too many inputs, we can bundle the inputs of the gate to get the complement of the output.

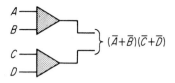

$$(\overline{A}+\overline{B})(\overline{C}+\overline{D})$$

Figure 6.21. A bundling example.

Example 6.6: Figure 6.18 is re-done using two less transistors in Figure 6.21 by bundling.

Example 6.7: We'll work a six variable example, not to achieve a minimum circuit (which we won't by a wide margin) but to illustrate the line of thought one might approach a problem with, and also to develop some useful tricks. The function is written in one form below.

$$f = BD\overline{E} + A\overline{B}\overline{C}D + BC\overline{D} + \overline{A}B\overline{C}\overline{D}E + A\overline{B}\overline{C}F$$
$$+ A\overline{B}DEF + \overline{B}CDEF \qquad (1)$$

Factoring out the B and $\overline{B}$ since one of these appears in every term:

$$B(D\overline{E} + \overline{A}\overline{C}\overline{D}E + C\overline{D}) + \overline{B}(A\overline{C}D + A\overline{C}F + ADEF + CDEF) \qquad (2)$$

Taking the B expression alone, we can see a potential *exclusive-or* in D and E in the first two terms, for which we already have a good solution (example above). So, applying the distributive law to the first and parts of the second term we get:

$$B\cdot[(D\overline{E} + \overline{A}\overline{C})\cdot(D\overline{E} + \overline{D}E) + C\overline{D}] \qquad (3)$$
$$= B\cdot\{(D\overline{E} + \overline{A}\overline{C})\cdot[(\overline{D} + \overline{E})D + (\overline{D} + \overline{E})E] + C\overline{D}\} \qquad (4)$$

Now in the first term of eq. 4 we can distribute again to get the complemented variables $\overline{A}$, $\overline{C}$ on an odd level so the complements will disappear in the transform:

$$D\overline{E} + \overline{A}\overline{C} = (D\overline{E} + \overline{A})(D\overline{E} + \overline{C}) \qquad (5)$$

Now from the *exclusive-or* of D and E (eq. 4) share the term; $(\overline{D} + \overline{E})$:

$$(\overline{D} + \overline{E})D = D\overline{E} \qquad (6)$$

getting for the B expression:

$$B\cdot\{[(\overline{D} + \overline{E})D + \overline{A}]\cdot[(\overline{D} + \overline{E})D + \overline{C}]\cdot$$
$$[(\overline{D} + \overline{E})D + (\overline{D} + \overline{E})E] + C\overline{D}\} \qquad (7)$$

In the $\overline{B}$ expression we can factor to:

$$\overline{B}\cdot[A\overline{C}(D + F) + DEF(A + C)] \qquad (8)$$

Now this is going to require an *inverter* for A and for C. But we require $DEF(A + C) = DEF(\overline{\overline{A}\overline{C}})$ in the $NAND$ function, and this latter term is available in the B expression, eq. 4. It has been factored, though in eq. 5 but by using the two terms of B containing $\overline{A}$ and $\overline{C}$ in eq. 5 or 7 and substituting, we find the other terms cancel:

$$DEF\cdot\overline{[(\overline{D} + \overline{E})D + \overline{A}]\cdot[(\overline{D} + \overline{E})D + \overline{C}]}$$
$$= DEF\cdot\overline{(D\overline{E} + \overline{A}\overline{C})} = DEF(\overline{D} + E)(A + C) = DEF(A + C) \qquad (10)$$

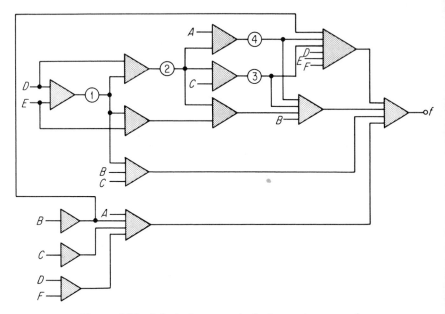

Figure 6.22. A factoring example (not meant as a good solution but only as an illustration, in the text, of a typical derivation argument).

We still require an inverter in the $C\overline{D}$ term of eq. 7. We can add the redundant term $B(C\overline{E})$ to eq. 7 since in eq. 10

$$\overline{DE} + C\overline{D} + C\overline{E} = D\overline{E} + C\overline{D}$$

so

$$B \cdot [\cdots + C\overline{D} + C\overline{E}] = B \cdot [\cdots + C(\overline{D} + \overline{E})] \qquad (11)$$

and we can share this $(\overline{D} + \overline{E})$ term with eq. 7.

Combining eqs. 7, 11 and 8, 9 we get:

$$f = B \cdot \{[(\overline{D} + \overline{E})D + \overline{A}] \cdot [(\overline{D} + \overline{E})D + \overline{C}] \cdot [(\overline{D} + \overline{E})D + (\overline{D} + \overline{E})E]$$
$$+ C(\overline{D} + \overline{E})\} + \overline{B}\{A\overline{C}(\overline{D} + \overline{F})$$
$$+ DEF \cdot \overline{[(\overline{D} + \overline{E})D + \overline{A}] \cdot [(\overline{D} + \overline{E})D + \overline{C}]}\} \qquad (12)$$

Multiplying through by B and $\overline{B}$ we get:

$$f = B \cdot [(\overline{D} + \overline{E})D + \overline{A}] \cdot [(\overline{D} + \overline{E})D + \overline{C}] \cdot [(\overline{D} + \overline{E})D + (\overline{D} + \overline{E})E]$$
$$+ BC(\overline{D} + \overline{E}) + A\overline{B}\overline{C}(\overline{D} + \overline{F})$$
$$+ \overline{B}DEF[(\overline{D} + \overline{E})D + \overline{A}][(\overline{D} + \overline{E})D + \overline{C}] \qquad (13)$$

To simplify implementation, let:

$$① = \overline{D} + \overline{E}$$
$$② = ① \cdot D = (\overline{D} + \overline{E})D$$
$$③ = ② + \overline{C} = (\overline{D} + \overline{E})D + \overline{C}$$
$$④ = ② + \overline{A} = (\overline{D} + \overline{E})D + \overline{A}$$

then:

$$f = B \cdot 4 \cdot 3(2 + 1 \cdot E) + B \cdot C \cdot 1 + A\overline{B}\overline{C}(\overline{D} + \overline{F}) + \overline{B} \cdot D \cdot E \cdot F \cdot 3 \cdot 4 \qquad (14)$$

Eq. 14 is implemented in Figure 6.22.

Transform Tricks

Let us list the tricks covered which supplement the Transform rules:

1) *Partial Multiplication*—$(\overline{A} + \overline{B})(C + D) = (\overline{A} + \overline{B})C + (\overline{A} + \overline{B})D$

   This is useful for separating complemented variables to the odd levels to be complemented in the Transform, from the uncomplemented variables to the even levels where they will not be complemented in the Transform.

   Text source: Example 1, 2, 3.

2) *Adding (or multiplying) a constant*—$(A + B)(C + D) + 0$

   This gets an equation in the wrong form for the Transform into a correct form, for the $NAND$, with the output an OR.

   Text source: Example 1.

3) *Associativity*—$D(\overline{A} + \overline{B} + C) = D[(\overline{A} + \overline{B}) + C]$

   This separates complemented variables (A, B) from the uncomplemented C ready for Partial multiplication (1) to separate them to the levels that will eliminate the inverters.

   Text source: Example 2.

4) *Bundling*—$\overline{\overline{\overline{ABD}}} = \overline{ABD}$ (in $NAND$s)

   Letting the complement of a signal be represented by the bundle of wires which are inputs to that block is called bundling. It eliminates gates.

   Text source: Between Examples 2, 3.

5) *Distributive law*—$AB + \overline{C}\overline{D} = (AB + \overline{C})(AB + \overline{D})$

   This factoring rule (and its dual) can serve to separate complemented variables to odd levels, and also to factor out common terms leaving correct equation form:

$$AB + CD\overline{E} + CD\overline{F} =$$
$$(\underline{AB + CD})(\underline{AB} + \overline{E}) + (\underline{AB + CD})(\underline{AB} + \overline{F})$$

(Shared terms are underlined.) It can be used to factor to a function form for which the solution is well known, like the exclusive-or, for example. It is useful as well as the general factoring tool.

Text source: Example 3.

6) *Add redundant terms, literals:*

a) Redundant literals may make gates identical:

$$(\overline{A} + \overline{C})B + (\overline{B} + \overline{C})A = (\overline{A} + \overline{B} + \overline{C})B + (\overline{A} + \overline{B} + \overline{C})A$$

(adding redundant $\overline{B}$ to the first term, and redundant $\overline{A}$ to the second makes the gates identical and can be shared.)

Redundant literals may eliminate gates:

$$X(D\overline{E} + C) = X(D\overline{E} + C + E) = X(D + C + E)$$

(if redundant, EX eliminates the $D\overline{E}$ gate.

Redundant literals may reduce complemented literals to odd levels:

$$X(\overline{D}E + \overline{C}) = X(\overline{D}E + \overline{C} + \overline{E}) = X(\overline{D} + \overline{C} + \overline{E})$$

(if $\overline{E}$ is redundant, all complemented literals now on odd level).

b) Redundant terms may make a factoring possible:

$$(\overline{A} + B)(A + \overline{B}) = (\overline{A} + B)(A + \overline{A})(A + \overline{B})(B + \overline{B})$$
$$= (\overline{A} + AB)(\overline{B} + AB)$$

Redundancy is what allows the possibility of some gates shared between even and odd levels replacing two gates.

Redundancy has many such uses.

Text source: Example 3.

7) *Getting a complement from a complex term:*

$$f_1 = \overline{A}BC$$
$$f_2 = A(B + D)$$
$$f_1 = \overline{A(B + D)} \cdot B \cdot C$$

Factoring with a Karnaugh Map

For problems in only a few variables, a technique for factoring $NAND$ (or NOR) functions on a Karnaugh Map has been developed which often yields quite clever results. This method makes use of considerable redundancy where advantageous, and also allows us to use the full logical power of the $NAND$ (and NOR) functions, unavailable easily in the Transform method.

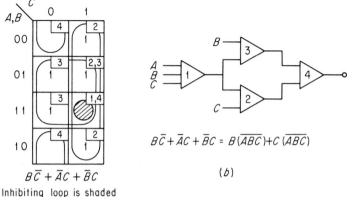

$$B\overline{C} + \overline{A}C + \overline{B}C$$

Inhibiting loop is shaded

(a) Numbers in boxes refer to gate numbers of (b) covering that box within a loop.

$$B\overline{C}+\overline{A}C+\overline{B}C = B(\overline{ABC})+C\,(\overline{ABC})$$

(b)

Figure 6.23. Illustrating map factoring $(NAND)$.

The method is based on a simple argument. In the function of the map of Figure 6.23a, we require the loop B AND NOT the shaded loop ABC, OR loop C AND NOT the shaded loop ABC:

$$B(\overline{ABC}) + C(\overline{ABC}) = B(\overline{A} + \overline{B} + \overline{C}) + C(\overline{A} + \overline{B} + \overline{C})$$
$$= \cancel{\overline{A}B} + \cancel{B\overline{B}} + B\overline{C} + \overline{A}C + \overline{B}C \qquad (14)$$

(redundant terms crossed out).

Note this factored expression is better (four transistors) than simple algebraic factoring:

$$B\overline{C} + \overline{A}C + \overline{B}C = B\overline{C} + C(\overline{A} + \overline{B}) \qquad \text{(five transistors)} \qquad (15)$$

This is because we used redundancy.

Now notice that the technique of taking a loop of ones including a few bothersome zeros, and intersecting it with the complement of the looping of those zeros, takes the form of a product term times the complement of a product term. But instead of multiplying this out, note as above that the complemented term is now in the form of a $NAND$ function:

$$B(\overline{ABC}) + C(\overline{ABC}) \qquad (16)$$

Now, by the Transform method, this yields the block diagram of Figure 6.23b.

This can be interpreted as follows: Loops on the Karnaugh Map representing the input literals to $NAND$ blocks that get inserted on even levels of gating act as ones; loops representing on odd level gates act as zeros. A loop of zeros (gate on an odd level) will *inhibit* any area of intersection with a loop of ones (even level gate) if the zero loop gate goes to the input of the one loop gate.

Thus, we could have approached the problem of Figure 6.23a as follows: (see gate nos. in 6.23b). Take loop A, B, C (gate 1: $\overline{A \cdot B \cdot C}$); take loop C and inhibit it with loop A, B, C. This yields (gate 2: $\overline{C \cdot 1}$); take loop B and inhibit it with loop A, B, C. This yields (gate 3: $\overline{B \cdot 1}$); take these two inhibited loops, 2, 3 and inhibit from the unity loop (the loop of the whole map) with them—this will yield all the zeros of the map; this is the output gate 4. This argument also yields Figure 6.23b. Thus we generate both all the 1's and all the 0's of the map.

With the provision that a loop of ones can inhibit their intersection with a loop of zeros if the 1's gate is an input to the 0's gate, we can extend this simple factoring technique to arbitrarily many levels of factored gating. (Note that an inverter is the loop of a single variable, with literal value 1.)

The *permissible loops* then are those that can be made from use of uncomplemented literal loops only with or without inhibition from other such loops. Thus the permissible loops without inhibition are shown for 3 and 4 variables in Figure 6.24. Any others must be generated from these by inhibiting one or more from one another. Note the all zero cube is always the most difficult, requiring the inhibition from the unity loop of all loops

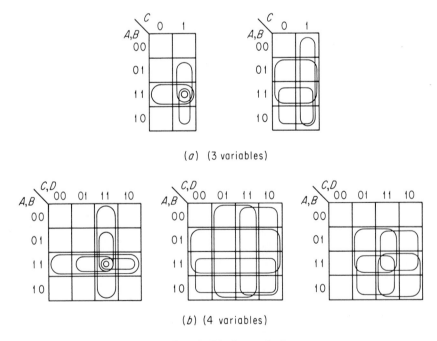

(a) (3 variables)

(b) (4 variables)

Figure 6.24. Permissible first order loops.

of opposite level necessary to cover the complement of the value in the all zero cube. Thus to get the 000 cube of Figure 6.23a covering a 0, it is necessary to inhibit all the loops necessary to cover the 1's, from unity.

Method of Map Factoring

1) Restricting oneself to permissible loops, loop a selection of ones or zeros or both.

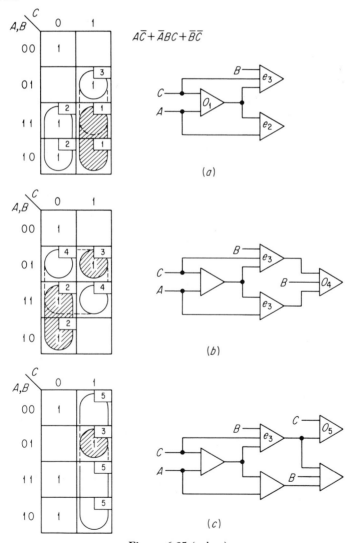

$$A\bar{C} + \bar{A}BC + \bar{B}\bar{C}$$

(a)

(b)

(c)

Figure 6.25 (a, b, c).

2) Using loops already chosen as inhibitions, attempt to cover remaining ones, and/or zeros.

3) Repeat (2) until all ones and zeros are covered. Last level of loops (for $NAND$) must be zeros (must be an OR) so if last level is ones, inhibit the ones from unity, i.e., complement the output.

These rules are simple but are no measure of the complexity and subtlety they may beget in application since they give little in the way of guidance.

Example 6.8: In Figure 6.25 a step by step example is worked. In Figure 6.25a the loop B, C inhibited by A, C is chosen, and loop A inhibited by A, C is chosen. This gets us all but one of the ones. We can get the remaining term $\overline{A}\,\overline{B}C$ by getting the remaining zeros looped and inhibiting unity, the whole map with all the zero loops. Two zeros are covered by the loop of Figure 6.25b where loop B is inhibited by the one loops generated in Figure 6.25a. The final zero is achieved in Figure 6.25c. Inhibiting the whole map with the zero loops yields all the ones (Figure 6.25d) but to end on a loop of zeros we inhibit the one's from unity, i.e., we complement the result.

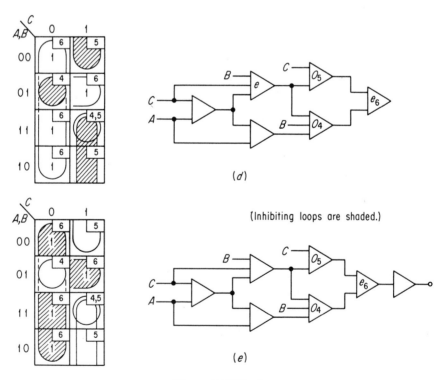

(Inhibiting loops are shaded.)

Figure 6.25 (d, e).

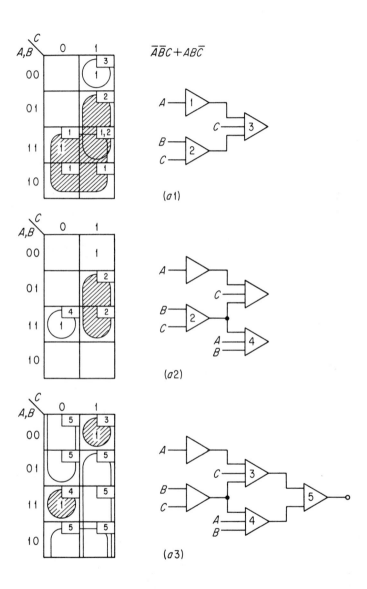

Figure 6.26 (a1, a2, a3). Two map factorings of a single three – variable function.

To analyze a block diagram of *NAND* functions, draw a loop on the map for the input variables to each block and observe the inhibitions as a loop (gate) drives another. Given a block diagram this will enable you to follow how it was (or could have been) originally derived by map factoring and also to check the result without the algebraic techniques of the Transform.

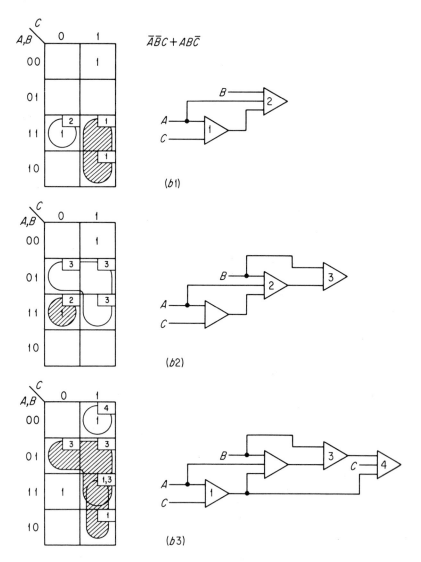

$\overline{A}\overline{B}C + AB\overline{C}$

(b1)

(b2)

(b3)

Figure 6.26 (b1, b2, b3).

Example 6.9: Analyze Figure 6.26 (b_4) and (a_3) to see how these two block diagrams are derived and compare with the derivations in Figure 6.26. (Note analysis is shown by working backwards from b_4 to b_1, a_3 to a_1. Then study the two derivations of equivalent circuits b_4, a_3.

Example 6.10: Figure 6.27 gets another solution to the problem of Figure 6.13. Here bundling is used.

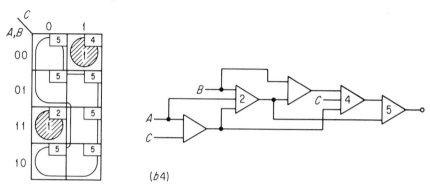

Figure 6.26 (b4).

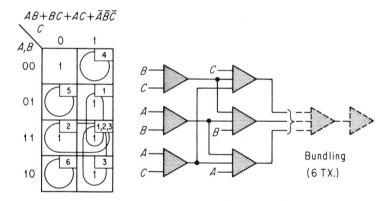

Figure 6.27. Bundling applied to the example of Fig. 6.12.

The Logic Power of the NOR and NAND

Now we are in a position to exploit the basic logical power of the $NAND$ (and NOR) functions beyond that of the Boolean connectives. This power is simply that, by the Transform to Boolean form, a single $NAND$ (NOR) gate can act as both an AND and an OR if it drives both an even and an odd level. Thus a single $NAND$ gate can sometimes replace two Boolean gates. We have already observed this phenomenon in the analysis rules and examples for the Transform method. This was shown in our analysis of Figure 6.13b and Figure 6.13c, where the "blank" level gates are those driving both odd and even levels. These "blank" level gates we transformed, splitting into two gates, an AND, and an OR. Now we shall see how this power of the $NAND$ can be made use of in synthesis.

To be effective in a function in both an even level and an odd level, a gate must partake of both the ones and the zeros of the function. Indeed, a "blank" level gate, representing two Boolean gates, one AND and one OR, corresponds in map factoring to a loop which includes both ones and zeros. As such it cannot enter into the actual function, rather it acts as an inhibitor in a resultant loop of zeros and as an inhibitor in a resultant loop of ones as well. Sometimes, it acts as an inhibitor for generating other "blank" level gates. These are very useful and often fruitful because the first set of loops chosen is usually chosen primarily for purposes of looping the remaining ones and zeros, and often does not drive the output gate, not entering directly the transmission function, the one's or zero's being recovered by loops it helped generate. As such these worker gates are like catalysts and since not driving the output gate need not loop only ones or only zeros.

Indeed, in picking the initial loops, a good rule of thumb criterion governing their selection should be: Choose them not for purposes of covering some ones or zeros first, but for facilitating the generation of loops that will cover the ones and zeros.

Example 6.11: A simple example is developed, loop by loop, in Figure 6.28 which uses the power of the $NAND$ in that two of the gates represent loops that contain both ones and zeros (Figure 6.28a gates 1, 2). The inhibiting loops are shaded in each map, the loops generated by the inhibition together with some input variables are unshaded. If the reader analyzes the circuit of Figure 6.28c with the Transform Analysis rules, he will find that gates 1 and 2, blank level gates corresponding to the two loops of mixed ones and zeros in Figure 6.28a, each split in two, into an AND, and an OR (or an AND and an inverter). Thus in $NAND$s, the circuit of Figure 6.28e takes seven gates; its Boolean inverse Transform takes 9 gates, plus the necessary inverters on odd level inputs.

This additional logic power of the $NAND$ (NOR) is paid for by its logic weakness when implementing cascaded AND's (study Figure 6.29). As we'll see in the next section on the NOR Tree, however, this problem often is illusory and the benefits would seem to outweigh this disadvantage in an environment rich with a broad scope of problems such as found in a computer.

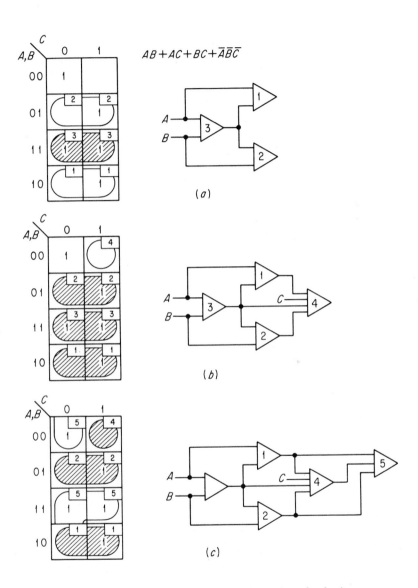

Figure 6.28 (a, b, c). An example illustrating the basic power of the *NAND* function.

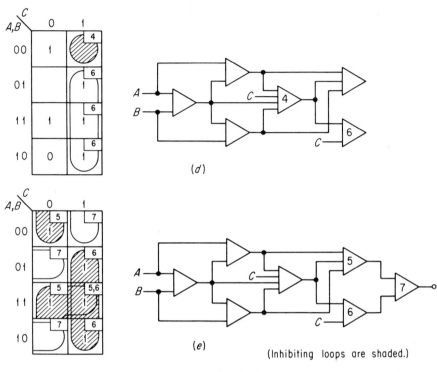

(d)

(e)

(Inhibiting loops are shaded.)

Figure 6.28 (d, e).

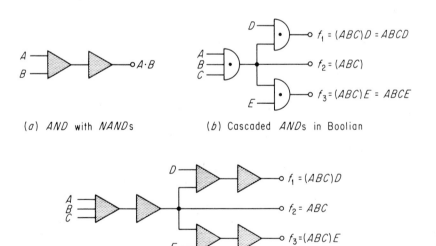

(a) *AND* with *NAND*s

(b) Cascaded *AND*s in Boolian

(c) Cascaded *AND*s in *NAND*s

Figure 6.29. Logic weakness of the *NAND* in cascaded *AND* circuits.

Example 6.12: One of the two most important three variable functions, the complement of the binary sum of three bits, (two bits and an input carry) utilizes the basic power of the $NAND$ for its minimal net—7 transistors. It is developed, one gate at a time, factoring on the Karnaugh map in Figure 6.30. Inhibiting loops are shaded and numbered loops correspond to the numbered gates. It is important for the reader to work through each of the examples derived, in detail, if he is to develop any proficiency with map factoring.

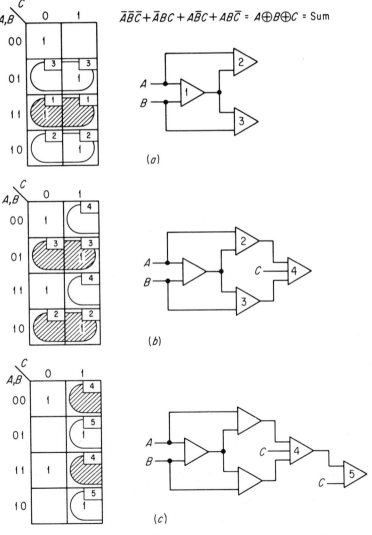

$$\overline{A}\overline{B}\overline{C} + \overline{A}BC + A\overline{B}C + AB\overline{C} = A \oplus B \oplus C = \text{Sum}$$

Figure 6.30 (a, b, c). Map factoring of the complement of the sum-modulo-two of three variables.

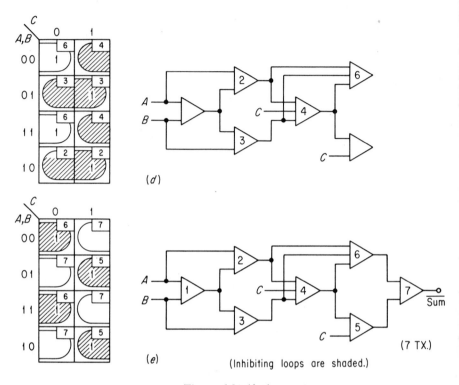

Figure 6.30 (d, e).

Example 6.13: The other important three variable functions, the binary sum of three bits (sum-module-two), also makes good use of this power. This also requires but 7 transistors in its minimal net developed in Figure 6.31.

If we add a carry output to either the sum or its complement, we get a full adder, a very important circuit. By investigating the map loopings of each gate in Figures 6.30, 6.31, we note that all the terms of the carry function (Figure 6.32a) are present in both circuits. From maps (a) and (c) in Figure 6.30 we find the carry terms (loops 1 and 5) for the "$\overline{\text{Sum}}$" circuit of Figure 6.30e. These need only be combined in an output gate as shown in Figure 6.32b. From map (c) in Figure 6.31 we find that the carry terms (loops, 1, 2, and 3) for the "Sum" circuit of Figure 6.31d. These need only be combined in an output gate as shown in Figure 6.32c. Thus a minimal full adder circuit requires 8 transistors.

Since the "Sum" and "$\overline{\text{Sum}}$" and the "carry" are all self dual functions (check this), implementing them in the same circuit with *NOR*s, the dual of

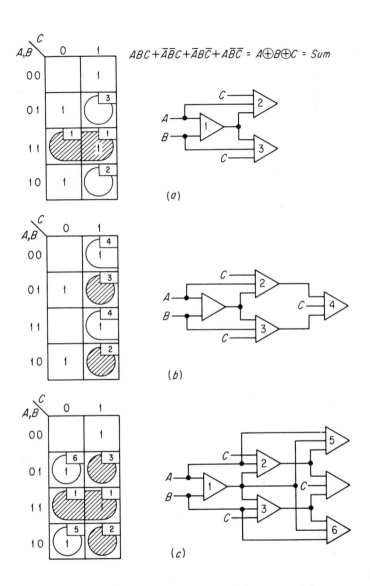

$ABC + \bar{A}\bar{B}C + \bar{A}B\bar{C} + A\bar{B}\bar{C} = A \oplus B \oplus C = Sum$

Figure 6.31 (a, b, c). Map factoring of the sum-modulo-two of three variables.

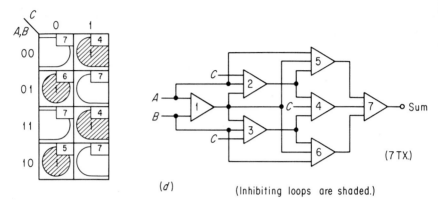

(d)

(Inhibiting loops are shaded.)

Figure 6.31 (d).

NANDs, realizes the same functions. Thus Figure 6.32b realizes the "$\overline{\text{Sum}}$" and the "carry" independent of whether *NORs* or *NANDs* are used, and similarly for Figure 6.32c.

Four variable problems are handled the same way.

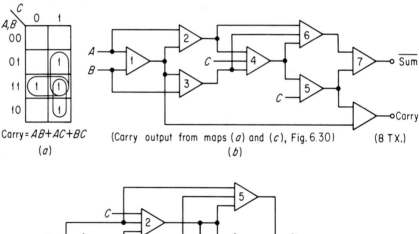

Carry = $AB+AC+BC$

(a)

(Carry output from maps (a) and (c), Fig. 6.30)

(b)

(8 TX.)

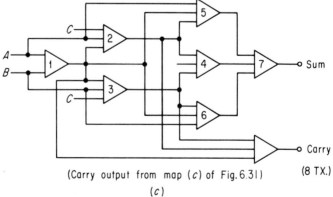

(Carry output from map (c) of Fig. 6.31)

(c)

(8 TX.)

Figure 6.32. Full adders; Figs. 6.30 and 6.31 with the carry output added.

Example 6.14: Three equivalent solutions for one four variable problem are given in Figure 6.33 with the first fully worked out, loop by loop. The last two, b, c, have their loops for all gates drawn on their associated Karnaugh map. The reader is invited to analyze these solutions for himself. Figure 6.27 gives another four variable problems. Here bundling is used on the output.

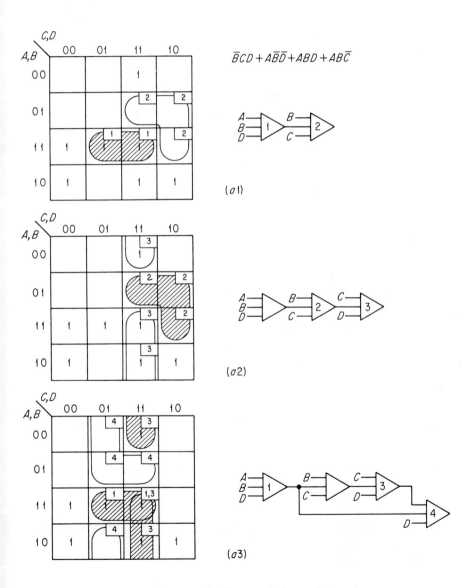

$$\bar{B}CD + A\bar{B}\bar{D} + ABD + AB\bar{C}$$

$(a1)$

$(a2)$

$(a3)$

Figure 6.33 (a1, a2, a3). Three equivalent solutions to a joint variable problem.

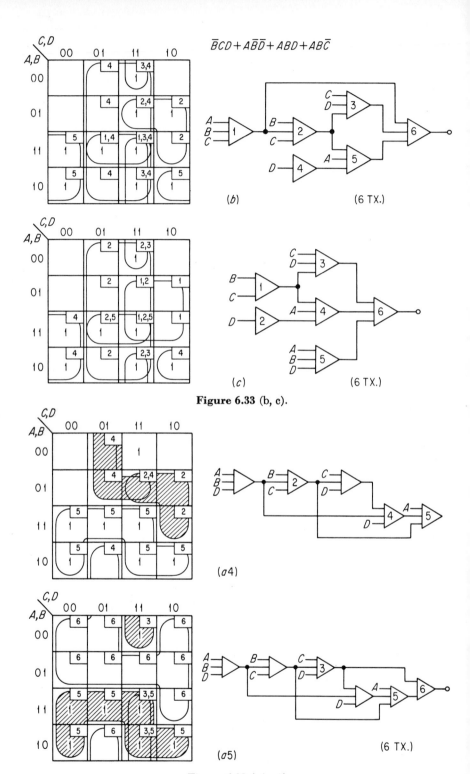

$$\overline{B}CD+A\overline{B}\overline{D}+ABD+AB\overline{C}$$

(b)   (6 TX.)

(c)   (6 TX.)

Figure 6.33 (b, c).

(a4)

(a5)   (6 TX.)

Figure 6.33 (a4, a5).

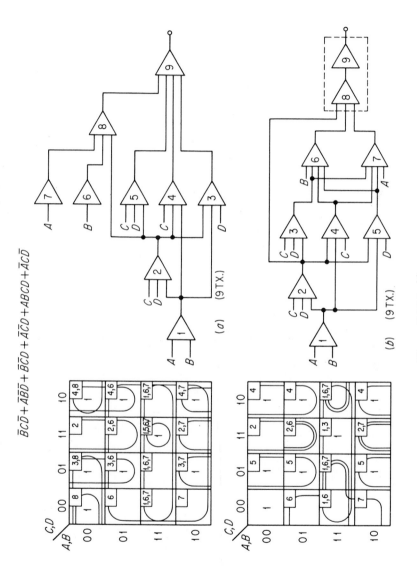

$$\bar{B}C\bar{D} + \bar{A}B\bar{D} + \bar{B}\bar{C}D + \bar{A}\bar{C}D + ABCD + \bar{A}C\bar{D}$$

Figure 6.34 (a, b).

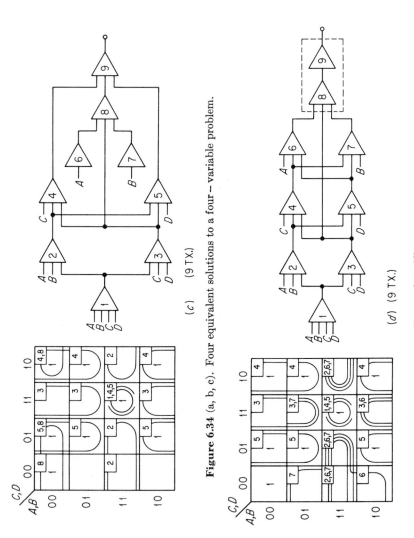

Figure 6.34 (a, b, c). Four equivalent solutions to a four – variable problem.

Figure 6.34 (d).

Example 6.15: Figure 6.34 gives four equivalent solutions to a four variable problem. The reader is urged to study their structure for insight into map factoring techniques. Figure 6.34a and b both use the power of the *NOR* as is easily seen. Note the symmetry of (d).

Example 6.16: Figure 6.35 is another exercise for the reader. Note that it uses a "blank" level gate to generate another "blank" level gate.

Example 6.17, 6.18: The three solutions of Figure 6.36 and that of Figure 6.37 should be analyzed as the writers have done in previous examples. Every worked problem improves technique, for map factoring is an art and can be taught only by example.

Example 6.19: Finally, the solution worked out in Figure 6.38 deserves careful study. A very clever circuit, note that one gate drives three separate levels.

The reader is invited to work all these examples searching for alternative, even better solutions. Only through such practice can map factoring be mastered. A few tries at five and six variable maps should be made also.

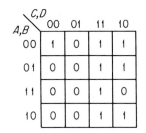

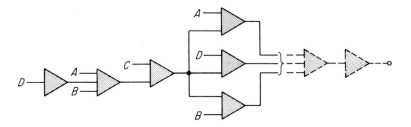

Figure 6.35. A four – variable example with bundling.

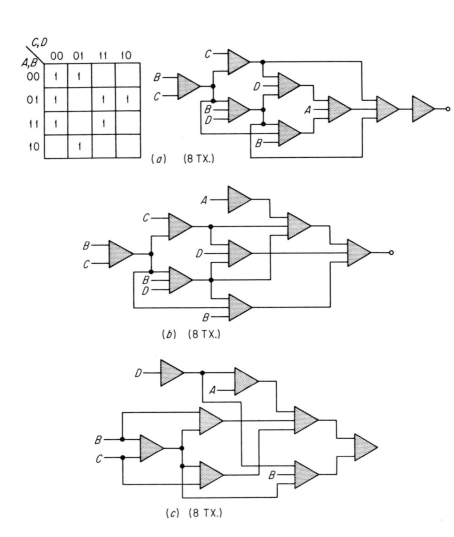

Figure 6.36. Three equivalent solutions to a four–variable problem.

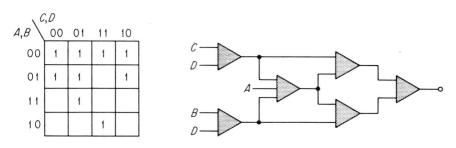

Figure 6.37. A symmetrical factoring.

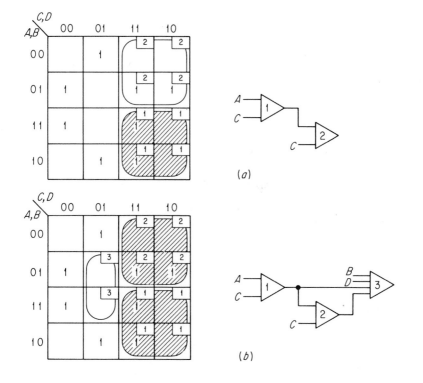

Figure 6.38 (a, b, c) (continued).

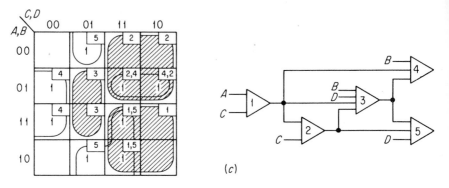

Figure 6.38 (a, b, c). Example using a gate in three separate levels.

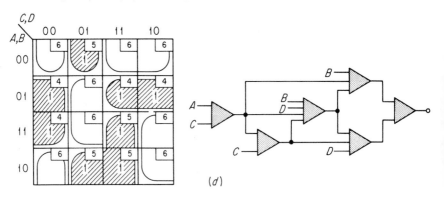

Figure 6.38 (d).

The NAND-NOR Tree

Here we'll consider one aspect of the problem of *ANDs* driving *ANDs* in cascade, purportedly an expensive circuit in the *NAND* function, two *NANDs* per *AND* (see Figure 6.29). In developing the *NAND* Tree as an important counter-instance we will find it also very useful for high speed approximations for factored multiple-output circuits.

The classical solution to the problem of generating all of the 2^n canonical terms of n variables, or equivalently, all of the $2^{(2^n)}$ functions of n variables is a matrix of *AND*'s cascaded, a tree circuit. This is shown for three variables in Figure 6.39, and an indication of how it continues to branch with more variables at the top. (To get all the functions of n variables one merely *OR*'s together all distinct subsets of these canonic terms.) This circuit is also useful as a decoder where we decode from an n-bit code to a one out of $2n$-bit code.

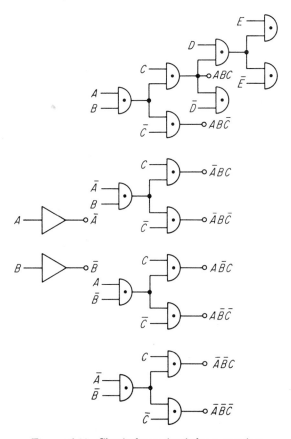

Figure 6.39. Classical tree circuit for generating all canonical terms of three variables.

This circuit would appear to be a worst case for the $NAND$ function since to put AND's in series requires two $NAND$ gates per AND (Figure 6.29). Here it requires 12 gates and 2 inverters (Figure 6.39) and it would appear by applying the Transform that in the $NAND$ it would cost 24 gates and 2 inverters. Surprisingly enough, the $NAND$ function can actually do this job more efficiently than the ANDs in terms of number of gates. As we'll see, the $NAND$ requires but 8 gates and no inverters, exactly as many gates as if we had done the ANDs in one level of gating but requiring three inverters.

The $NAND$ Tree for two variables is shown in Figure 6.40. Note that it has four gates, each an output giving one of the four canonic terms of two variables—and there are no dummy inverters to make the $NAND$ look like

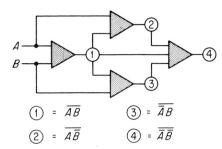

① = $\overline{\overline{A}B}$ ③ = $\overline{\overline{A}B}$

② = $\overline{A\overline{B}}$ ④ = $\overline{\overline{A}\,\overline{B}}$

Figure 6.40. The $NAND$
tree for two variables.

an AND as in Figure 6.29. The
terms are complemented product
terms so that when the different
functions of two variables are
required, gating together different
combinations of these four outputs
will cancel the inversion (in the
output gate) and yield the desired
function. All of the 16 functions of
two variables can be synthesized
from this tree (except the constant
1) adding but one gate per function
to "$NAND$" the terms together.

The $NAND$ Tree is a completely systematic structure, generalizable
for any number of variables. (Practically, the increasing fan-in and drive
constraints limit its size.) The Tree for 3 variables is shown in Figure 6.41.
Notice it uses but 8 gates, one for each output, and no inverters.

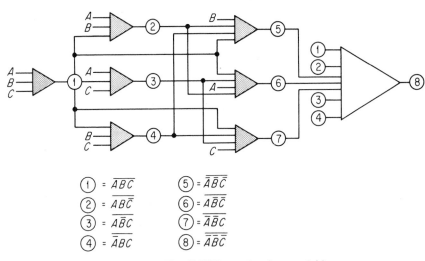

① = $\overline{ABC}$ ⑤ = $\overline{\overline{A}\,\overline{B}\,\overline{C}}$

② = $\overline{AB\overline{C}}$ ⑥ = $\overline{A\overline{B}\,\overline{C}}$

③ = $\overline{A\overline{B}C}$ ⑦ = $\overline{\overline{A}B\overline{C}}$

④ = $\overline{\overline{A}BC}$ ⑧ = $\overline{\overline{A}B\overline{C}}$

Figure 6.41. The $NAND$ tree for three variables.

Algorithm for Generating the NOR-NAND Tree

(n is the number of input variables and x $(0 \leq x \leq n)$ is a particular level
of $NAND$ gates.)

   1) Each level (except level a) receives as inputs, to respective $NAND$
      gates, specific sets of all possible sets of combinations of $(n - x)$
      input variables;

2) Each *NAND* gate which receives a set of inputs as specified in (1) also receives as inputs the outputs of all higher level *NAND* gates which have input sets including the input variables to this gate.

3) Level n having no input variables ($n - n = 0$ from (1)), receives as inputs the outputs of *all* higher level *NAND* gates (since all input sets include the empty set).

4) The number M_x^n of *NAND* gates in any given level x for n-input tree is:

$$M_x^n = C_x^n = \frac{n!}{(n - x)!x!}$$

Thus the total number of *NAND* gates in a complete tree is:

$$\sum_{x=0}^{n} C_x^n = \sum_{x=0}^{n} \frac{n!}{(n - x)!x!} = 2^n$$

With a little attention to them, the reader will find that the three variable tree of Figure 6.41 and the Algorithm above for generating it and higher order trees, clarify each other.

The *NAND-NOR* Tree in Multi-Output Problems

A much more interesting application of the *NAND-NOR* Tree is as a high speed approximation for factored multiple output problems. These are usually difficult to do well, but with the Tree some surprisingly good circuits can appear as fast as one can draw the circuit.

The method is simple. For a three multi-output problem, delete all gates in the three variable tree not terms in one of the outputs or necessary for generating such. *NAND* together the terms for each function. It may be necessary to remove some inputs which are redundant.

Example 6.20:

$$f_1 = AB\overline{C} + A\overline{B}C$$
$$f_2 = ABC + A\overline{B}\overline{C}$$
$$f_3 = \overline{A} + \overline{B} + C$$

There are no reductions possible and no shared terms in two levels of gating requiring 10 *NAND* gates. Figure 6.42 truncates the 3 variable tree for a quick 6 gate solution. The circled A input to gate 1, Figure 6.42, can be removed as redundant.

Another use for the tree is to embed it in a larger problem requiring the generation of several canonic terms (or functions) of some variables.

Example 6.21:

$$f = AB\overline{DE} + \overline{A}B\overline{CE} + \overline{CD}E + \overline{AB}C\overline{D} + \overline{F}$$
$$= (AB + \overline{C})(\overline{A}B + \overline{D})(\overline{A}B + E) + \overline{F}$$

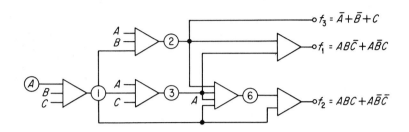

Figure 6.42

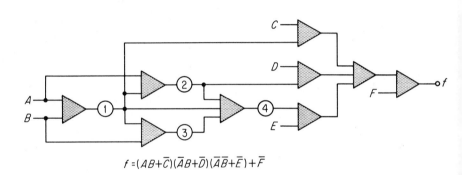

$$f = (AB+\bar{C})(\bar{A}B+\bar{D})(\bar{A}\bar{B}+\bar{E})+\bar{F}$$

Figure 6.43. Embedding a $NAND$ tree in a larger problem as generator of the terms.

Now in this factored form we need to generate the terms AB, $\bar{A}B$, $\bar{A}\bar{B}$. These we can get immediately from the $NAND$ Tree. The implementation is shown in Figure 6.43. If we had not used the tree it would have cost us five $NAND$ elements to generate the A, B terms instead of the four of the Tree.

5) Use the NOR-$NAND$ tree to get factored multiple output solutions in $NAND$ and NOR:

    a) $f_1 = \Sigma\,(0, 1, 4, 5, 11, 15)$
       $f_2 = \Sigma\,(0, 9, 6, 11, 12, 15)$

b) $f_1 = \Sigma\ (2, 3, 10, 11, 12, 15) +$ don't cares $(1, 7, 8, 9)$
   $f_2 = \Sigma\ (1, 3, 10, 11, 15) +$ don't cares $(2, 12)$

c) $f_1 = \Sigma\ (1, 5, 6, 12)$
   $f_2 = \Sigma\ (1, 2, 5, 6, 12)$
   $f_3 = \Sigma\ (5, 7, 9, 12) +$ don't cares $(1, 2, 6)$

d) $f_1 = \Sigma\ (2, 5, 6, 13, 14)$
   $f_2 = \Sigma\ (5, 7, 13, 14)$
   $f_3 = \Sigma\ (2, 6, 7, 13, 15)$

1) Analyze:

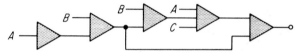

2) Analyze:

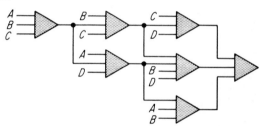

3) Analyze: (2) And (3) Assuming The NOR

4) Synthesize in Factored NOR And NAND:
First use the Transform method, and then the map factoring method.
 a) $\Sigma(2,3,5,7,8,12,14)$
 b) $\Sigma(0,4,6,7,10,14) +$ don't cares $(5,9,13,15)$
 c) $\Sigma(1,3,4,6,8,10,11)$
 d) $\Sigma(1,3,7,9,15) +$ don't cares $(0,2,8)$
 e) $\Sigma(3,7,9,14,15)$

References

H. M. Sheffer, "A Set of Five Independent Postulates for Boolean Algebras", Trans. Amer. Math. Soc., **V.** 14 (1913) pp. 481–488.

J. Earle, "Synthesizing Minimal Stroke and Dagger Functions". IRE Conv. 1960, Part II,
PGCT—Special Supplement, CT-7, Aug. 1960.
——; "Implementing *NOR* Logic", IBM TR 00.08000.697

ARITHMETIC

OPERATIONS

7

Introduction

The speed of the arithmetic unit of a digital computer is often used as a measure of the value of the entire machine. This statement, less true today than several years ago, is still strong enough to dictate many of the fundamental decisions involved in the design of a computer. As an example: Using present day components, the fastest arithmetic units are of the parallel, binary form. Therefore, it is not surprising to find that the fastest scientific computers of today are binary, parallel machines. It is the purpose of this chapter to explain, in a rather fundamental way, the methods used by digital computers for performing parallel, binary arithmetic.

Binary Addition

The principles of binary addition are even less complex than those used in decimal arithmetic. It should be remembered that there are but two symbols, zero (0) and one (1), in the entire system. When a single binary digit, called a bit, is added to another bit, there are but four conditions that could exist.

(a) 0 plus 0 = 0

(b) 0 plus 1 = 1

(c) 1 plus 0 = 1

(d) 1 plus 1 = 0 with a carry of "1"

A functional device that will perform this operation is called a half adder. Such a device will have two inputs: one for each of the digits to be added, and two outputs. The first output, called the sum line, is used to indicate the value of the resulting sum. The second output, called the carry line, will contain the value of the carry. The truth table for a half adder is shown below.

Input X	0	0	1	1
Input Y	0	1	0	1
Output Sum	0	1	1	0
Output Carry	0	0	0	1

"Half Adder Truth Table"

From this table, the Boolean expressions for the half adder are obtained.

$$S = \overline{X}Y + X\overline{Y}$$
$$C = XY$$

There exist many methods for implementing these two equations. Three such implementations are shown in Figure 7.1.

A half adder is sufficient for the low order position of a parallel adder, but all other positions must have the capability of adding three bits together. This condition occurs since a carry from the next lower position

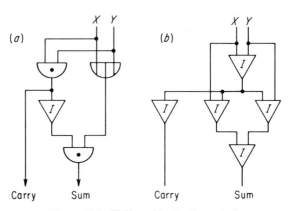

Figure 7.1. Half – adder implementations.

must be added to the two incoming bits. A functional device that will add three binary bits together is called a "full adder." The truth table for a full adder is shown below.

Input	X	0	0	0	0	1	1	1	1
	Y	0	0	1	1	0	0	1	1
	Carry In	0	1	0	1	0	1	0	1
Outputs	Sum	0	1	1	0	1	0	0	1
	Carry Out	0	0	0	1	0	1	1	1

From this truth table, we are able to obtain the two Boolean expressions for the full adder:

$$S = \overline{X}\,\overline{Y}C_i + \overline{X}Y\overline{C}_i + X\overline{Y}\,\overline{C}_i + XYC_i$$
$$C_{\text{out}} = \overline{X}YC_i + X\overline{Y}C_i + XY\overline{C}_i + XYC_i$$

The "carry out" expression may be reduced by the use of a Karnaugh map.

$$C_{\text{out}} = XY + XC_i + YC_i$$

Several implementations of the full adder expressions are shown in Figure 7.2. A parallel, binary adder may now be constructed from a half adder and a series of full adders as shown in Figure 7.3.

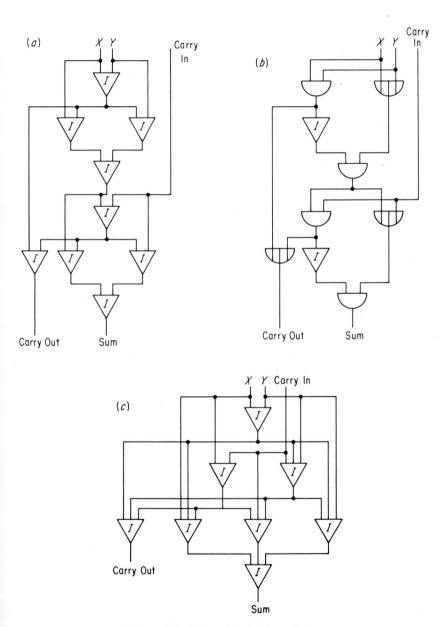

Figure 7.2. Full − adder implementations.

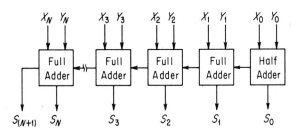

Figure 7.3. Functional binary adder.

Three registers are normally affixed to functional adder to complete the implementation. The two binary numbers to be added are placed in Registers A and C while the sum, when it is completed, is placed in register B. Register A and register B are often combined and drawn as one double register and called an accumulator register. It should be pointed out that the gating from the adder to the accumulator must be held long enough to permit a ripple carry to propagate the entire length of the functional adder.

Binary Subtraction

A functional subtractor may be designed by following the same method outlined for the design of a functional adder. The authors would like to point out that functional subtractors are not used in present day machines; but before proceeding with the actual methods used, it is advisable to look at the truth table for a half subtractor and a full subtractor. The truth table for a half subtractor $(X - Y)$ is given below.

Menuend X	0	1	0	1
Subtrahend Y	0	0	1	1
Difference	0	1	1	0
Borrow	0	0	1	0

The reader should observe that when a "1" is subtracted from "0", a borrow sign is propagated to the next *higher* position. This borrow signal is used to reduce the difference of the next higher position by "1." Since we now have borrowed a "1" from the next higher position, the menuend in the first position is "10" giving us a difference of "1."

The truth table for a full subtractor is shown below. In this case, Y is subtracted from X and the incoming borrow signal is also subtracted from X. The basic algebraic equation is therefore $X - Y - B_{in}$.

X	0	0	0	0	1	1	1	1
Y	0	0	1	1	0	0	1	1
B_i	0	1	0	1	0	1	0	1
Difference	0	1	1	0	1	0	0	1
Borrow Out	0	1	1	1	0	0	0	1

The Boolean expressions as obtained from the truth table are:

$$\text{Difference} \;\; = \overline{X}\,\overline{Y}B_i + \overline{X}YB_i + X\overline{Y}B_i + XYB_i$$
$$\text{Borrow Out} = \overline{X}\,\overline{Y}B_i + \overline{X}Y\overline{B}_i + \overline{X}YB_i + XYB_i$$

The "Borrow Out" expression may be reduced by Karnaugh mapping.

$$\text{Borrow Out} = \overline{X}Y + \overline{X}B_i + YB$$

With the above truth table in mind, we will work several example problems.

$$
\begin{array}{rl}
7 = & 0111 \\
\text{minus } 5 = & \underline{0101} \\
2 = & 0010
\end{array}
\qquad
\begin{array}{rl}
 & \overset{\frown}{B} \\
5 = & 0101 \\
\text{minus } 2 = & \underline{0010} \\
3 & 0011
\end{array}
\qquad
\begin{array}{rl}
 & BBB \\
8 = & \overset{\frown\frown\frown}{1000} \\
\text{minus } 1 = & \underline{0001} \\
7 & 0111
\end{array}
$$

When a number is subtracted from a smaller number, a negative difference is obtained.

$$
\begin{array}{rl}
 & \quad\;\; \overset{\frown}{B} \\
3 \;\; = & 0\;0\;1\;1 \\
\text{minus } \underline{4} \;\; = & \underline{0\;1\;0\;0} \\
-1 & 1\;1\;1\;1
\end{array}
$$

Using this form of subtraction, we obtain what is called the "two's complement" representation of negative numbers:

$$
\begin{array}{rcl}
-1 & = & 1\;1\;1\;1 \\
-2 & = & 1\;1\;1\;0 \\
-3 & = & 1\;1\;0\;1 \\
-4 & = & 1\;1\;0\;0 \\
-5 & = & 1\;0\;1\;1
\end{array}
$$

A "1" located in the highest order position may be used to indicate that the number is negative. If our word length is 4 bits, the largest positive number we may represent is 0111 (Decimal 7) while the largest negative number is

1000 (Decimal -8). The high order bit of the binary number may therefore be interpreted as a sign bit. This complemented method of representing negative numbers is not too familiar to most of us except when a one is subtracted from zero on a desk calculator. In this case, the calculator will show an answer of 999999 (called ten's complement), which is the decimal equivalent of the two's complement in binary. Individuals prefer to represent negative numbers as a minus sign followed by an absolute value. In order to obtain this type of representation in the binary system from the two's complemented form, another subtraction operation is required. The two's complemented number is subtracted from a row of zero's, equal to the work length, preceded by a single "1" in the next higher position.

Example: 1 1 0 1 is equal to what in absolute value?

$$
\begin{array}{r}
1\ 0\ 0\ 0\ 0 \\
\text{subtract} \quad 1\ 1\ 0\ 1 \\
\hline
0\ 0\ 1\ 1 \quad = \quad -\ 0\ 0\ 1\ 1 \quad = \quad -3
\end{array}
$$

It should be observed that a complete parallel subtraction operation was required to convert the two's complemented number into absolute value. It is for this reason that two's complements are not too widely used in present-day computers. In place of the two's complement system, a one's complement is used. With this system, we introduce a difficulty with zero, but the conversion of numbers is much simpler.

Example of one's complement representation of negative numbers:

$$
\begin{array}{rcl}
+1 & = & 0\ 0\ 0\ 1 \\
+0 & = & 0\ 0\ 0\ 0 \\
-0 & = & 1\ 1\ 1\ 1 \\
-1 & = & 1\ 1\ 1\ 0 \\
-2 & = & 1\ 1\ 0\ 1 \\
-3 & = & 1\ 1\ 0\ 0
\end{array}
$$

As with the two's complement, the high order bit may be thought of as being a sign. To convert a one's complemented number to absolute value, one merely inverts all bits.

Example: 1010 in one's complement form, is equal to what in absolute form?

$$
\begin{array}{c}
1\ 0\ 1\ 0 \\
\downarrow\ \downarrow\ \downarrow\ \downarrow \\
-\ 1\ 0\ 1 \quad = -5
\end{array}
$$

We may obtain the one's complement representation of negative numbers from the previously designed functional subtractor by connecting the "borrow out" from the high order position to the lowest position. The low order position must now be a full subtractor in place of the half subtractor previously used. This connection is called "end around borrow."

Example:

$$
\begin{array}{ccc}
 & & B\ B\ B \\
5 & = & 0\ 1\ 0\ 1 \\
\text{minus}\quad 7 & = & 0\ 1\ 1\ 1 \\
\text{End around} & & 1\ 1\ 1\ 0 \\
\text{Borrow} & & \longrightarrow 1 \\
\hline
& & 1\ 1\ 0\ 1 \quad = \quad -2 \text{ in one's complement}
\end{array}
$$

When a negative number in one's complement form is added to a larger positive number, the result should be positive. To obtain the correct positive value when adding, an end around carry must be used.

Example:

$$
\begin{array}{rcl}
-2 & = & 1\ 1\ 0\ 1 \\
\text{Add}\quad +3 & = & 0\ 0\ 1\ 1 \\
\text{End around} & & 0\ 0\ 0\ 0 \\
\text{Carry} & & \longrightarrow 1 \\
\hline
& & 0\ 0\ 0\ 1 \quad = \quad +1
\end{array}
$$

Subtraction by Complement Addition

In order to reduce the hardware requirements of a computer, it has been found advisable to develop some method whereby subtraction may be performed without the use of a functional subtractor. It has been noted that if one wishes to subtract a plus 5 from a plus 7, the same results may be obtained by adding a minus 5 to a plus 7.

When the one's complement method is used, it becomes a rather simple procedure to convert a plus 5 to a minus 5.

Example:

$$
\begin{array}{rcl}
+7 & = & 0\ 1\ 1\ 1 \\
\text{subtract}\quad \underline{(+5)} & = & 0\ 1\ 0\ 1 \\
+2 & &
\end{array}
\qquad
\begin{array}{rl}
& 0\ 1\ 1\ 1 \\
\text{add } (-5) & 1\ 0\ 1\ 0 \\
\text{End around} & 0\ 0\ 0\ 1 \\
\text{Carry} & \longrightarrow 1 \\
\hline
& 0\ 0\ 1\ 0 \quad = \quad +2
\end{array}
$$

An end around carry was required since the -5 was used in the one's complemented form. This method of performing subtraction requires a functional adder with end around carry and the ability to one's complement any binary number. Several examples are shown below.

$$
\begin{array}{rcl}
+3 & = & 0\ 0\ 1\ 1 \\
\text{Subtract} \quad \underline{(+2)} & = & \underline{0\ 0\ 1\ 0} \\
+1 &&
\end{array}
\qquad
\begin{array}{l}
\phantom{\text{add}}\ \ 0\ 0\ 1\ 1 \\
\text{add}\ \ \underline{1\ 1\ 0\ 1} \\
\phantom{\text{add}}\ \ 0\ 0\ 0\ 0 \\
\phantom{\text{add}\ \ }\longrightarrow\ 1 \\
\phantom{\text{add}}\ \ \overline{0\ 0\ 0\ 1} \ =\ +1
\end{array}
$$

$$
\begin{array}{rcl}
5 & = & 0\ 1\ 0\ 1 \\
\text{Subtract} \quad \underline{(-1)} & = & \underline{1\ 1\ 1\ 0} \\
+6 &&
\end{array}
\qquad
\begin{array}{l}
\phantom{\text{add}}\ \ 0\ 1\ 0\ 1 \\
\text{add}\ \ \underline{0\ 0\ 0\ 1} \\
\phantom{\text{add}}\ \ 0\ 1\ 1\ 0 \ =\ +6
\end{array}
$$

$$
\begin{array}{rcl}
+2 & = & 0\ 0\ 1\ 0 \\
\text{Subtract} \quad \underline{(+4)} & = & \underline{0\ 1\ 0\ 0} \\
-2 &&
\end{array}
\qquad
\begin{array}{l}
\phantom{\text{add}}\ \ 0\ 0\ 1\ 0 \\
\text{add}\ \ \underline{1\ 0\ 1\ 1} \\
\phantom{\text{add}}\ \ 1\ 1\ 0\ 1 \ =\ -2
\end{array}
$$

$$
\begin{array}{rcl}
-2 & = & 1\ 1\ 0\ 1 \\
\text{Subtract} \quad \underline{(-1)} & = & \underline{1\ 1\ 1\ 0} \\
-1 &&
\end{array}
\qquad
\begin{array}{l}
\phantom{\text{add}}\ \ 1\ 1\ 0\ 1 \\
\text{add}\ \ \underline{0\ 0\ 0\ 1} \\
\phantom{\text{add}}\ \ 1\ 1\ 1\ 0 \ =\ -1
\end{array}
$$

As far as the arithmetic operations of a machine are concerned, the one's complemented form of representing negative number is quite satisfactory. But as previously explained, individuals do not like to see negative numbers written in this form. For this reason, complemented numbers must be converted to absolute value with sign before they are printed by a computer. An argument now develops on where these complemented numbers should be converted. Some machines do not convert complement numbers until they are actually being sent to an output device. Other machines are built on the principle that complemented numbers should not be permitted to leave the arithmetic unit until they have been converted to absolute value with sign. With the latter method, complemented numbers will not appear in memory which may ease the programming job on complex problems. Arguments of this type are rather weak and similar arguments may be given for any method. Present-day machines are being built using both methods, and it is obvious that there is no clear cut reason for selecting either method.

A Complete Addition Subtraction Method

If complemented numbers are not permitted to leave the arithmetic unit and negative numbers are going to be sent to the unit in absolute value, then it is clear we will have to alter somewhat the addition and subtraction procedures. In the following procedure, it should be remembered that negative numbers will enter and leave the arithmetic unit in absolute form as shown below. A six-bit word length is assumed and a one in the high order position is read as a minus sign.

$$
\begin{array}{rcl}
 & & \text{Sign bit} \\
 & & \downarrow \\
+2 & = & 0\ 0\ 0\ 0\ 1\ 0 \\
+1 & = & 0\ 0\ 0\ 0\ 0\ 1 \\
+0 & = & 0\ 0\ 0\ 0\ 0\ 0 \\
-0 & = & 1\ 0\ 0\ 0\ 0\ 0 \\
-1 & = & 1\ 0\ 0\ 0\ 0\ 1 \\
-2 & = & 1\ 0\ 0\ 0\ 1\ 0 \\
-3 & = & 1\ 0\ 0\ 0\ 1\ 1 \\
\end{array}
$$

A functional arrangement which will handle the entire problem of adding and subtracting is shown in Figure 7.4. This arrangement requires only one set of complementing gates and uses a functional adder with end around carry. It is understood that in this parallel, binary machine, only one word at a time is available from main memory. The information in register "C" is either added to or subtracted from the contents of register "A," with the answer appearing in register "B." The answer is then moved into register "A", destroying the previous contents. From register "A," the information may be gated back to the adder for use in the next problem or may be sent to memory. Register "A" is initially filled by placing the information in register "C" and giving a "clear and add" instruction. This instruction will clear register "A" and then add the contents of "C" to "A" (which is empty), placing the answer in register "B." The information in "B" is then moved into register "A." It should be noted that each register has a sign bit associated with it. This sign position does not feed through the adder. The "True-Complement" gate on register "A" will gate out either the number in "A" or the one's complement of the number in "A." With this functional arrangement, we may now establish a set of rules for addition and subtraction. It is assumed, registers "A" and "C" have been loaded with data and the number in "C" is to be added to or subtracted from "A."

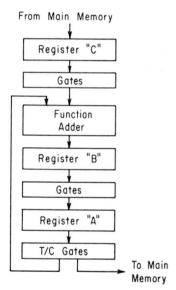

Figure 7.4. A functional arrangement for adding and subtracting.

Addition Rules

Rule 1 If Registers "C" and "A" have alike signs, add the contents of Register "C" to contents of Register "A."

Rule 2 If Registers "C" and "A" have unlike signs, add the contents of Register "C" to the 1's complement of Register "A."

After the addition operation, three more rules are used to eliminate complement number in Register "A."

Rule 3 If Registers "C" and "A" have alike signs (note: no sign changes occurred in Rules 1 and 2), the sign of Register "A" is left unchanged.

Rule 4 If Registers "C" and "A" have unlike signs and, if no end around carry occurred, Register "A" is complemented and the sign of Register "A" is left unchanged.

Rule 5 If Registers "C" and "A" have unlike signs and an end around carry has occurred, change sign of Register "A."

The complementing of Register "A" (Rule 4) may be accomplished by recirculating the information through the adder by way of the complementing gates.

Subtraction Rule

Change the sign of register "C" and proceed with the same rules as used for addition.

Examples:

Addition

			Sign bit ↓	
	+5	=	0 0 0 1 0 1	in register "A"
Add	+4	=	0 0 0 1 0 0	in register "C"
			Use Rule One	
			0 0 1 0 1	Output of register "A"
			<u>0 0 1 0 0</u>	Output of register "C"
			0 1 0 0 1	Input to register "B" then
			0 0 1 0 0 1	Moved into register "A"
			Using Rule Three	the sign of register "A" is left unchanged
			0 0 1 0 0 1	Answer in register "A"
	+7		0 0 0 1 1 1	Contents of "A"
Add	−3		1 0 0 0 1 1	Contents of "C"

Using Rule Two

1 1 0 0 0	Output of register "*A*"
0 0 0 1 1	Output of register "*C*"
1 1 0 1 1	Input to register "*B*" then
0 1 1 0 1 1	moved into "*A*"

Using Rule Four

0 0 0 1 0 0	Answer in register "*A*"

Add   −2   −4

1 0 0 0 1 0	Contents of "*A*"
1 0 0 1 0 0	Contents of "*C*"

Using Rule One

0 0 0 1 0	Output of register "*A*"
0 0 1 0 0	Output of register "*C*"
0 0 1 1 0	Input to register "*B*" then
1 0 0 1 1 0	moved to register "*A*"

Using Rule Three

1 0 0 1 1 0	Answer in Register "*A*"

Add   −7   +7

1 0 0 1 1 1	Contents of "*A*"
0 0 0 1 1 1	Contents of "*C*"

Using Rule Two

1 1 0 0 0	Output of "*A*"
0 0 1 1 1	Output of "*C*"
1 1 1 1 1	Input to "*B*" then
1 1 1 1 1 1	moved to "*A*"

Using Rule four

1 0 0 0 0 0	Answer in Register "*A*"

Examples Subtraction

Sub   +7   +8

0 0 0 1 1 1	Contents of "*A*"
0 0 1 0 0 0	Contents of "*C*"

Using subtraction rule,   sign of "*C*" is changed

0 0 0 1 1 1	Contents of "*A*"
1 0 1 0 0 0	Contents of "*C*"

Using Rule Two

1 1 0 0 0	Output of "*A*"
0 1 0 0 0	Output of "*C*"
0 0 0 0 0	

End Carry   ⟶ 1

0 0 0 0 1	Input to "*B*" then move
0 0 0 0 0 1	to "*A*"

Using Rule five

1 0 0 0 0 1	Answer in "*A*"

Sub   +8   −2   =

0 0 1 0 0 0	Contents of "*A*"
1 0 0 0 1 0	Contents of "*C*"

Using subtract rule

0 0 1 0 0 0	Contents of "A"
0 0 0 0 1 0	Contents of "C"

Using Rule 1

0 1 0 0 0	Output of "A"
0 0 0 1 0	Output of "C"
0 1 0 1 0	Input to "B" then
0 0 1 0 1 0	moved into "A"

Using Rule three

0 0 1 0 1 0	Answer in "A"

The two zero problems ($+0$, -0) may be solved by adding a circuit that will force the sign to plus when the "A" register contains all zeros.

Binary Multiplication

Binary multiplication is a rather simple operation when performed with pencil and paper. The binary multiplication table for a single bit times a single bit is shown below.

	0	1
0	0	0
1	0	1

With this table in mind and an understanding of binary addition, it is now possible to perform binary multiplication.

Examples:

$$
\begin{array}{r}
5 \\
\times 2 \\
\end{array}
\;=\;
\begin{array}{r}
101 \\
\times 10 \\
\hline
000 \\
101 \\
\hline
1010 \\
\end{array}
\;=\; \text{ten}
$$

$$
\begin{array}{r}
6 \\
\times 7 \\
\end{array}
\;=\;
\begin{array}{r}
0\,1\,1\,0 \\
0\,1\,1\,1 \\
\hline
0\,1\,1\,0 \\
0\,1\,1\,0 \\
0\,1\,1\,0 \\
0\,0\,0\,0 \\
\hline
0\,1\,0\,1\,0\,1\,0 \\
\end{array}
\;=\; 42
$$

As a result of the simplicity of the binary multiplication table, all partial products are either zero or equal to the multiplicand shifted to the left some number of positions. The multiplication problem may therefore be reduced to selectively gating the multiplicand, through a shifting device, into a parallel adder. The other set of inputs to the parallel adder will be fed from a register used to store the running sum of the partial products. It should be noted that the fully developed product may be double word length (sum of number of bits in multiplier and multiplicand). For this reason, it would appear that four full word length registers would be required. One full word length register each for the multiplier and the multiplicand, plus a double length register for the product. But upon close examination, one may notice that after the first partial product is obtained, the low order bit of the multiplier is no longer needed and this bit position may be used to store other information. One additional bit position of the multiplier register will become free after each partial product is formed. Upon examination of the development of the product, it may be noted that the first running sum cannot be longer than one word length. The next running sum of the partial products will be no longer than one word length plus one bit.

In other words, the register used to store the running sum of the partial products must be one word length for the first operation and will require an additional bit position after each addition. Since the multiplier register requires one less bit position after each addition and the product register requires one more bit position, it is possible to share one word length register between the two requirements. Such a method is outlined below. Although not shown, it is assumed that a fourth register "B" will store the results of the addition operation temporarily before placing the sum in register "A."

Example:

$$\begin{array}{cc} 19 & 10011 \\ \underline{\times 11} \quad = & \underline{\times 01011} \end{array}$$

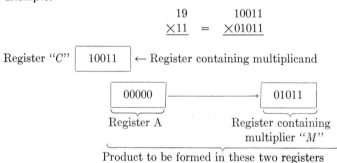

Register "C" | 10011 | ← Register containing multiplicand

Register A

Register containing multiplier "M"

Product to be formed in these two registers

Step I   Since the right hand bit of the multiplier is "1", the multiplicand is added to the register below it. It is understood that a "B" register is used to store the sum temporarily before moving it into Register "A".

The registers now appear as shown below.

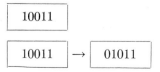

Step II   The information in the bottom two registers is now shifted one position to the right.

Step III   Since the right hand bit of the multiplier is again a "1", the multiplicand is added to the register below.

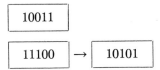

Step IV   The information in the bottom two registers is shifted one position to the right.

Step V   Since the right hand bit of the multiplier is now a zero, nothing is added to the bottom register.

Step VI   The information in the bottom two registers is shifted one position to the right.

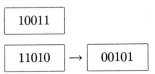

Step VII   The right hand bit of the multiplier is a "1", therefore the multiplicand is added to the register below.

Step VIII The information in the bottom register is shifted one position to the right.

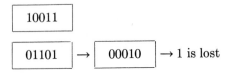

Step IX   The right hand bit of the multiplier is a zero so nothing is added to the bottom register.

Step X   The information in the bottom registers is shifted once more. Since we now have completed five shift operations (the bit size of the multiplier), the operation is complete. The multiplier has been completely destroyed and the ten bit product now appears in the bottom two registers.

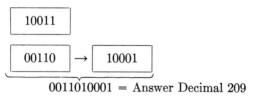

0011010001 = Answer Decimal 209

Binary Division

When binary division is performed with pencil and paper, it appears as shown below.

Example (a): Divide 6 by 2

$$\left.\begin{array}{ccc} 6 & = & 110 \\ 2 & = & 010 \end{array}\right\} \text{Shown as 3 bit words}$$

$$\begin{array}{r} 1\ 1\ \ =\ 3 \\ \phi\ 1\ 0\ \overline{)\ 1\ 1\ 0} \\ \underline{1\ 0} \\ 1\ 0 \\ \underline{1\ 0} \end{array}$$

Example (b): Divide 39 by 12

$$\left.\begin{array}{ccc} 39 & = & 100111 \\ 12 & = & 001100 \end{array}\right\} \text{Shown as 6 bit words}$$

$$\begin{array}{r} 1\ 1\ .\ 0\ 1\ \ =\ 3\frac{1}{4} \\ 1\ 1\ 0\ 0\ \overline{)\ 1\ 0\ 0\ 1\ 1\ 1\ .\ 0\ 0} \\ \underline{1\ 1\ 0\ 0} \\ 1\ 1\ 1\ 1 \\ \underline{1\ 1\ 0\ 0} \\ 1\ 1\ 0\ 0 \\ \underline{1\ 1\ 0\ 0} \end{array}$$

Since we are working in the binary system, each of the quotient bits must be either a zero or a one. Therefore, each of the trial divisor is either zero (0 X divisor) or equal to the divisor (1 X divisor). This reduces the division operation to one of trial subtractions, using the divisor as the subtracthend and the dividend as the menuend. A "1" is recorded in the quotient register each time the subtraction is successful (a positive remainder). In the preceding example (a), the first trial subtraction should be:

$$
\begin{array}{ll}
\;\; 0\,1\,1\,0 & \text{Dividend} \\
\text{sub}\;\; \underline{0\,0\,1\,0} & \text{Divisor}
\end{array}
$$

This subtraction would yield a negative result when performed on paper since a human would assume a series of "0's" in the high order positions of the dividend. But within a computer, the arithmetic unit must be told that these high order positions are "0's". This would imply that almost a full word length of "0's" must be affixed to the high order of the dividend. This is impractical, but we shall assume it to be true for the time being. Continuing with our example:

$$
\begin{array}{l}
\;\; 0\,0\,0\,0\,1\,1\,0 \\
\;\; \underline{0\,0\,1\,0} \\
B\;\; 1\,1\,1\,0\,1\,1\,0
\end{array}
$$

these bits moved down unchanged

negative number

Since this first trial subtraction was unsuccessful, a zero is recorded in the high order bit of the quotient and the dividend is left unchanged. The next trial subtraction is performed after the dividend is shifted one position to the left. Shifting the dividend left produces the same effect as shifting the divisor right.

zero introduced by shifting

$$
\begin{array}{l}
\; 0\,0\,0\,1\,1\,0 \\
\text{sub}\;\; \underline{0\,0\,1\,0} \\
 B\;\; 1\,1\,1\,1\,1\,0
\end{array}
$$

negative number; record a zero in quotient register

$$0\,0 = \text{quotient}$$

The dividend is shifted left and another trial subtraction taken:

$$
\begin{array}{ll}
\;\; 0\,0\,1\,1\,0\,0\,0 \\
\text{sub}\;\; \underline{0\,0\,1\,0} \\
\;\; 0\,0\,0\,1\,0\,0\,0
\end{array}
$$

Positive Number

This time the trial subtraction gave us a positive remainder which means that the divisor went into the dividend. A "1" is therefore placed in the next lower position of the quotient and the result of this subtraction will be used as the new dividend. Our quotient at this point is 001. The new dividend is shifted left one position and a trial subtraction taken.

```
      0 0 1 0 0 0 0
sub   0 0 1 0
      0 0 0 0 0 0 0            0011
```

Positive number; place "1" in quotient register

In this case, the dividend has been reduced to zero and the problem is complete.

The procedure just outlined is satisfactory for a pencil and paper method but has some rather severe hardware requirements for implementation in a computer. The first hardware requirement encountered was that of the high order zeros affixed to the dividend. This problem, if left unaltered, would require a register of almost two word lengths to contain the dividend. This requirement of a double length register is not too severe if it were not for the fact that a full word length of zeros should be affixed to the low end of the dividend. This requirement occurs when a small number is divided by a larger number. At this point, we have a triple length register required for the dividend and a double length register for the quotient. The double length register requirement for the quotient since we may obtain a full word length of integer quotient and a full word length of fraction. Since multiplication required basically three registers (B register not counted), most computers employ a division method based on the use of these same three registers. The first restriction employed will be that of allowing only a single word length register for the quotient. The quotient could be restricted to only an integer by prohibiting the machine from dividing numbers by smaller numbers. Or the quotient could be restricted to a fraction by limiting the division operation to problems where the dividend is smaller than the divisor. It has become common procedure to select the latter method. The reason for this selection is rather clear when one considers the average quotient obtained in a fixed word length machine. The average quotient will be close to one. If an integer quotient had been selected, the high order bits would be seldom used and significance would be lost. But if a fraction quotient is selected, then a full word length of significant bits will be obtained when the answers are close to one. This restriction of limiting the quotient to a fraction may seem rather harsh, but it is only a slight inconvenience to the programmer. A three-register arrangement for performing binary division is shown below.

Example:

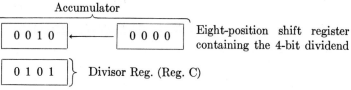

Accumulator

| 0 0 1 0 | ← | 0 0 0 0 | Eight-position shift register containing the 4-bit dividend

| 0 1 0 1 | Divisor Reg. (Reg. C)

Step I   Divisor is subtracted from dividend. A negative result is obtained which proves the restriction: Divisor larger than Dividend. If a positive result is obtained, the machine will indicate to the operator that a divide check has occurred. This type of check will also solve the problem of division by zero.

Step II The entire accumulator is shifted left one position and a subtract cycle taken.

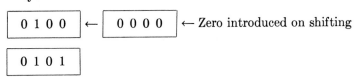

0 1 0 0 ← 0 0 0 0 ← Zero introduced on shifting

0 1 0 1

This subtraction 4 − 5 will produce a negative result and will indicate that the high order bit of the fractional quotient is zero. This bit will be stored in the right most bit of the 8-bit accumulator. In this case, this position is already a zero so it need not be changed.

Step III The accumulator is then shifted left one position and another trial subtraction taken.

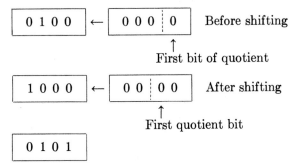

0 1 0 0 ← 0 0 0 0   Before shifting

↑
First bit of quotient

1 0 0 0 ← 0 0 0 0   After shifting

↑
First quotient bit

0 1 0 1

In this case, a positive remainder is obtained (8 − 5 = 3). The next quotient bit should therefore be a "1" and will be stored in the right most position of the accumulator. Since the subtraction was successful, the results of this subtraction will be used to replace the dividend.

0 0 1 1 ← 0 0 0 1

Step IV The accumulator is shifted and a trial subtraction is taken.

0 1 1 0 ← 0 0 1 0   Accumulator after shifting

0 1 0 1

Six minus five will give a positive result of "1" (0001) and a "1" will be stored in the right most bit of the accumulator. The result (0001) will be placed in the four left most bits of the accumulator.

$$\boxed{0\ 0\ 0\ 1} \leftarrow \boxed{0\ \vdots\ 0\ 1\ 1}$$

Step V   The accumulator is shifted and another trial subtraction taken.

$$\boxed{0\ 0\ 1\ 0} \leftarrow \boxed{\vdots\ 0\ 1\ 1\ 0}$$

$$\boxed{0\ 1\ 0\ 1}$$

Two minus five will give a negative result and the next bit of the quotient will be zero.

The operation is terminated at this point since one more shift operation will place the high order bit of the quotient in the dividend register. The operation was discontinued after the trial subtraction following the fourth shift (4 bit word). The quotient is now located in the four right most bits of the accumulator. It should be remembered that this is a fraction and should be written as .0110. The remainder (.0010) is located in the left most bits of the accumulator.

Since the right hand four bits of the accumulator are not used except to store zeros on the first trial subtraction, the division operation may be extended to double procession. In other words, a fraction part of the dividend may be loaded into these four positions before the division operation is started. Problems such as 0110.0110/1000 may be performed. The quotient will still contain only four bits, but the remainder may be divided by the divisor after the four bits of quotient have been sent to memory. The right hand four bits of the accumulator are set to zeros and four more bits of quotient may be obtained by giving a divide instruction.

These four zero positions of the accumulator may be put to use in another way. If the dividend proves to be larger than the divisor, then th dividend may be shifted right until it appears smaller. Each single shift to the right effectively divides the dividend by two. It is up to the programmer to record the number of right shifts taken and to alter the quotient accordingly.

Problems: (all numbers listed below are in decimal)
I.   Add in Binary
   (a) 21 plus 37
   (b) 15 plus 47
   (c) $15\frac{1}{2}$ plus $14\frac{3}{4}$

(d) $12\frac{13}{16}$ plus $1\frac{3}{16}$

(e) 62 plus 41 plus 31

II. Subtract in Binary (use functional subtractor)

(a) 7 from 9

(b) 1 from 16

(c) 5 from 4

(d) 15 from 14

III. Using the Add-Subtract method outlined for absolute numbers with signs, perform the following operations:

(a) Add $+7$ to $+15$

(b) Add $+8$ to -1

(c) Add -13 to $+5$

(d) Add -5 to -13

(e) Sub $+3$ from $+14$

(f) Sub -7 from $+8$

(g) Sub $+5$ from -5

(h) Sub -13 from -8

IV. Using the methods outlined for a computer, perform the following (assume word length of four):

(a) Multiply 5 by 7

(b) Multiply 13 by 5

(c) Multiply 6 by 13

(d) Divide 5 by 7

(e) Divide 1 by 6

(f) Divide 3 by 5

(g) Divide 4 by 7

8

One way of introducing sequential circuits or sequential machines is to mention some familiar examples of them. The ordinary combination lock is a mechanical sequential machine. A particular sequence of turns to certain numbers is required before the mechanism generates an output signal which opens the lock. Further, the tumblers remember where you are in the sequence. Thus, if you turn to the first number in the correct sequence, you can leave and come back the next day; now completing the sequence will still open the lock. Also, there is always a way of resetting the tumblers, usually by twisting the dial completely once or twice.

An electro-mechanical example is the stepping relay in the dial telephone system. In dialing a sequence of digits, not only the numbers but the sequence is remembered. Here there is a large number of outputs, namely all of the telephones in that dial system. Here, hanging up the receiver returns the system to its initial state.

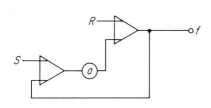

Figure 8.1. Simplest electronic sequential circuit.

The simplest electronic sequential circuit is shown in Figure 8.1. Suppose S and R are both 0. Remembering that the NOR function is a 1 only if all its inputs are zero, we see that it is impossible for us to know the value at f just from knowledge of the inputs as given above. If $f = 0$, then node ⓐ $= 1$ and f remains 0 (see Figure 8.1). On the other hand, if $f = 1$, then node ⓐ $= 0$ and f remains 1. Either state is possible; the feedback loop is remembering which input was last a 1 (assuming S and R, if both 1, never drop to 0 at the same time.)

For suppose $R = S = f = 0$. If S goes to 1, node ⓐ drops to 0 and f will go to 1 since $R = 0$ also. Now even though S goes back to 0, $f = 1$ will hold ⓐ $= 0$ and $f = 1$, perpetuating itself and storing the fact that the S input was last a 1.

If we now bring R along up to 1, f will drop to 0. Since $S = 0$, ⓐ will be forced up to 1 holding $f = 0$ even after R goes down. Thus $f = 0$ will now perpetuate itself which can be interpreted to mean that the circuit is storing or remembering the information that the R input was last a 1. Usually the restriction is made that S and R are never allowed to be 1 at the same time, because this forces both outputs ⓐ and f to 0 and if both are removed near simultaneously, the symmetry of the circuit makes the resulting state unpredictable. Actually, if ⓐ $= f = 0$ does not cause trouble, $S = R = 1$ can be allowed providing one knows that one of them will drop significantly before the other. The result is then predictable, the loop remembering which was the last input to be 1.

This simple sequential circuit in vacuum tube version is called an Eccles-Jordan flip-flop. Flip-flop, latch, trigger, toggle—all these names have been used.

Just below on the scale, are a class of feedback machines, that are *almost* sequential circuits. An example is Shannon's Black Box. Dr. Shannon actually built a working model of this and copies have been sold by novelty companies especially around Christmas time. It is a plain black box with a switch on it. If you turn the switch on, the top of the box opens and a hand comes out which turns off the switch.

The idea of this mechanism seems to have an unanalyzable appeal, especially for logicians. The authors have had a great deal of fun in contriving similar situations. Of these, the most interesting one is the inverse of Shannon's Black Box. Here, one would have a similar black box with a switch on it. The box would flash lights, play music, or merely make rumbling noises. When you turn off the switch, the noise stops and out comes a hand which turns the switch back on again.

In this borderline class there are many useful circuits; however, most important for us are single-shots, pulse extenders. We will use sequential techniques to design these in a later chapter.

Now if we abstract the quintessential properties of sequential circuits as manifested in these examples, we find a common functional dependence of the output s on *sequences of combinations of input values*, where by sequence is meant at least two successive (different) input conditions. Thus we have the

Definition

A sequential circuit is one whose sequences of output s are functionally dependent on sequences of input conditions.

The most general form of a transistor sequential circuit is shown in Figure 8.2. The delays shown are understood to be scattered lumped and distributed delays throughout the network, not a single lumped delay in the box marked "delay". Further, these distributed-lumped delays are independently variable though not without constraints. For example, individual transistors, as opposed to wiring delay, have switching delays that vary not only with time as components age, but more importantly they vary individually depending on their loading, whether turning on or off, the slope of the input signal, fluctuations in the power supply, ground plane and circuit elements, change in their gain, thus their switching threshold, and even temperature, etc.

From Figure 8.2 we can see that the functional dependence of the outputs $(z_1, z_2, \cdots z_r)$ of a sequential circuit at time t is in general, on the inputs $(x_1, x_2, \cdots x_p)$ *and* the state of the feedback loops $(f_1, f_2, \cdots f_q)$ both at time t (or Δt earlier where Δt is the delay in the logic of the output network). Most authors take this functional dependence of the outputs on the inputs and state of the circuit as a definition of sequential circuits. (Since Figure 8.2 is the most general form, not all the elements shown must be there, of course. Indeed combinational circuits are but a special degenerate case of sequential circuits where the feedback is absent.)

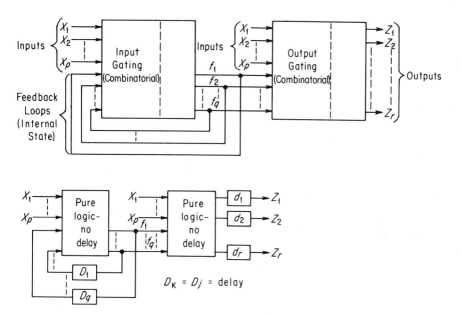

Figure 8.2. The general form of an electronic asynchronous sequential circuit. (a). The p inputs, q feedback loops, and r outputs form an adequate and minimal set of nodes or test points for the analysis or synthesis of sequentia (circuits). The contents of the boxes may be treated as contained in "black boxes" except at the beginning of analysis (for convenience, not necessity) and at the end of synthesis when their contents are specified, an end goal of synthesis. "Delay" segments refer to the distributed and scattered lumped delays of the gating inherent in all physical circuits. It is not implied these delays are lumped at the output as drawn. (b). While (a) is a fairly realistic description even though abstract, (b) depicts the simplified mathematical model we shall abstract to simplify the size and complexity of analysis and synthesis. Fundamental is the separating out of "+ One" in the form of "delay" from the combinatorial parts of the network.

Analysis

Rather than merely presenting the rules of the method to be developed here* for analysis and synthesis of asynchronous sequential electronic circuits, we will try to develop the method with the reader so he may gain the understanding necessary to use the rules intelligently and intuitively.

---

* The superstructure of the theory and methods presented in this chapter is taken from D. A. Huffman's Doctoral dissertation "The Synthesis of Sequential Switching Circuits," E.E. Dept., M. I. T., 1953. This work was done largely for relay circuits and the interpretations and extensions in terms of electronic circuit are those of the authors.

So much is still an art, it is as important to develop one's intuition in this field as it is to learn the rules of the game.

In analysis, we are presented with a switching circuit involving feedback for which we must develop systematic tools of analysis. By analysis, we mean tabulating (preferably the minimum) data about the circuit such that from this information the values of all outputs of the circuit may be predicted at any future time, given initial conditions at sometime and every subsequent input change to the circuit). One fundamental and natural assumption is that all input conditions last long enough for the circuit to settle into a stable state.

Stability and Non-Stability

In considering the transistor circuit of Figure 8.3, we note that it contains a loop connecting its output f back to inputs; thus it potentially has memory and (if so) its operation will differ for different sequences of inputs. (Feedback is a necessary but not a sufficient condition for semi-permanent or non-transient storage. Figure 8.3a, for example, has feedback but no memory. The reader is encouraged to check this and to determine why this is so.)

Since the parameter "time" is the essential ingredient of memory that we've not dealt with before (note the depence on it of "sequence" and "memory" for their meanings to be defined), and the sense of this dimension is completely lacking in our main manipulative tool, Boolean Algebra, which is a-temporal, a reasonable first step in sequential analysis is to separate "time" from the pure "instantaneous" elements of our logic blocks.

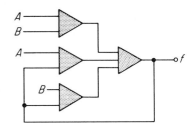

Figure 8.3. Net with feedback for analysis.

We replace Figure 8.3 by Figure 8.4 which lumps and makes explicit the delay inherent in every transistor circuit. In Figure 8.4 the double triangle $NAND$ block depicts the pure logic function which operates instantaneously, and the rectangle with the "Δt" (Δt an increment of time) is an element of pure delay abstracted and separated from the logic and connecting wires, lumping all time dependencies of both these.

This is the first simplifying assumption we make to derive an abstract model which can be more readily handled by nature of its simplified form. Later we shall study the effects and malfunctions as a result of departure of the circuit from our model and learn their symptoms and cure. The

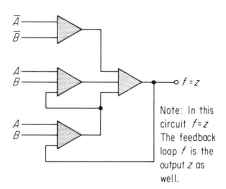

Figure 8.3 (a). A net with feedback but which does not exhibit the characteristics of "memory." f is completely determined by the inputs, A, B, alone and is independent of the present internal state of the circuit. Despite the feedback, this is a purely combinational circuit.

Note: In this circuit $f = z$ The feedback loop f is the output z as well.

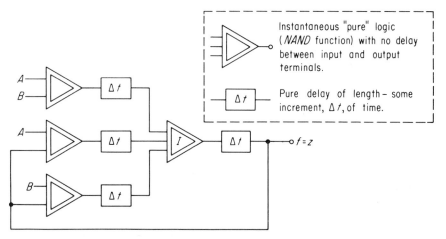

Instantaneous "pure" logic (*NAND* function) with no delay between input and output terminals.

Pure delay of length – some increment, Δt, of time.

Figure 8.4. Circuit of Fig. 8.3 with the delays made explicit. Each Δt lumps transistor delays and wiring delays at the output of the most significant delays, the transistors. All Δt's are independently variable with respect to each other and with time. First step in idealizing the circuit of Fig. 8.3 in an abstract model.

justification for this inverted approach to reality is in the simple and unifying concepts and methods which result.

These deltas are independently variable delays depending for their magnitude on the loading of the transistor, its characteristics, whether it is turning on or off, and several other parameters. Our second simplifying assumption in our abstracted model is that these delays are all equal and all path lengths are equal as they happen to be in Figure 8.4. Now since the delay through all paths from input to output, f, are the same length, we may replace our circuit with that of Figure 8.5.

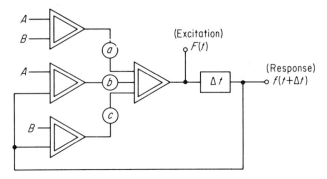

Figure 8.5. Final step in idealization of Fig. 8.3. The simplifying assumptions which constitute this model of the original circuit are necessary not only for understanding the way such circuits as Fig. 8.3 are analyzed and synthesized, but for any reflective criticism of the methods as well.

The magnitude of the delay does not concern us except relative to the time between input changes. However, we will retain the independent and unpredictable delay of each relative to the other. Otherwise our model would not exhibit some of the realistic problems and properties which are necessary to characterize some of the significant aspects of sequential behavior.

We distinguish timewise between the two ends of the delay line (Figure 8.5) by $F(t)$ and $f(t + \Delta t)$ where the former signal, $F(t)$ becomes $f(t + \Delta t)$, an increment Δt time later. We will subsequently drop the functional notation $F(t)$ and $f(t + \Delta t)$ and use only F and f, but their differences as functions of time should be remembered. $F(t)$ is the *excitation* applied to the circuit and $f(t + \Delta t)$ is the *response* of the circuit.

Now that we have idealized our circuit we must seek the key for describing its performance. A little thought shows that to do this requires us to show the state of the feedback loop $f(t + \Delta t)$ for not only all input combinations, but for all input sequences of combinations. How do we start? Certainly the easiest time to observe the feedback loop is when it is neither changing nor about to change; these will be the stable states of the circuit.

The first thing to do is hold the inputs constant at some set of values. Then for such a condition, there are two possibilities:

    a) $f(t + \Delta t) \neq F(t)$ non-stable
    b) $f(t + \Delta t) = F(t)$ stable

In condition (a), we know that after a delta time interval or less $f(t + \Delta t)$ is going to change to the "exciting" value $F(t)$; the circuit is in an unstable state. In condition (b) however, as long as the inputs remain the same, there is nothing to change the system and it is in a stable state; excitation equals the response. A listing of all the stable states, and all the non-stable states together with the directions of transitions between states for all instabilities, will completely describe the circuit performance of f for all possible conditions. We need to compare all the excitations $F(f, A, B; t)$—since F is a Boolean function as well as of time—with all the output values $f(F; t + \Delta t)$. $F(t)$ is combinational for a particular value of t so we may write from Figure 8.5.

$$F(t) = A \cdot B + A \cdot [f(t + \Delta t)] + B \cdot [f(t + \Delta t)]$$

Deriving the Excitation Matrix and Flow Table

In general the excitation is a Boolean function of the response and of the inputs. A convenient representation of this equation is the Karnaugh map plotting the function $F(t)$, particularly if we separate the feedback variable

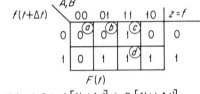

$$F(t) = A \cdot B + A \cdot [f(t+\Delta t)] + B \cdot [f(t+\Delta t)]$$

Figure 8.6. Stopping time at t, $F(t)$ is purely combinational for fixed t. Combinational analysis yields the K-Map and equation above from Fig. 8.5.

$f(t + \Delta t)$ from the input variables A, B. Figure 8.6 shows the function such that horizontal movement in the map means a change in the input variables and a vertical movement in the map means the value of the feedback loop is changing.

Now for each input combination we can compare the values of $F(t)$ (in the matrix) with each value of $f(t + \Delta t)$ on the left for each row to determine the stable and non-stable states. With the stability criteria of Figure 8.7 in mind, we look at the upper left hand square of the map of

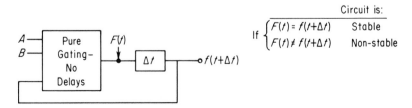

Figure 8.7. Generalized form of Fig. 8.5 emphasizing stability conditions.

Figure 8.6 (box ⓐ) where $A = B = f(t + \Delta t) = 0$). The value of $F(t)$ is 0. Since $f(t + \Delta t) = F(t)$ (the input variables constant), this is a stable state of the circuit. That is, (reference to Figure 8.5) with A and $B = 0$, and the feedback loop 0, the excitation to $f(t + \Delta t)$ at $F(t)$ is zero, as should be verified logically in the block diagram of Figure 8.5. Since the excitation matches the response we say the system is stable.

Since the map of Figure 8.6 shows the values of the excitation function $F(t)$, we call it the *excitation matrix*. Note that time has been separated out and remains only in the time difference of the values $F(t)$ in the excitation matrix and the response $f(t + \Delta t)$ for that row.

Moving horizontally to the square where $f(t + \Delta t) = A = 0$, $B = 1$, (box ⓑ) we find another stable state. But in the next square (box ⓒ) $A = B = 1$ and the response $f(t + \Delta t) = 0$, while the excitation $F(t) = 1$. This is unstable and in Δt time $f(t + \Delta t)$ will change to 1. Still assuming we remain in the column where $A = B = 1$, as always in transition, the circuit operation moves vertically down to the square where $f(t + \Delta t) = 1$ (box ⓓ.) Since the excitation here is still 1, this is a stable state and no further changes will occur unless initiated by the inputs.

These stable states and the transitions between them may be depicted as in the transition matrix of Figure 8.8. The stable states of Figure 8.8 are denoted by circles; the unstable by dots. The arrow shows the transition that occurs when a non-stable state is entered.

An alternative way of tabulating the stable and non-stable states along with their transitions, codes each state with a number as shown in Figure 8.9. This gives every state a name (number) for reference. This table shows us the flow of transitions when we change the input variable combination. Stable states are circled numbers. Unstable numbered states are uncircled with the number telling us to what stable state the circuit will go. This *flow table* is a convenient notation for describing part of what earlier was the object of analysis. The *flow table* characterizes the state sequences of the circuit in response to input sequences.

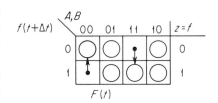

Figure 8.8. Transition matrix for Fig. 8.6.

Assume the circuit is in the stable ① state of Figure 8.9. $A = 0$, $B = 1$, and the circuit has a stable response $f(t + \Delta t) = 0$. Referring back to Figure 8.5, since $A = 0$, $a = b = 1$, and since $F(t + \Delta t) = 0$ node $c = 1$ and the system is stable with zero response. Thus the circuit operation checks with the flow table description.

If we now bring A up to 1, the circuit's operation moves horizontally to state 2 (uncircled). This is unstable sending the circuit to stable ②.

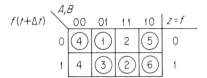

Figure 8.9. Flow table for Figs. 8.6 and 8.8.

Now the 0 response $f(t + \Delta t)$ has gone to 1. Comparing this again to Figure 8.5, bringing A to 1 ($B = 1$) forces ⓐ to 0 driving $F(t)$ to 1. At this moment $1 = F(t)$, $f(t + \Delta t) = 0$. Excitation does not match the response and this is unstable state 2. After time Δt, $f(t + \Delta t)$ becomes 1 forcing ⓑ and ⓒ to 0 locking the feedback loop into the stable ② state with $F(t) = f(t + \Delta t) = 1$.

If we now release A to 0, the circuit state moves horizontally in the flow table of Figure 8.9 to stable state ③. We are now back to the original input conditions, $A = 0$ and $B = 1$, but we have changed the state of the feedback loop from 0 to 1. (The reader should verify that the rest of the transitions and stable states predicted by the flow table do in fact correspond to the circuit action of Figure 8.5.)

If B now drops to 0, the circuit moves through unstable 4 to stable ④. Releasing B to 1 returns the circuit to the original stable ① state. We have thus set the flip-flop to a 1 state and then "reset" it to a 0 state. Here the A was a set signal, and B a reset signal, but because of the symmetry of the flow table if we had let A be normally 1 and B be normally 0 (the opposite of before) the circuit would normally sit in states ⑤ and ⑥ for the 0 and 1 states when unexcited and the roles of set and reset would be reversed for A and B. In using a circuit like this, A might at times be acting like a set and at other times be resetting. Another way of looking at the circuit is to say that if both A and B were pulsed simultaneously from ① or ③, providing there was no skew, the state of the feedback loop would not change; that is, we would not change rows but go to ⑤ or ⑥ respectively.

A Comparison Example

By way of comparison, analyze the circuit of Figure 8.10 which is the dual of Figure 8.1.

First write the excitation function

$$F(t) = \overline{S} + R \cdot [f(t + \Delta t)]$$

Plotting this on the map of Figure 8.10'a separating input from feedback variables, comparison of the excitation values of the map with the feedback response values of the rows, makes manifest the stable and unstable states and the transitions which are recorded in the flow table of Figure 8.10'b.

Comparing this to the flow table of Figure 8.9, we can see these differences: in Figure 8.10'b the set (S) and the reset (R) lines are both normally up instead of one up and one down as in Figure 8.9. When S drops to 0 and returns to 1 while $R = 1$, we move through ② to state ③, the 1-state of the

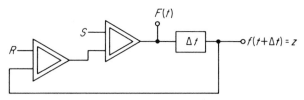

Figure 8.10. Set-reset flip-flop for analysis. Circuit ideal-ized as our model of circuit reality requires.

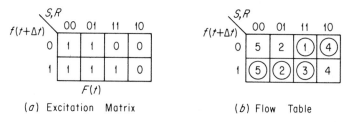

(a) Excitation Matrix   (b) Flow Table

Figure 8.10′. Excitation matrix and flow table for Fig. 8.10.

flip-flop. The same sequence for R alone takes us through ④ to ①, the 0 state.

As opposed to Figure 8.9, this flow table is not symmetrical, and if both inputs are simultaneously pulsed, the circuit will set to a 1-state through ⑤. The ability displayed in Figure 8.9 of exhibiting bi-stability for two different input conditions as opposed to the one condition of Figure 8.10′b is mainly what the extra transistors of Figure 8.3 over Figure 8.10 are accom-plishing.

As long as the simplifying assumptions we have made about the delays in the circuit are approximately valid so that we can lump the delay at one point in the feedback loop without changing the circuit operation, this analysis procedure is effective and accurate. Significant departures from the model, however, can result in hazardous operation. The nature of these hazards and how they can be avoided is discussed in the next chapter. Now, we will drop the lumped delay equivalent of the circuit and the time func-tional notation for the excitation and the output in the figures and equa-tions, though not in our minds. The excitation function diffuses into the distributed delays of the circuit. In reality no one point of the circuit can be pinpointed as the excitation. The model, however, should be kept in the back of the mind, to be brought out whenever a basic insight into transistor sequential circuits is needed.

A More General Example

A test of the power of our analysis methods will be the more formidable circuit of Figure 8.11. One complication here we have not before encountered except in Figure 8.2, is the gating labelled with output Z, a combinational

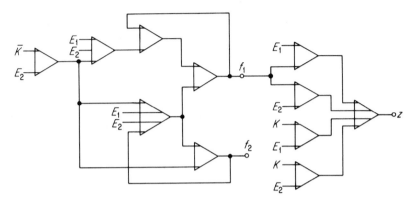

Figure 8.11. An analysis example with more challenge—for flexing our newly acquired muscles, our analytic tools.

function of the inputs and one of the feedback loops. We shall concentrate temporarily, however, on the two feedback loops, f_1 and f_2. We may write the excitation functions from the logic remembering the F's are combinational for fixed t which allows treating the feedback loops as inputs.

$$F_1 = [(\bar{K} + E_2) \cdot \bar{E}_1\bar{E}_2 + f_1][K\bar{E}_2 + E_1 + E_2 + f_2]$$
$$= \bar{K}\bar{E}_1\bar{E}_2 f_2 + Kf_1 + E_1F_1 + E_2f_1 + f_1f_2$$
$$F_2 = [K \cdot \bar{E}_2 + E_1 + E_2 + f_2] \cdot [\bar{K} + E_2]$$
$$= E_1\bar{K} + E_2 + f_2\bar{K}$$

These equations are plotted on the Karnaugh map—excitation matrix of Figure 8.12. Note that for more than one feedback loop, their excitation equations are all plotted, superimposed on a single matrix rather than on separate matrices for each. This is so that stability of the feedback loops may be a property of the combination of all the feedback loops and stability in the sequential circuit may be defined for the circuit as a whole independent of how many feedback loops implement it. Also, note that the K-map form is maintained as we jump to 5 variables in Figures 8.12 and 8.13.

Now compare the excitation entries in the matrix with the combination

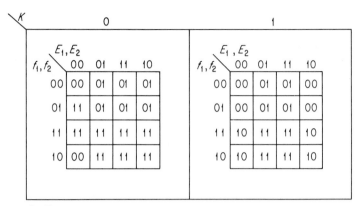

$$F_1 = \overline{KE_1\overline{E}_2}\, f_2 + Kf_1 + E_1 f_1 + E_2 f_1 + f_1 f_2$$

$$F_2 = E_1\overline{K} + E_2 + \overline{K}f_2$$

Figure 8.12. Excitation equations for Fig. 8.11 plotted on the excitation matrix. Note 5-variable K-Map form. (Equations derived in the text.)

f_1,f_2 \ E_1,E_2,K	000	010	110	100	001	011	111	101
00	①	5	6	8	②	4	7	③
01	9	⑤	⑥	⑧	2	④	⑦	3
11	⑨	⑪	⑫	⑭	15	⑩	⑬	16
10	1	11	12	14	⑮	10	13	⑯

Figure 8.13. Flow Table for Fig. 8.11, derived from Fig. 8.12.

of feedback loop values on the left for stability. Take the first row, $f_1 = f_2 = 0$. We place circled numbers in the flow table for all boxes in that row which contains the excitation functions $F_1 = F_2 = 0$. These are the stable states. Namely, states ①, ②, and ③ in the flow table of Figure 8.13. In row $f_1 = 0, f_2 = 1$, states ④ through ⑧ are stable. We continue filling in the stable states in the flow table from the excitation matrix.

Now we can investigate the non-stable conditions. Starting with the top row of Figure 8.12, we look for those columns in that row where the excitations differ from the feedback loops. This is true for the $\overline{E}_1 \cdot E_2 \cdot K$ column. The excitation is $F_1 = 0$, $F_2 = 1$. Thus f_1 is stable but f_2 will tend towards 1. This will bring the circuit operation to the $f_1 = 0$, $f_2 = 1$ row of the same column. This is stable state ④ in Figure 8.13 so we put an uncircled 4 in the non-stable box. Continuing the argument we fill in the flow table as done in Figure 8.13. The reader should verify all of the transitions for himself.

Now we can handle the combinational output function in an output matrix. Writing the Z output equation from Figure 8.11:

$$Z = (f_1 + E_1)(f_1 + E_2)(K + E_1)(K + E_2)$$

We plot this on a Karnaugh map which we will call the *output matrix*, Figure 8.14. Since the equation is in P of S form, we plot the zeros of the function. Even though Z is not a function of f_2 the output matrix is plotted

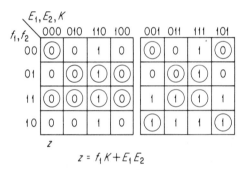

$$z = f_1 K + E_1 E_2$$

Figure 8.14. Output matrix, for Fig. 8.11, associated with the flow table of Fig. 8.13. Outputs corresponding to stable states in the flow table of Fig. 8.13 have been circled in the output matrix for convenience in tracing output sequences (from the output matrix) associated with input sequences and the resulting flow through the states of the circuit (from the flow table).

on a K-map identical to that of the excitation matrix. Otherwise, as we'll see, there'll be no clear correspondence between the stable states and the outputs. If there are more than one output they should be superimposed on the same matrix just as for multiple feedback loops. This gives an immediate picture of the state of all outputs, unavailable if they were spread among several maps.

Now the formal analysis of the circuit is completed, and we may go back and from given initial conditions and subsequent input sequences discern the corresponding sequence of outputs from the flow table and the output matrix. To give meaning to the problem, we'll assume the following interpretations for the variables: E_1 and E_2 are error signals telling us something has gone wrong at their respective sources. The circuit, we'll see, stores the information an error has occurred until K comes along sampling the information in the circuit and then resetting it to its initial state.

Suppose the circuit is in state ① of Figure 8.13. We see that if K goes to 1 alone, or at the same time as E_1 (states ② and ③, the feedback loops are left unchanged) sampling finds no errors stored and leaves the circuit alone. However, if we are in state ⑨ and K goes to 1 alone or with E_1, and then goes down again, we go through ⑮ or ⑯, respectively, and return to ①. Thus when K goes up and then down alone or with E_1, we always end in the zero-zero condition of the feedback loops (that is, the first row of the flow table). Thus after sampling the stored error K resets the circuit for the next cycle.

Starting again in state ① we see that raising E_1 alone or E_2 alone or both together alone, the feedback loops change to the zero-one condition (states ⑧, ⑤, and ⑥). When they are released the circuit goes to ⑨ and the feedbacks are one-one (storing an error). However, the same sequences starting from state ⑨ leave f_1 and f_2 unchanged (states ⑭, ⑪, ⑫.) So the error signals alone or together will "set" the circuit to ⑨, the one-one condition of f_1 and f_2. Further errors leave the circuit alone.

The remaining input combinations show that when an E_2 error signal comes along at the same time as a K reset signal, the E_2 overrides the K and the circuit sets or retains an error if in ⑨ (states ④, ⑦, and ⑩, ⑬ on the fall of the signals), independent of $E_1 \cdot K$ overrides E_1, however, as shown in states ③ and ⑯.

Apparently an E_2 error is more important than an E_1 so that it must not be lost should it occur during reset, whereas E_1 would be ignored at this time.

In looking back on our analysis, it is not clear why it was required to have four stable states of the feedback loops (the four rows of the flow table). The problem is similar to the set-reset latch of Figure 8.10 with some combinational gating in the set and the reset lines. This required only one feedback loop with two states. However, if we now look at the output function in Figure 8.14, we see the first term is $f_1 \cdot K$. Thus we require an output when K goes to one if $f_1 = 1$ (samples and finds a stored error). But K serves to reset the circuit to zero. Thus we are sampling the circuit at the same time we are resetting it. If we had only two stable states and K came along while $f_1 = 1$, f_1 would go to zero as a result of K and $K \cdot f_1$ would give us only a short transient 1 output if any at all.

However, we can see in the flow table that f_1 changes only on the fall of K. So long as K is up, f_1 will not change and we can sample it with K. Inspection of the flow table shows that f_2 on the other hand changes on the rise of the set or reset pulse, temporarily storing the bit until the input signal drops; then f_1 follows f_2.

The second term of the output function (Figure 8.14), $E_1 \cdot E_2$ shows that both errors occurring as the same time is so significant that we do not wait for the sampling pulse K, but immediately give an output.

Thus for each stable state of the flow table, the corresponding box of the output matrix tells us the output of the circuit in that state. Given an initial state we can trace the sequence of states of the circuit from the input sequence while the corresponding tracing in the output matrix tells us the sequence of outputs. Thus we have satisfied our goals of analysis.

Eccentric Behavior in Sequential Circuits

Some of the more eccentric behavior possible in sequential circuits are brought together in the excitation and transition matrix of Figure 14′a. Starting in the transition matrix, column 1, the box marked X, the dotted lines indicate the circuit might go next to any state, stable or unstable, in

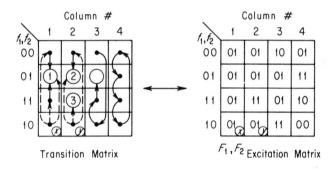

Column #	Nature	Name of Condition
1	Useful	Non-critical race (at $\widehat{X}$)
2	Bad	Critical race (at $\oslash$)
3	Useful	Multiple Transition
4	Good or bad depending on whether you want an oscillator or not.	Oscilator(s), cycle (of non-stable states)

Figure 8.14′. Analytical forms of an eccentric sequential circuit and an exhaustive cataloging, with comments, of sequential eccentricities.

that column. From the excitation matrix we note that box x has an excitation requiring both feedback loops to change. This is called a race condition since the next state is determined by which feedback loop wins or ties the race. However, no matter which transition occurs in column 1, we always end in stable state ①—thus the race is fixed. Since the final state is assured, this is called a *non-critical race*. The non-critical race can often be used in synthesis to simplify a circuit.

The similar excitation in box y of column 2 is more serious, however. Depending on the outcome of the race, the circuit may end up either in state ② or ③. This is called a *critical race* and is to be avoided.

Column 3 is an instance of a multiple-transition where the circuit passes through more than one non-stable state before reaching a stable one. These are also useful for simplifying circuits.

Column 4 is a closed loop of non-stable states. Both feedback loops are oscillators in this column. Although sometimes oscillations are deliberately designed, in most cases such loops are to be avoided.

These are instances of all the possible departures from the transitions we've been dealing with where stable states were separated by at most one stable state. These are listed in Figure 8.14′a along with comments as to whether each is useful or to be avoided.

Synthesis

The Flow Table: The synthesis of sequential circuits follows analysis procedure in reverse. Nonetheless, it is always more difficult to synthesize than analyze. The problem is analogous to parallel parking. It is harder to get into a tight parking space than to get out. The reason is, there are only a few positions outside from which you can get in—but there are many more positions inside from which you can get out. Similarly, analysis is unique, but with synthesis there are always many alternate paths we can take along the way resulting in different circuits, but all operating according to the same specifications. We will leave these subtleties to a later chapter, now, and except for some hints along the way, concentrate on the mechanics of synthesis yielding *a* circuit solution.

The first step in the process of synthesis is the reverse of the last in analysis. We must go from a word description of the problem to a flow table description. This is not always easy to do since our verbal descriptions are usually less precise than that of the flow table. The flow table forces us to specify the circuit action desired for every possible sequence of inputs. The flow table is for sequential circuits what the function table was for combinational circuits. As examples, we will not try to idealize the problem to simplify the transitions from word description to flow table, but present them as they might arise in actual computer design.

Problem 1: The carry output of a serial-parallel adder, is to be stored in a sequential circuit when a "store" control signal comes along. The circuit must hold the carry value until the sum is stored in the circuit and the carry is transferred to the least significant bit position of the sum-register so that it can be added to the next number. At this time, the "store" signal goes down and the store-carry circuit must reset to get ready for the next possible carry. The carry will always go up (if at all) before the "store" signal; also the carry will go down as the adder is cleared for the next cycle before "store" goes down. This time after the carry goes down (if it went up at all) and "store" is up, is the memory in the circuit. It remembers, for example, that the carry was a 1 when the control signal arrived even though the carry may now be zero.

There are two inputs, C, the carry, and S, the "store signal". The output is to remain 0 until $C \cdot S = 1$. We know C goes to 1, if at all, before S goes to 1. The circuit should store the value of C when S comes along and hold it until S goes down, which should reset the circuit to zero. The timing chart of the input conditions and required circuit response is shown in Figure 8.15.

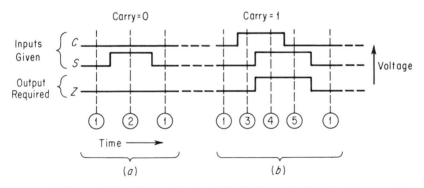

Figure 8.15. Timing Chart and Stable States for Problem 1.

We can discern the stable states by looking at those points in the timing chart where inputs and output remain at fixed values. The stable states are numbered on the chart. The particular numbering has no significance and is arbitrary. The numbers act as "names" for the states for purposes of reference. Notice that resetting (S to 0) always returns the circuit to the 0 state.

00	01	11	10	Z
①	2			0
1	②			0

(a)

00	01	11	10	Z
①	2		3	0
1	②			0
		4	③	0
		④		1
				1

(b)

00	01	11	10	Z
①	2		3	0
1	②			0
		4	③	0
	5	④		1
1	⑤			1

(c)

00	01	11	10	Z
①	2	—	3	0
1	②	—	—	0
—	—	4	③	0
—	5	④	—	1
1	⑤	—	—	1

(d)

Figure 8.16. Writing the primitive flow table for Problem 1, step by step.

We start the flow table by writing down all possible combinations of input variables in cyclic code at the top of the table as in Figure 8.16a. A column is provided at the right for the output values.

Starting in stable state ① with output 0 (Figures 8.15a and 8.16a), the store signal may come along while the carry is still zero. This moves the circuit operation horizontally in the table of Figure 8.16a to the column, $C = 0$, and $S = 1$. But when this change first occurs, the system is unstable so we put an uncircled 2 in this square; this indicates a transition through nonstable 2 to the stable state ② which we write below is in the next row. The output, Z, for ②, is still zero in Figure 8.15a so a 0 is entered for that row in the Z column of Figure 8.16a. Although, in this instance, it is not *apparent* that a change in response is required, a non-stable state is always assumed in the transitions between stable states while writing the initial flow table. Later, when the flow table is completed, and the problem thus fully specified, we may delete unstable transitions if possible. Although the necessity in this case is not apparent at this point, other transitions might require it when the table is completed. Further, we may or may not choose to delete a non-stable state, depending on which obtains a better circuit solution. It is more general to have them in, particularly since they are easier to remove than insert. Also, as we'll later discuss, there may be more than one way of removing these transitions, and these can best be seen only when the table is completed with all transitions indicated through non-stable states.

Following the sequence of Figure 8.15a, S next returns to 0 and the circuit returns to its initial state 1. Thus in Figure 8.16a, when S goes down, the operating point moves left horizontally from ② to the column $C = S = 0$. This non-stable state returns us to ① so we put an uncircled 1 here.

The other possible sequence is shown in Figure 8.15b. A carry comes along, then $S \rightarrow 1$ and Z follows staying a 1 as long as $S = 1$, even after $C \rightarrow 0$. Thus in the flow table (Figure 8.16b), starting in ①, $C \rightarrow 1$, $S = 0$

so we put a nonstable ③ in the box of that column and in the same row as ①. This moves the operating point to a new stable state and a new row—circled 3 in the third row directly below 3. As seen from the timing chart, the output $Z = 0$, for this state and we enter this 0 at the right. Again, for generality, we assign each stable state its own row, although once the flow table is written, we shall learn to see how best to combine rows of stable states.

S then goes to 1 and both $C \cdot S = 1$, thus the operating point moves from ③ to the left, through 4 and down to stable ④ in a new row. In ④ we want $Z = 1$ (from Figure 8.15b) as indicated on the right of Figure 8.16b. When the carry goes down we define a new state ⑤ with output 1 (Figure 8.16c). This figure shows that now when $S \to 0$ from ⑤, the circuit returns to its initial state ① and we enter an unstable 1 to the left of ⑤. Note that the nonstable states correspond to the transitions in the timing chart where response is slightly delayed behind input and no signal has a perfect rise time. This is shown more clearly in the exaggerated redrawing of Figure 8.15b in Figure 8.17. Here the nonstable states are indicated as well as the stable ones.

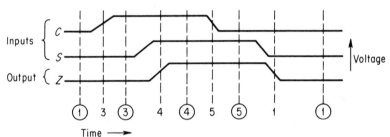

Figure 8.17. Timing Chart of Fig. 8.15(b) redrawn with exaggerated slopes of rises and falls of input and output signals—thus the non-stable states can be depicted.

Since we have specified all given transitions, we may now ask, what about the blank spaces in the table of Figure 8.16c? These correspond to sequences of inputs about which we were given no information or were told they would not occur. Alternatively these sequences may occur but we "don't care" what happens when they do. We indicate these situations by a line in the box. The completed flow table is shown in Figure 8.16d. Actually, we may observe from the nature of this problem that no other sequences should occur. For example, once the carry goes up, no ripple carry will change it so we would never move from ③ to the $C = S = 0$ column in that row. We also know that C always comes before S ruling out any sequence S then C or even C and S at the same time.

You will notice in Figure 16d that we have assigned one stable state to each row and to each row corresponds a stable state. A flow table with this property we will call a *primitive flow table*.

Problem 2: A very useful device in binary circuits is a scale of two counter. This circuit is of great historical importance and continues to have many applications in binary counters and control circuitry. (It should be noted that the broad general power of the methods developed here allow us to suit the circuit to the task; thus subverting the general importance of any one circuit.) Its required operation is shown in Figure 8.18.

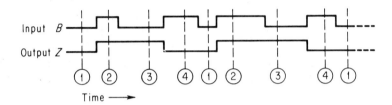

Figure 8.18. Timing Chart for Problem 2. The B-pulse width and the time between pulses may, as indicated, or may not be varied (beyond the minimum for resolution in the circuit). Essential point is Z changes state on the rise of every B-pulse.

We observe that the output f changes state on the rise of every B input-pulse, counting one bit in a scale of two. This circuit is often called a D. C. Binary Trigger. It is D. C. (as all the circuits derived by these methods) operating independent of the rise time of the input pulse. A trigger whose input pulse must be shortened artificially is an A. C. Binary Trigger.

The heading of the primitive flow table has only one variable, thus only two columns plus an output column. It is shown in Figure 8.19. Starting with $B \cdot Z = 0$ as stable state ① at the left of the timing chart, when $B \to 1$, the circuit operating point moves horizontally in the flow table to unstable 2 and down to stable state ②. Here we put a 1 in the output column as required by the timing chart. When $B \to 0$, we move through 3 and down to ③ with the output still 1. We have now counted one pulse in the radix 2.

The rise of another pulse moves us to ④ with Z going to 0 and removing the pulse returns the circuit to ①, the zero state. Thus we have counted the

$$
\begin{array}{c}
B \\
\begin{array}{cc|c}
0 & 1 & Z \\
\hline
① & 2 & 0 \\
3 & ② & 1 \\
③ & 4 & 1 \\
1 & ④ & 0 \\
\end{array}
\end{array}
$$

Figure 8.19. Primitive flow table for Problem 2.

pulses in binary. This completes the primitive flow table, noting there are no "don't care" conditions.

Problem 3: In many problems, the complexity and size of the timing chart is prohibitive and the flow table must be derived directly from the word statement. Although this is not true of this problem, we shall frequently omit the chart to give practice in going directly to the flow table.

This circuit is to have three inputs A_1, A_2, A_3 and three outputs Z_1, Z_2 and Z_3. When any input A_k goes up, its corresponding output Z_k is to go up and stay up after A_k goes down. When A_k goes up, all other outputs other than Z_k go or remain down. Only one input is ever up at a time. Only one input variable ever changes at a time. It is possible for the circuit to start with all the outputs down. This state will occur when the machine is turned on—the mechanism is ignored here for simplicity.

We can simplify the writing of the primitive flow table by eliminating all the columns representing input conditions which are "don't cares,"

A_1, A_2, A_3

000	001	010	100	$Z_1 Z_2 Z_3$
①	2	4	6	000
3	②	—	—	001
③	2	4	6	001
5	—	④	—	010
⑤	2	4	6	010
7	—	—	⑥	100
⑦	2	4	6	100

Figure 8.20. Primitive flow table for Problem 3.

namely all those where more than one input is up. In Figure 8.20, assuming we start in ① with all outputs down, any of the inputs may go up alone bringing us to ②, ④, or ⑥. The outputs immediately change to match the inputs. The input going down brings us back to the 000 column to states ③, ⑤, and ⑦ respectively, each with the same output as its previous state. All other states in rows ②, ④, and ⑥ are don't cares since only one variable ever changes at a time and only one input is ever up at a time.

From every stable state in the first column, when A_3 goes up, the operating point moves to ② with the output, 001. Similarly to ④ and ⑥ for the third and fourth columns.

Malformed Flow Tables: There are two general problems in writing flow tables that are usually ignored in much the same fashion as was done in the three preceding examples. These two general flow table problems are: (1) where to begin and (2) where to end?

Consider the store-carry circuit of problem 1. Here we slyly announced we would begin the flow table at the circuit operation point when all inputs and outputs are zero. But if the reader is not timid in the face of the authors' brazenness, one might question whether the statement of the problem gave reason to choose one beginning over another and whether such an initial beginning affects the flow table.

One place to start a circuit is in the state it is in when the machine is turned on. Reasonably we might argue in this example, that the carry certainly is down but the store flip-flop might go to 1 as the power supplies are turned on. Assuming an initial output of 0, this starts the operation in state ⑥ of Figure 8.21. Operation moves to ① if S is subsequently turned off, unless a carry comes along. At this time, this cannot be a true carry but a result of other flip-flops falsely going on when the machine was started up, so the operating point moves to ⑧ and gives a zero output not letting the false carry through. When the false carry is reset we go back to ⑥ and eventually to ①. Assuming the same initial input conditions but an initial output of 1, we get state ⑦ in the table. The rest of the table is as before in Figure 8.20.

The result (Figure 8.21) is a different flow table which although it will not be clear until later, requires 50% more memory elements and a much greater cost than the first flow table. We will call this type of flow table as one with a malformed initialization.

If it is possible for the machine to start in these states these remedies might be necessary but there are usually better and more economical ways of handling this problem. However, if one gets into this problem by accident, beginning the flow table in the wrong place, there is an easy way to detect this condition and remedy it. Note that internal to the flow table of Figure 8.21, there is no way of getting into states ⑥ and ⑦ and no way into ⑧ except through ⑥ or ⑦ (or by starting the machine there). If there is no way of get-

C,S				
00	01	11	10	Z
1	⑥	8	—	0
1	⑦	8	—	1
—	6	⑧	—	0
①	2	—	3	0
1	②	—	—	0
—	—	4	③	0
—	5	④	—	1
1	⑤	—	—	1

Figure 8.21. Problem of starting a sequential machine.

ting into a state, there is no reason to specify circuit action in leaving it, so the entire rows of ⑥, ⑦, and ⑧ can be deleted. This leaves our original table.

In general, in the specifications of the circuit to be synthesized, there should be some statement depicting an initial or normal "rest" state. In a counter for example, there is usually a first number in the sequence. In the store-carry circuit of problem 3, the normal inactive condition is: all inputs and output at 0. Although one *can* start anywhere in a table, there is always the possibility of starting in the middle of a long sequence without realizing all the past history of the circuit—since it hasn't been written yet. This can result in a table where this first state can be entered only when the machine is turned on. So it is best to look for a passive state with a past history remembered no longer than the last change of variable, if there appears no clear initial state.

The problem of where to end a flow table is a more difficult and serious problem.* If we didn't recognize that state ④ of Figure 8.19 should lead us back to our initial state when $B \to 0$, we might have written the flow table of Figure 8.22.

Notice that, except from the point of view of economy, there is nothing wrong with a circuit with this flow table, for the job at hand (provided it terminates somewhere returning to a proper state previously defined.) The outputs as a function of the input sequence are exactly what was required for the binary trigger operation of problem 2.

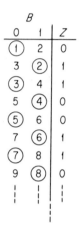

Figure 8.22. A binary trigger flow table where the designer didn't know where to stop.

This circuit has little esthetic appeal, however, and is unnecessarily costly. The trouble is that many of the states in this table are equivalent. If the designer had the somewhat belated foresight to end with state ⑧, for example and, go back to ① (or ⑤**) on the fall of B, there are tests for equivalency among states which will be developed later and these methods would reduce the table to the original one. However, these methods in general require our knowledge of all possible sequences from a given state. But if our flow table is unfinished, as in Figure 8.22, we don't know all the sequences. If we don't know all the sequences, we can't test for equivalent states. But if we can't test for equivalent states, we can't finish the flow table.

This dilemma can arise when the flow table is written sloppily* or when the problem is inadequately specified. For example, the timing chart of Figure 8.18 is just such an inadequate specification. (Ignoring the stable state markings which were assumed in syntheses), nothing whatever is told us of what is to happen to the right of this timing chart. We need some information in the original specifications which implies, or preferably explicitly states how to recognize the end of a sequence in the sense that the next state will be one already defined. Further, we must have this information for every sequence of the flow table.

* See the next chapter on Equivalence.
** Notice that if returned to five, the first part of the table, one through four, is a malformed initialization.

One other problem arises in ending a flow table, either through careless-
ness or deliberately in the design of diabolical machines. It is illustrated in
Figure 8.23. This is a flow table for a booby trap bomb. It has only two internal states, the initial primed state ① and the exploded state ②-③. It is
characteristic of exploded states that there is no way out. Once in row ②-③,
the operating point is there to stay. So we must be careful lest a row of a
flow table contain only stable states (Figure 8.23a) or lest the table contains
an unbroken cycle of states (Figure 8.23b), unless an inert lifeless machine

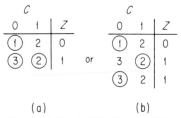

Figure 8.23. A diabolical machine.

state is our goal. Such a flow table may be said to have a malformed termi-
nation. Even the malformed is not useless as illustrated by the fact that
the authors once actually had to design the circuit of Figure 8.23 for a machine. There was only one input pulse a day, just after the machine was
started; this was the signal for other operations to start and continue, so
this pulse was held until the machine was shut off. In short, once a flow
table is completed, symptoms of malformations are states that can't be
gotten into and states that can't be gotten out of.

Merging: Although the process of synthesis was supposed to be the reverse
of analysis, the flow tables of synthesis problems 1–3 (Figures 8.16d, 19, 20)
differ from, for instance, the analysis example of Figure 8.13 in one respect.
Our synthesized primitive flow tables have uniquely one state per row
whereas Figure 8.13 has several states in each row. This combining of the
rows of the primitive flow table is called *merging*. The result, such as Figure
8.13, is called the *merged flow table*.

Notice that, as in Figure 8.13, the rows of the flow table are associated
with the states of the feedback loops. Eventually, in our synthesis we shall
assign feedback states to each row. We are now using "state" in a different
sense than before so we define an *internal state* as a state of the feedback
loops. It refers to an entire row of the flow table, thus it may also conven-
iently be called a *row state* alternatively for some contexts. For our previous
use of states referring to circled numbers, for example ① or ②, we will use
the phrase *total state*, when necessary to distinguish them from internal

states. It is implied that these states are stable. Notice that the difference between these is: *an internal state* (or *row state*) is defined independent of the input combinations by only the feedback loop state; a *total state* is defined by an internal state *and* the input combination. For example, total state ① of Figure 8.13 is defined by the internal state 0, 0 (of f_1, f_2) and the input combination, 0, 0, 0 (E_1, E_2, K). These definitions distinguish between the state of the memory elements of a sequential circuit (internal state) and the state of the whole sequential circuit including inputs, internal

$$A,B$$

	00	01	11	10	Z
Internal state (x)	4	①	2	3	0
Internal state (y)	4	1	②	3	1

Figure 8.24. A pair of similar row states for comparison.

states, and output combination (total state). These refer to the two parts of the general form of a sequential circuit, the two boxes of Figure 8.2.

Let us compare the two internal states in Figure 8.24, part of some larger flow table. These two rows states have different outputs, and different input combinations (columns) for their total states. They have just one thing in common. Their next states for each input combination are the same. When A and B both $\rightarrow 0$, the next state for both rows is stable ④. When $A \rightarrow 0$ and $B \rightarrow 1$ both row states go next to state ①.

Now a row state serves only to determine an ordered set of next states, one for each input combination. A total state serves only to determine an ordered set of output values, one for each output. Note that the outputs defined in the primitive flow table refer not to the row but to the total state. If the ordered sets of two or more row states are the same as they are in Figure 8.24, there is no need to distinguish between them; we can combine the two row states into one row, the common ordered set of next states—providing of course we don't lose the outputs associated with the total states of the two merged rows. The merger of Figure 8.24 is shown in Figure 8.25. We can justify this merged row by noting that there is no difficulty, after merging, in distinguishing total states 1 and 2 and

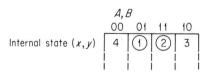

$$A,B$$

	00	01	11	10
Internal state (x,y)	4	①	②	3

Figure 8.25. Merged form of Fig. 8.24.

thus their associated outputs. Whenever the feedback loops are in the internal state x, y (Figure 8.25), and $A = 0, B = 1$, we have uniquely specified total state ① and the output should be 0 (from Figure 8.24). On the other hand, in the same internal state of the feedback loops, $A = B = 1$ uniquely specifies total state ② and Z should equal 1 (from Figure 8.24). Thus, the outputs may differ for different total states within the same row state; merging may be done independent of the outputs.

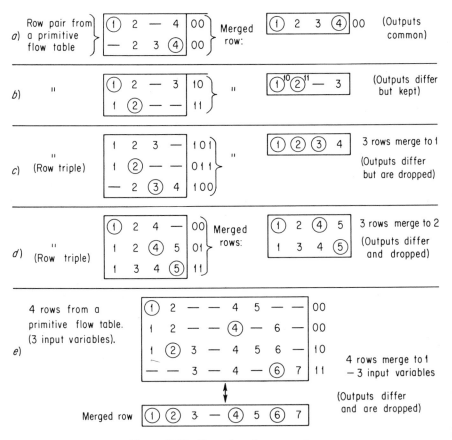

Figure 8.26. Examples of row merging.

The general rules for merging are as follows: (See Figure 8.26)

1) Two (or more) row states may be merged, irrespective of their outputs, if every next state number in corresponding columns, circled or uncircled, are the same.

2) Any number circled or not, can be merged with a "don't care" condition providing the other columns satisfy rule 1 or 2.

The procedure for merging two (or more) row states is:

1) Replace every pair (triplet, etc.) of uncircled numbers within each column by the same uncircled number in that column in the new merged row.
2) If one of the pair (triplet, etc.) of numbers is circled, replace them with the circled number.
3) A number, circled or not, and a don't care condition, gets replaced by the number. If all entries of a column in the to-be-merged rows are don't cares, they are replaced by a don't care.
4) The outputs may be dropped in the merged flow table if rows with different outputs are merged. The output information is still given in the primitive flow table. Alternatively, if useful, the outputs may be written to the upper right of their total states when rows with different outputs are merged. See Figure 8.26b, d for examples.

The justification for merging is that in so doing, we often cut down the number of feedback loops required, which, to a degree, leads to a more economical circuit. Practically, especially for the student, since almost nothing is known about choosing among the very large number of alternatives in a non-minimal row merger it is best to choose a minimal row merger which for simple cases yields at least a good, if not always the best, solution.

Examples of row merging are shown in Figure 8.26.

One pertinent question at this point: is the completely merged flow table unique?—or, more specifically, does the order in which rows are merged affect the result? The answer is, the merged table is uniquely independent of the order of merging if there are no "don't cares" in the transitions of the table. Since most flow tables arising from practical problems are dense with "don't care" entries, one should approach merging with some care. Often there are several ways one can merge a table—there may be more than one merging yielding the same number of minimal rows, and different mergings may result in different numbers of rows.

A survey first of all possible mergers is pre-requisite to choosing the minimal row merger (or any other, for that matter). For this survey we will develop a *merger diagram*. We draw lines connecting the total state numbers of all pairs of rows which can be merged. Just above and to the right of the number we put the outputs for that state. Note that we are here allowing a total state to denote a row state, but this is unambiguous since in the primitive flow table there is only one total state in each row state. As an example, look at the primitive flow table of Figure 8.27a.

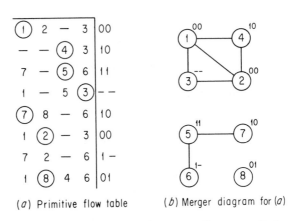

(a) Primitive flow table   (b) Merger diagram for (a)

Figure 8.27. Developing the merger diagram method.

Starting with row 1 we compare it with all succeeding rows for mergeability. We see it can merge with 4 so we draw 1 and 4 with their outputs adjacent, and connect them with a line. Next we see 1 can merge with 3 and we write 3 and its output, connecting it to 1 with a line. Finally, row 1 merges with row 2 and we connect 2 with 1. Row 1 won't merge with any other rows so we try the next row, 4. Comparing 4 with all the succeeding rows we find it merges with 2 so we connect them with a line. We need not compare a row with those above it for these merger possibilities have already been examined. (This merger diagram is shown completed in Figure 8.27b).

Next, row 5 is not already present in our diagram so we start this below in Figure 8.27b. Five merges with both 6 and 7 as indicated in the merger diagram. Note the outputs above each row number.

Note the number of possibilities. In the upper part of the merger 4 and 2, or 1 and 2 could be merged. But if, as in this case 2 is mergeable with both rows of the mergeable pair 1, 4, the reader may quickly verify that 2 may be merged with the merged row of 1 and 4; in other words 1, 2, and 4 may all be merged together. More generally, the test for mergeability of a number of rows is if all possible interconnections of merge lines exist among them. For three rows to merge, we need a triangle like that of 1, 2, and 4. There is another triangle, 1, 2, and 3, an equivalent alternate to the other, but note that since 3 and 4 are not mergeable we cannot merge 1, 2, 3, 4 all into one row. If we choose 1, 2, 4, we leave 3 alone; if we choose 1, 2, 3, we leave 4 alone. On the lower diagram, we have two choices: We could merge 5 and 7 leaving 6 alone or 5 and 6 leaving 7 alone. 8 will merge with no row.

The best rule to follow, when possible, if presented with several equivalent mergings, at least on the first pass at the problem, is the:

Multiple Merging Choice Rule:* When possible, merge so as to minimize or eliminate the output gating.

Thus if merging is done without merging rows with different outputs, it may be possible to code the feedback loops so that the outputs may be taken directly from the feedback loops. This saves the entire output gating. More important, taking the outputs from the feedback loops is the fastest way possible to get the outputs. Especially in medium and large scale computers, speed often overrides economy. Even so, since the output gating is saved, this choice frequently yields a very economical circuit. In relays, the output gating added no time delay at all. The situation is quite different for transistors. It should be emphasized that this is but a guide for the first pass at the problem and has no assurance of minimality (nor does any other rule for that matter).

Returning to our merger example of Figure 8.27 and applying the above rule we choose to merge 1, 2, and 3, all with the 00 output except for 3 with "don't cares" in both outputs which we assume to be 00. Thus 4 is left unmerged even though it *could* be merged in a different way. In the lower diagram the rule chooses to merge 5 and 6 with outputs 11 and $1-$, which becomes 11. 7 and 8 remain alone.

After our merger, we have 5 rows instead of 8. This merger choice is carried out in Figure 8.28. We show the outputs only because they are still common to each row.

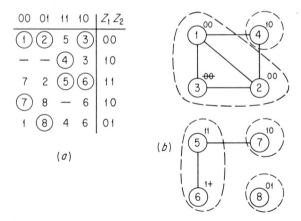

Figure 8.28. Merged flow table from Fig. 8.27. Applying the Multiple Merger Choice Rule, rows within the dotted lines of (b) above are merged yielding (a).

* This rule is derived from the experience of the authors and has been found possible and fruitful to use in a good majority of the type of sequential circuits currently used in computers.

Now that we know the rules of the game, let us practice with the simple merging of the 3 problems for which we wrote primitive flow tables.

Problem 1: The flow table from Figure 8.16d, its merger diagram and a minimum row merger in keeping with the Multiple Merger Choice Rule is shown in Figure 8.29. It would be instructive for the reader to make the merger diagram and merged flow table for problems 1, 2, and 3 (from Figures 8.16d, 19, and 20) and then compare them with the following. Thus in Figure 8.29 we went from 5 row states to 2. Note that there are two triangles in the merger diagram (Figure 8.29) with 3 common to both. The Multiple Merger Choice Rule decided the issue.

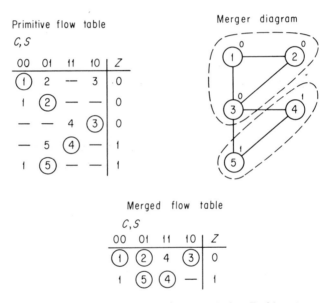

Figure 8.29. Merging techniques applied to Problem 1.

Problem 2: The merger situation is shown in Figure 8.30 (from Figure 8.19). There are no merger possibilities and so the primitive and the merged flow tables are identical.

Problem 3: Merging is unique in Figure 8.31, and the outputs for each row of the pair of merged rows is the same so we can show the outputs in the merged flow table.

Coding the Flow Table: Once we have settled on a particular merger of the flow table, we must code the row states into particular assignments of the feedback loops. The restriction on this coding is that all changes between row states must involve the change of only one feedback loop or if more than one, such that no critical race is possible.

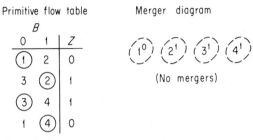

Primitive flow table

B

0	1	Z
①	2	0
3	②	1
③	4	1
1	④	0

Merged diagram also

Merger diagram

(No mergers)

Figure 8.30. Applying merger rules to Problem 2.

Primitive flow table

A_1, A_2, A_3

000	001	010	100	$Z_1 Z_2 Z_3$
①	2	4	6	000
3	②	—	—	001
③	2	4	6	001
—	—	④	—	010
⑤	2	4	6	010
7	—	—	⑥	100
⑦	2	4	6	100

Merger diagram

Merged flow table

A_1, A_2, A_3

000	001	010	100	$Z_1 Z_2 Z_3$
①	2	4	6	000
③	②	4	6	001
⑤	2	④	6	010
⑦	2	4	⑥	100

Figure 8.31. Merging applied to Problem 3.

We first try to make cyclically adjacent those row states between which there will be transitions. That is we first try to encode without races. This should be done before an actual coding is assigned. A good medium for studying adjacencies is the Karnaugh map.

First we assign a letter to each row state since the total state no longer denotes a row unambiguously in the merged flow table. Then we list those letter pairs which must be adjacent—that is, all pairs of rows with transitions between them. Then we try to fill in a Karnaugh map (not coded) for the number of feedback loops we expect to use with the letters such that these adjacencies are satisfied. If different outputs have not been merged, write these above the letters for their row in the K-map. Finally, we encode the rows and columns of the map with a cyclic code. This should be chosen, if possible, to minimize or eliminate the output matrix. A simple way of telling if the outputs can be taken directly from the feedback loops can be seen from the map. Assuming rows with different outputs have not been merged, all the outputs in a row (or column) are the same and $\frac{1}{2}$ the rows (columns) are 1 and $\frac{1}{2}$ are 0, that output may be taken from a feedback loop if it matches a cyclic encoding of the map. Since there may be different arrangements of letters on the map that satisfy the transition adjacencies, if one does not yield outputs from a feedback loop, another may.

Problem 1: Here encoding is no problem since we have only two rows in the merged flow table (Figure 8.32). No more than one feedback loop can change in a transition and since there is but one output, we assign this to the coding of the row states.

Problem 1:

f	C, S 00	01	11	10	Z
0	①	②	4	③	0
1	1	⑤	④	−	1

Figure 8.32. Problem 1 encoded, choosing values of the feedback, f, to yield the output, Z, directly.

Problem 2: The adjacencies required are listed in Figure 8.33b. Row A must be adjacent to row B because of the transition through unstable state 2. The other three adjacency requirements listed follow from similar arguments. These adjacencies are satisfied in the uncoded Karnaugh map of Figure 8.33c. The outputs of each row state are entered in the upper right hand corner of each square. Since the outputs in each column are the same, we encode the columns to correspond to the outputs. The row coding is arbitrary in the sense that no reason can be discerned at this stage for thinking one coding would be better than another. Indeed, it can be shown that the circuit in this case is invariant to the cyclic coding chosen, though this is not a general rule. We choose that of Figure 8.33d.

primitive-merged flow table

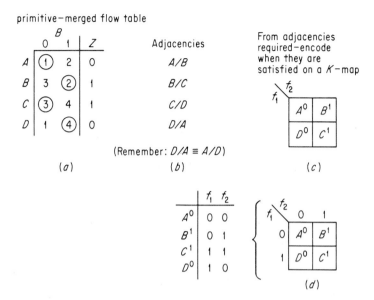

(Remember: $D/A \equiv A/D$)

(a)   (b)   (c)

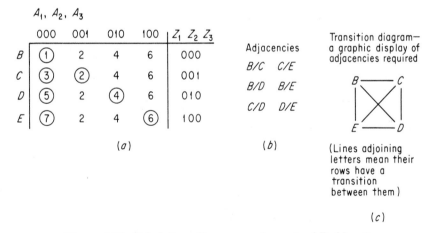

(d)

Figure 8.33. Encoding problem worked for Problem 2.

Transition diagram—
a graphic display of
adjacencies required

(a)   (b)

(Lines adjoining
letters mean their
rows have a
transition
between them)

(c)

Figure 8.34. Tabulating adjacency requirements of Problem 3.

Problem 3: Here it seems that all rows must be adjacent to each other as illustrated in the transition diagram of Figure 8.34c. This connects all rows which must be adjacent with a line. This cannot be satisfied in a Karnaugh

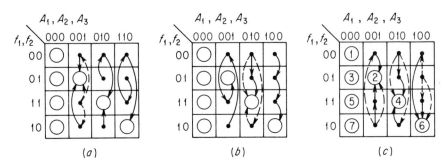

(a)   (b)   (c)

Figure 8.35. A few of many possible transition matrices which satisfy Problem 3 for a four row flow table.

map of two variables. But notice that in the second, third, and fourth columns (Figure 8.34a), where all the transitions actually occur, there is only one state in each column, thus we can set up non-critical races or multiple-transition codings. Some of the possibilities are shown in the transition matrices of Figure 8.35. There is nothing that seems to warrant one choice of coding over another at this point, so we arbitrarily choose that of Figure 8.35c.

Excitation Matrix: Now with the merged flow table and a coding for the row states, we can write the excitation matrix. We write the code of the row states in cyclic form in a column on the left of the matrix and write the input combinations across the top. Now for the corresponding squares of the flow table which are stable states, we enter in the excitation matrix the row state coding of that row. The excitation and the circuit response are the same so the circuit is stable. In the squares corresponding to nonstable entires of the flow table, we write the code of the row to which the circuit is going. "Don't cares" remain "don't cares."

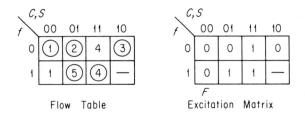

Flow Table   Excitation Matrix

Figure 8.36. The excitation matrix derived from the flow table of Problem 1.

Problem 1: Filling in the stable entries first, Figure 8.36, ①, ②, and ③ are stable and all in the row state coded zero. So a zero is entered in the corresponding squares of the excitation matrix. ④ and ⑤ both have the row state coded one, so a one is put in the corresponding squares. 4 is non-stable; we enter in its corresponding square, the coding of the row state to which the circuit is going, one. Similarly, non-stable 1 is going to the row coded zero so a zero is put in the corresponding square. The "don't care" remains a "don't care."

Problem 2: The coding assigned in Figure 8.33 codes the flow table of Figure 8.37. The stable and non-stable states in the excitation matrix are shown separately. The final matrix is shown in the right of the figure.

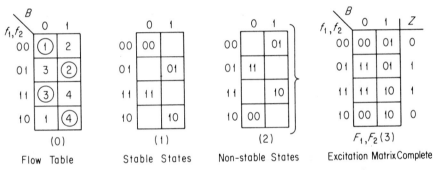

Figure 8.37. Constructing the excitation matrix for Problem 2, step by step.

Problem 3: The excitation matrix is shown in Figure 8.38. For convenience the stable states are circled. Notice that the missing columns have been inserted as "don't care" entries and a non-critical race coding has been assigned in the remaining columns except for the first. This corresponds to the transition diagram of Figure 8.35c. The only justification at this point for using the non-critical races over others is that when there is only one state in a column, experience shows that this assignment very often yields an economical circuit. This is justification enough for our first pass.

Output Matrix: Since the outputs will in the most general case, be functions of the input variables as well as all the feedback loops, the output matrix will start as the excitation matrix with the left column, the row state codings, and the top of the matrix with the input combinations.

For each stable entry of the merged flow table, we enter the output (or outputs) in the corresponding square of the output matrix. For the

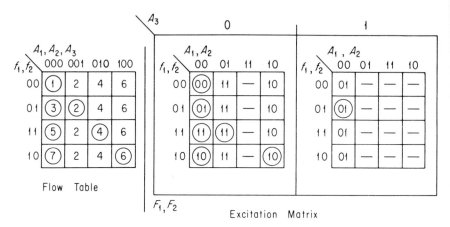

Figure 8.38. A five variable excitation matrix for Problem 3. Notice missing columns must be explicitly shown here with "don't cares."

outputs we go back to the primitive flow table. Thus, even though two total states with different outputs were merged to the same row state, here their outputs are separated.

Problems 1, 2: The output matrices for problems 1 and 2 are trivial since we merged and coded such that the outputs were available directly from feedback loops. These are shown in Figure 8.39.

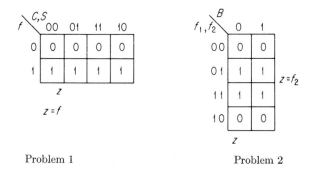

Figure 8.39. Output matrices for Problems 1 and 2.

Problem 3: Figure 8.40 shows the output matrix for all the stable states of the flow table. But what outputs are to be specified for the non-stable states left blank in the output matrix of Figure 8.40.

The statement of the problem gives us no requirements on these so we shall for now treat these as "don't cares."

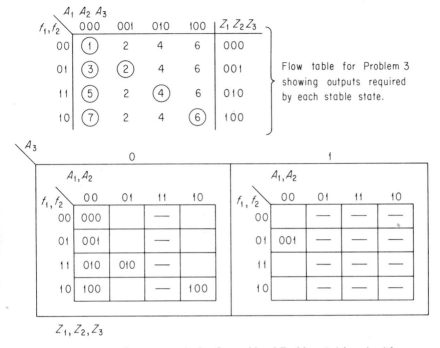

Flow table for Problem 3 showing outputs required by each stable state.

Z_1, Z_2, Z_3

Figure 8.40. Output matrix for flow table of Problem 3 (above) with stable state outputs entered.

Implementation: The final steps in synthesis is to write the excitation and output equations and implement these circuit logic blocks. It may be necessary to plot the excitation and output matrices on Karnaugh maps although for small problems such as those of this chapter, they may already be in this form. For large numbers of variables, the Quine-McCluskey method is recommended.

Problem 1: Figure 8.41 shows the equations for this problem and Figure 8.42 illustrates implementation in the $NAND$ and the NOR logic blocks.

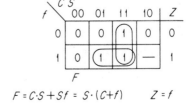

Figure 8.41. Excitation matrix equations and output equation for Problem 1.

$$F = C{\cdot}S + Sf = S{\cdot}(C+f) \qquad Z = f$$

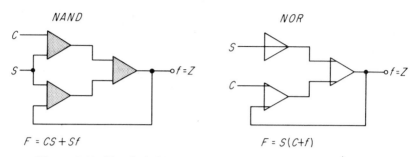

$$F = CS + Sf \qquad\qquad F = S(C+f)$$

Figure 8.42. Two logic block implementations of a solution to Problem 1.

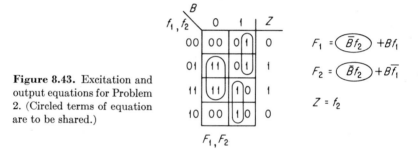

Figure 8.43. Excitation and output equations for Problem 2. (Circled terms of equation are to be shared.)

$$F_1 = \boxed{\overline{B}f_2} + Bf_1$$

$$F_2 = \boxed{\overline{B}f_2} + B\overline{f_1}$$

$$Z = f_2$$

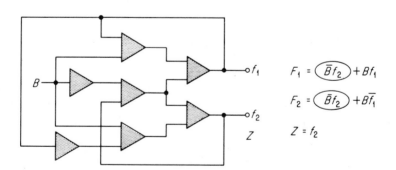

$$F_1 = \boxed{\overline{B}f_2} + Bf_1$$

$$F_2 = \boxed{\overline{B}f_2} + B\overline{f_1}$$

$$Z = f_2$$

Figure 8.44. A straightforward implementation of the excitation equations (Fig. 8.43, Problem 2).

Problem 2: Figure 8.43 derives the excitation equations for this problem. Note that for more than one feedback loop, our excitation matrix comes out in a form for which multiple-output techniques are readily adaptable. This is also true of the output matrix with more than one output.

In the excitation matrix of Figure 8.43 we can readily see the common term $B \cdot f_2$. Implementation of these equations for the $NAND$ logic block is shown in Figure 8.44.

This circuit is further discussed in a later chapter.

The reader is urged to trace through these circuits to see that they do indeed perform so as to satisfy the original specifications.

Problem 3: The excitation matrix of Figure 8.38 is somewhat tricky because of the "don't cares." We want to choose these such as to minimize the excitation circuit. A reasonable choice of "don't cares" is shown in Figure 8.45. The "don't care" entries are distinguished by a horizontal line through that box. A similar problem exists in filling in the "don't cares" of the output matrix. A reasonable choice is shown in Figure 8.46.

These are implemented in Figure 8.47.

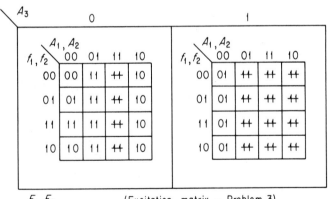

F_1, F_2 (Excitation matrix — Problem 3)

$$F_1 = A_1 + A_2 + \overline{A_3} f_1$$
$$F_2 = A_2 + A_3 + \overline{A_1} f_2$$

Figure 8.45. The excitation equations for Problem 3 derived. Entries with lines through them are the "don't care" choices made.

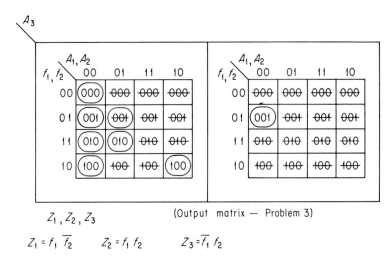

Z_1, Z_2, Z_3 (Output matrix — Problem 3)

$$Z_1 = f_1 \overline{f_2} \qquad Z_2 = f_1 f_2 \qquad Z_3 = \overline{f_1} f_2$$

Figure 8.46. Output equations derived for Problem 3.

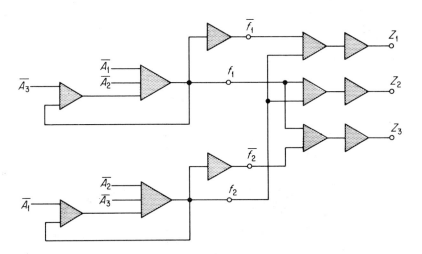

Figure 8.47. An implementation of the excitation and output equations (Figs. 8.45, 8.46) for Problem 3.

ASYNCHRONOUS TRANSISTOR SEQUENTIAL CIRCUITS II: ADVANCED THEORY

9

In the previous chapter we studied the basic methods of synthesis and analysis. We review them here.

Analysis

1. Excitation Matrix: From the block diagram of the circuit, write the excitation equations and plot on an excitation matrix.

If it is a device rather than a logic circuit so that the equations are not apparent or if there is doubt of circuit action due to hazards or races, determine the value of each entry in the matrix by assigning the corresponding values to the inputs and feedback loops and determining the resulting values impressed on the feedback loops.

2. Output Matrix: If the outputs do not come directly from the feedback loops, write the output equations and plot the output matrix. If the outputs do appear only from the feedback loops, they are already shown in the row coding of the feedback loops.

3.a Transition diagram: Plot the stable and non-stable states indicating transitions with arrows and races with dotted arrows.

OR

3.b Flow Table: Plot the stable and non-stable states using circled numbers for stable states and uncircled for non-stable states.

The transition diagram is better than the flow table if any races or multiple transitions are present, as these are difficult to indicate in the flow table.

Synthesis

1. Flow table: Convert the word specifications to flow table form. If feasible, a timing chart can be useful. Make sure all possible sequences are accounted for.

2. Test for equivalent states (see next section).

3. Merge: Draw the merger diagram and merge to minimize the output matrix if possible.

4. Encode the merged flow table: Determine the adjacency requirements and plot the rows on a Karnaugh map to satisfy these (if possible). Look for possible non-critical races that may be useful. If transition requirements cannot be met, another feedback loop must be added. Encode the Karnaugh map with a cyclic code to minimize the output matrix if possible.

5. Excitation and output matrix: Using the code assigned, fill in the excitation and output matrices. If the outputs may be taken from the feedback loops, the output matrix is not necessary.

6. Implement in logic blocks: Using any "don't cares" to simplify the excitation equations and output equations, implement in the given logic blocks.

Equivalence

Figure 9.1 shows part of a flow table for a sequential circuit. Suppose we look only at the terminal operation of this circuit such that we can observe only the outputs for each input we apply. But, it is easy to see from the flow table that for every allowable input starting in either state ① or ③ gets us to the same next state, regardless of the starting state. This means, of course, that the outputs will be the same after one change of input regardless of the initial state. Since both states ① and ③ have the same steady output as well, there is no way we can tell state 1 and 3 apart by observing only the terminal action of the circuit. This means that we can combine the two states and replace those two rows of the flow table as in Figure 9.2.

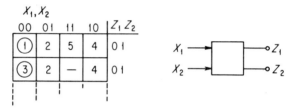

Figure 9.1. Equivalence example.

Notice that row merging while reducing the number of rows does not change the number of total states as does removing equivalent states.

This simple case of equivalence (above) can be tested for by looking for total states (*in the primitive flow table*) with the same outputs (for each input condition) and with identical next states. A "don't care", of course, can be equated with the same next state as in Figure 9.2.

More complicated equivalence can occur, however.

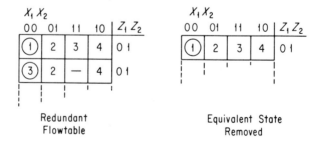

Figure 9.2. Equivalence removed.

Equivalency Condition

Two total states (in the primitive flow table) are equivalent if and only if their outputs (for each input condition) are the same (within a "don't care") and there exists no sequence of inputs starting from one of the states that gives a different sequence of outputs if started in the other state.

Essentially this says, if there is no detectable difference at the output of the circuit no matter which of two stable states we start in for all possible sequences of inputs, there is no need to distinguish between the states.

In testing a flow table for equivalencies, the primitive flow table should be used and equivalencies considered only between stable states in the same column. After equivalencies are removed, merging can be performed. If merging is done first, some possible equivalencies may be lost.

00	01	11	10	$Z_1 Z_2 Z_3$
(1)	2	7	3	0 0 0
1	(2)	7	8	0 1 0
9	6	5	(3)	0 1 0
10	2	5	(4)	1 1 1
11	6	(5)	4	1 0 1
9	(6)	5	8	0 1 0
11	6	(7)	4	1 0 1
9	2	7	(8)	1 1 1
(9)	6	5	3	0 0 0
(10)	2	5	3	0 0 1
(11)	2	5	8	0 0 1

Primitive Flowtable

00	01	11	10	$Z_1 Z_2 Z_3$
(1)	2	7	3	0 0 0 A
(4)	6	5	3	
1	(2)	7	8	
9	(6)	5	8	0 1 0 B
9	6	5	(3)	
10	2	5	(4)	1 1 1 C
9	2	7	(8)	
11	6	(5)	4	1 0 1 D
11	6	(7)	4	
(10)	2	5	3	0 0 1 E
(11)	2	5	8	

Partitioned Flowtable

Figure 9.3. Partitioning for equivalence test.

The first step is to partition the rows of the flow table into groups with the same outputs. The flow table of Figure 9.3 is an example to be tested for equivalency. Its partitioning is also shown with each partition labeled with a letter for reference.

Since the first test for equivalence is that the two states have the same outputs, we can restrict our comparisons to states within the same partitions, and which occur under the same input conditions. (Note that permitting the order of the rows does not change the flow table.) The simplest case of equivalence is found in partition D. States ⑤ and ⑦ have the same outputs and the same next states so they are equivalent. The succeeding argument is summarized in Figure 9.4.

1 and 9 are potentially equivalent in partition A; 1 is equivalent to 9 if 2 is equivalent to 6 and 5 is equivalent to 7. This is so if the corresponding next states are equivalent. We have already shown that 5 is equivalent to 7 so it remains to test 2 and 6. 2 is equivalent to 6 if 1 is equivalent to 9. But our original problem was: is 1 equivalent to 9? We can resolve this circular argument by observing the outputs for all possible sequences among these states. There is no detectable difference so we may say the states 1 and 9, 2 and 6, are equivalent.

In general, we can say that if state a is equivalent to b if c is equivalent to d, and c equivalent to d if a is equivalent to b, then both a is equivalent to b and c is equivalent to d.

State 4 is equivalent to 8 if 5 is equivalent to 7 which was already shown.

It remains to test the last possibility that 10 is equivalent to 11. But non-stable 3 and 8 each go to different partitions so the next outputs will differ and 10 cannot be equivalent to 11.

We can now replace each set of equivalent states by the state of the set with the lowest number (arbitrarily) and change every appearance of the other numbers of the set in the flow table to this number. The primitive flow table for this example with redundancy removed is shown in Figure 9.5.

Now the table can be merged to further reduce the number of rows.

The question arises whether removing equivalencies is unique, that is, is the flow table with all equivalencies removed independent of the order in which they were removed? Huffman has proved that it is unique when there either are no "don't care" entries in either the flow table or outputs, or if the flow table satisfies a uniformity of "don't cares" condition.

A flow table is said to have uniform "don't cares" if every row of an equivalency partition has "don't cares" (if at all) only in the same columns. Examples of parititions meeting this requirement is shown in Figure

*5 ≡ 7
1 ≡ 9 if (2 ≡ 6)(5 ≡ 7)
2 ≡ 6 if (1 ≡ 9)(5 ≡ 7)
*1 ≡ 9
*2 ≡ 6
4 ≡ 8 if 5 ≡ 7
*4 ≡ 8
10 ≡ 11 if 3 ≡ 8
3 ≢ 8
10 ≢ 11

("∗" means the result of an equivalence argument)

Figure 9.4. Equivalent states of Fig. 9.3.

00	01	11	10	$Z_1 Z_2 Z_3$
①	2	5	3	000
1	②	5	4	010
1	2	5	③	010
1	2	5	④	111
1	2	⑤	4	101
⑩	2	5	3	001
⑪	2	5	8	001

Figure 9.5. Equivalent states combined.

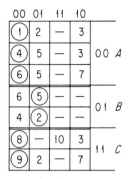

	00	01	11	10	
①	2	—	3		
④	5	—	3	00	A
⑥	5	—	7		
6	⑤	—	—		
4	②	—	—	01	B
⑧	—	10	3		
⑨	2	—	7	11	C

Figure 9.6. Partition A, B have uniform "don't care's"; C has non-uniform "don't care's."

9.6, partitions A and B. Non-uniform "don't cares" are shown in partition C.

An example of a non-unique flow table is given in one partition of Figure 9.7. Assuming we have already determined that 5 and 8, 7 and 9 are not equivalent, we can see that 1 is equivalent to 3, and 4 is equivalent to both 2 and 3, but 2 and 3 are not equivalent.

In Figure 9.8, two different partial flow tables are shown resulting from the two different choices ($4 \equiv 3$ and $4 \equiv 2$). Clearly the figure 9.7 does not have a unique equivalent without redundant states.

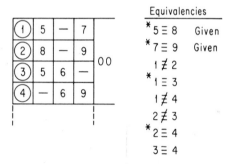

	00			Equivalencies
①	5	—	7	*$5 \equiv 8$ Given
②	8	—	9	*$7 \equiv 9$ Given
③	5	6	—	$1 \not\equiv 2$
④	—	6	9	*$1 \equiv 3$
				$1 \not\equiv 4$
				$2 \not\equiv 3$
				*$2 \equiv 4$
				$3 \equiv 4$

Figure 9.7. A non-unique partition.

				00
①	5	6	7	
②	8	6	9	

				00
①	—	5	7	
②	8	—	9	
③	5	6	9	

Figure 9.8. Non-unique reductions of Fig. 9.7.

Hazards*

Until now we have been working with a model of transistor circuits which was admittedly an oversimplification. We assumed the delays in each transistor and its associated circuit were fixed and equal and could be

* Based on: Huffman, "The Design and Use of Hazard-Free Switching Networks," JACM, v. 4, 41, Jan. 1957, pp. 47–62.

lumped at one point in the feedback loop. This model was useful in developing the theory of asynchronous sequential circuits, but we now need to study the effects of deviations from this model. From this point of view any significant deviations from desired operation reflect themselves as *hazards*, as potential or actual malfunctions of the circuit. All of these arise from distributions of delays in the circuit other than as assumed in our model.

All hazards arise from significant differences in delays among paths propagating the same signal. There are four kinds of hazards, three of which arise in the circuit when one variable is changing; they can be detected and corrected, two logically, the third with delay insertion (or deletion). These latter three are 1) the static hazard, 2) the dynamic hazard, 3) the essential hazard. The fourth kind of hazard arises when more than one variable is changing and will be called a multi-variable hazard. This can be of any of the three above kinds and may sometimes be handled logically or more usually by delay insertion or deletion.

The static and dynamic hazards are characterized by the fact that they both are caused by different path lengths of a signal in reaching the feedback loop response, whereas the essential hazard is caused by different path lengths for a signal to two different feedback loop responses. Static and dynamic hazards affect combinational circuits as well; the essential hazard occurs only in sequential circuits. But static and dynamic hazards in combinatorial circuits are significant only as they affect the operation of any sequential circuit at their outputs—thus all hazards are essentially sequential problems.

The static hazard causes an output to change transiently when it was supposed to remain static at one value during the change of a single variable. It is significant when the false transient is long enough to cause an unwanted transition in the sequential circuit resulting in the circuit changing state when it was not supposed to, or changing to a wrong state. *The static hazard is distinguished from the dynamic one in that it is caused by the differing delays of a signal between two paths to a single feedback response—the signal and its inversion.* The usual culprit is the delay through an inverter relative to the uninverted signal's path. The static hazard may be eliminated logically, or diminished by inserting delay.

The dynamic hazard causes an output to change three or more times when it is supposed to change only once during the change of a single variable. Thus if following an input variable change an output is supposed to go 11110000 a dynamic hazard can cause the changes 111101000. If the first and second changes both last long enough to cause transitions, the sequential circuit may malfunction and end in the wrong state. *The dynamic hazard differs from the static hazard in that there must be three or more differing delay paths of a signal to a single feedback response—one or more are the signal and its inversion. The dynamic hazard occurs only in factored circuits.* It may be eliminated logically, or it may be diminished by inserting delay.

The essential hazard causes a false transition to an improper state of a sequential circuit during the change of a single input variable. It appears only in circuits with at least two feedback loops. *The essential hazard is caused by differing delays of a signal to different feedback responses; it occurs only in sequential circuits.* This hazard cannot be eliminated logically, but can only be eliminated by delay. Its effects can be *diminished* logically however.

There are also multi-variable static, dynamic, and essential hazards involving the same conditions but several variables rather than a single one changing. In certain special cases, similar techniques will eliminate or diminish these hazards. *Generally,* however, *these cannot be wholly eliminated* which is one reason why asynchronous circuits try to change only one variable at a time.

Static Hazards: Consider the circuit of Figure 9.9 and the effects of a delay through the inverter which is of the same order as the AND and OR in series.*

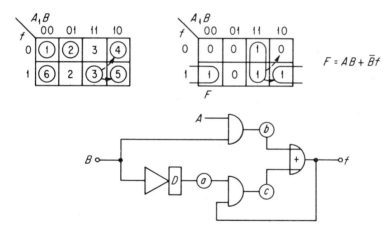

$$F = AB + \bar{B}f$$

Figure 9.9. Example of a static hazard.

* This situation can easily occur in many different situations. A few examples are: In some saturating circuits a turn off time of one transistor can overlap several turn on times and two or more turn off times of other transistors. Also, in diode circuits the diodes can be very much faster than the transistor inverter. Different wire lengths between transistors in the back panel wiring may make wire capacitive delay significant in one path relative to another.

Starting in state ③ of Figure 9.9, if B goes to 0, f should remain 1 (state ⑤). When B goes to 0 node b, which was holding f at 1, drops to 0. Node a is supposed to change to a 1 and together with f raise node c to 1 which in turn holds f up when b drops. But because of the inverter delay, node a is still a zero when b goes down, and f drops. If a changed to one in time before f drops entirely, there will be but a transient negative blip in f. But, with the inverter delay, f can go to 0 before a changes to a 1. Thus in trying to pass from state ③ to ⑤ the static hazard has jumped the circuit to ④ which is stable and incorrect. The static hazard has caused a malfunction.

In this instance the delay need not be large; the delay through one AND (node b) need only be less than through an inverter and an AND (node c). This is a static hazard since the output was supposed to remain static or constant at 1 during the transition.

Huffman has shown that the existence of potential static hazards may be determined directly from the excitation matrix (or Karnaugh map), and how they may be eliminated by logic means. The problem arises when an output or feedback response is to remain constant during a transition which is not contained in a loop of the mapping. In Figure 9.9, for example, the excitation matrix shows the hazard occurs when trying to make a transition from the AB loop (state ③) to the $\bar{B}f$ loop (state ⑤). The transition does not occur within a loop, but between loops. This means that two gates, corresponding to the two loops, are trying to change at the same time. As we leave the AB loop that gate is turning off; as we enter the $\bar{B}f$,

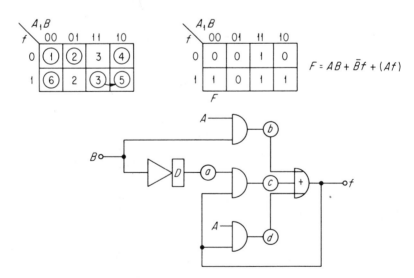

Figure 9.10. Static hazard removed from the circuit of Fig. 9.9.

that gate is turning on. We have a race between them and if AB goes off before $\bar{B}f$ goes on (node b goes to 0 before node c goes to 1), then we may lose the output signal transiently or permanently if it gets latched in.

The way to eliminate a static hazard is to add a redundant gate (loop) covering both the initial and terminal state of the transition and thus the transition itself as shown in Figure 9.10. This gate (loop) will be a constant 1 during the transition, unaffected by the single variable change, and will hold the output at 1 while the other gates are changing. The reader may verify this by tracing the same transition as above, from ③ to ⑤ in the circuit of Figure 9.10 and see how the redundant gate, node d ensures no hazard condition occurs and the transition occurs properly.

Anytime a transition between loops of 1's occurs where the transition is not covered by a loop, a static hazard exists. Depending on the distribution of delays in the circuit, the hazard may or may not cause malfunction. The hazard may be eliminated by adding a redundant gate whose loop covers the transition. Sometimes inserting delay in the other path to ensure its change won't reach the output first is sufficient to diminish the likelihood of the hazard causing malfunction. However, there are static hazard conditions where no amount of delay can remove the hazard; indeed adding delay to remove one hazard may simply create another. For example in Figure 9.10, the hazard occurs in the transition from ③ to ⑤ if node b drops before c comes up. So we might insert enough delay at b to ensure B will pass through the inverter, the delay (node a) and reach node c before B affects node b. Then this hazard would not occur on this transition. But, now, note that we have ensured that a hazard will occur in

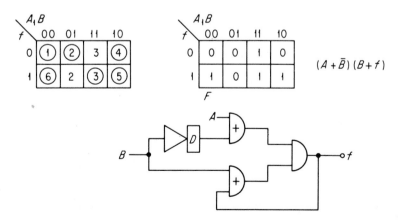

Figure 9.11. A static hazard in the zeros but one which does not cause malfunction.

the transition from ⑤ to ③. Our inserted delay ensures that b will not come up before c goes down—thus malfunction. Quite often also, especially in factored circuits, the path length delays may be just such as to remove the occurrence of the hazard, so this should be checked before redundant hazard terms are added.

The static hazard can occur in the zeros of the function as well. The excitation matrix of Figure 9.9 is written from the zeros in product of sums form in Figure 9.11. In the transition leaving the loop $(B + f)$ (state ①) and going to the loop $(A + \bar{B})$ (state ②), we do not make the transition within a loop; thus two gates (loops) will be changing at the same time while trying to hold the output to zero. With the delay as shown, the race can result in f transiently going to 1. Note that in this instance this will simply put the circuit in non-stable 2 and it will return to its proper state and no malfunction will occur providing the blip on f doesn't affect the output network it is driving. Malfunctions in state transitions can occur equally well in the zeros, however.

Fortunately, Huffman has proved that if you eliminate (logically) the hazards in the ones (zeros) there can be no hazards in the zeros (ones). Thus we need get rid of only the one, the other will follow.

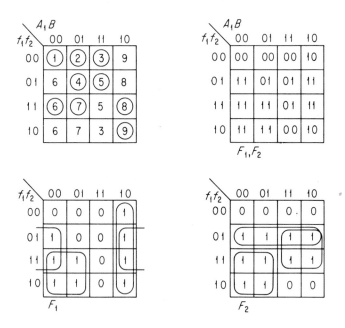

Figure 9.12. A static hazard in the feedback loops.

Figure 9.12 shows that static hazards can occur in the feedback variables. Here there is a static hazard in f_2 in the transition 6 to ⑦. Notice the static hazard also in the transition from ⑥ to 5. One must be careful here. The static hazard can often cause failure in only one direction of a transition. Since in the flow table of Figure 9.12, we can never make the transition from 5 to ⑦ the presence of the hazard in the delay distributions of the circuit must be checked. The same holds for the hazard from 6 to ⑥. Note the hazard between ④ and ⑦ in f_2. This is a mild trap. Despite the hazard, there is no possible transition between these states so we needn't worry about the hazard. The same could hold for the transition ⑦ to 5. We must go back to the primitive flow table to determine if a transition actually can occur between these two states. In merging we have lost this information. This is an important step in removing static hazards; after detecting a hazard check in the primitive flow table if that transition is possible.

The theory for static hazards in factored circuits is not well developed, but they may be detected by looking for a variable change affecting more than one gate and during which the output is to remain static, but there is no gate unchanging which holds the output static. In general this is not simple to test nor locate, but is a matter of exhaustion.

The Dynamic Hazard: Consider the circuit of Figure 9.13 during the transition ⑨ to 10 to ⑩. When B goes from one to zero f should also go from one to zero. To start with B at 1, a is holding the output up. When B goes to zero, a will go up and the output will drop before the change in B at b can affect c, when it does, b goes to 1. Suppose d is delayed, then c drops to zero and the output goes back up. Finally d will drop and c goes up with the output going down again. In the transition, f has gone from 1 to zero: 1010 in this sequence. This may result in a false input and subsequent malfunction of the sequential circuit fed by this circuit although it causes no malfunction in this circuit other than transient. Note that there are three paths from the input B signal to the feedback response; this is a necessary condition; also necessary is that at least one of the paths involves the inversion of the variable and at least one does not.

The necessary and sufficient conditions for a dynamic hazard is that at least two signals B and $\overline{B}$ appear in the expression for making the output a 1, and at least two signals (not the same two though one may be in common) B and $\overline{B}$ which appear in the expression for making the output a zero. The factored equations from the circuit of Figure 9.13 are

$$F = (AB_1 + \overline{A} + \overline{C})(\overline{A} + \overline{B_3})C + B_2f$$

For the transition condition, A, C, are 1 and F becomes

$$F' = \left(B_1\overline{B_3}\right) + B_2f$$

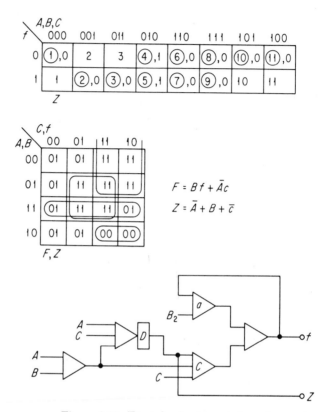

Figure 9.13. Example of a dynamic hazard.

The circled term contains the necessary two B literals, one a complement. The complement of F' gives the terms holding F to 0 in this condition:

$$F' = (\overline{B}_2 + f)(\overline{B}_1 + B_3) = \overline{B}_1\overline{B}_2 + \overline{B}_2B_3 + \overline{B}_1f + \overline{B}_3$$

The circled term contains the necessary B literals, not the same two, one a complement.

The dynamic hazard may sometimes be handled with delay, but sometimes it is simpler to refactor the function to remove the condition. Although generally, the dynamic hazard is not an important problem, particular attention to be given to it if the $NAND$ or NOR functions are being used. Especially the techniques of this book tend with their multiple inversions in factored $NAND$ circuits with redundancy to generate these dynamic hazard type situations. This hazard does not cause malfunctions easily, but if observed can be removed easily since it is a result of the circuit structure, not of the logic structure of the problem.

The Essential Hazard:* Unlike the previously discussed hazards, the essential hazard manifests itself only in sequential circuits. The essential hazard also is unique in that it is not a result of the particular logic design, as in the static and dynamic hazards, but inherent in the logical structure of certain sequential problems. Thus, unlike the other hazards, it cannot be removed by a logical change in the design. The best that can be done is that delay may be inserted to diminish the likelihood of malfunction due to the hazard. Unger has shown that the presence of an essential hazard can be seen by the presence of a particular structure in the flow table.* That structure is exhibited in the partial table of Figure 9.14a. Two columns of the flow table (merged or primitive) must have the structure shown (at least) where the asterisked box may be any entry except non-stable 2. If the hazard causes malfunction, the circuit will follow a transition from non-stable 2 to the state entry in the box with the asterisk instead of to stable ②

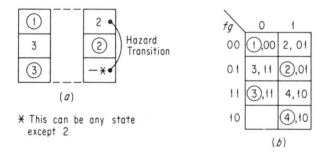

(a)

* This can be any state except 2

Figure 9.14. The flow table structure signalling the presence of an essential hazard.

We will trace the overall operation of the circuit (independent of how it is designed) in the combination flow table and excitation matrix of Figure 9.14b. Suppose the circuit is in state ① and the input goes to 1. Further let us suppose the input signal change is delayed in the circuit in reaching feedback f after the signal change appears at g. Then g seeing itself in state ① and the input going to 1, moves over, in operation to 2 where it sees an excitation changing it to 1. Responding to this excitation g's operation moves down to ②. Meanwhile, back at the f feedback, it as yet sees no change in the input so it thinks it is still in ①. But then f sees g

---

* Unger's thesis, MIT. The essential hazard turns out to be what Huffman had previously observed in his paper on hazards, what he called multiple-order hazards.

go to 1, since f is 0, fg is 1, and f thinks it is still in the left column, f obedi-ently moves down to unstable 3, sees the excitation and goes to a 1. At this moment, as f is going to 1, f is in state 3 and g is in state ②. When f becomes 1, both feedbacks see the response as 11, f moves down to ③ and g down to 4. Now g's excitation turns it off and as the input change finally reaches f, it moves over a column to 4 and as g becomes zero, together, f and g move down to ④ and the wrong hazard transition has occurred.

Note that if the input change still did not reach f at ③, g going to zero in 4 would move the operation of g to ④ and of f to the blank box below. If the excitation to f in the blank box were a 1 f would stay there until the input change arrived and then move over to ④. If it were a zero, however, f would turn off and return to ① and g to 2 and the whole thing would start all over. This is because if there is, say, a non-stable 1 (excitation 00) in the blank box, when f moves there with g in ④ we have entered another essential hazard starting from ④ as before we started in ①. The symmetry of the table with a 1,00 in the blank box shows there is an essential hazard starting in every state; the structure of Figure 9.14a appears beginning in any of them. Thus, with this particular flow table (this is a binary trigger, see Figure 9.15 these multiple essential hazards make it possible that a transition from any state could take the circuit into any of the states de-pending on the length of the delay. However, such delays would have to be considerable; besides one malfunction is as bad as any other.

Let us see, in a circuit, how the essential hazard can cause malfunction. The binary trigger of Figure 9.15 has been designed, duplicating the shared term so that the input T could be clearly delayed to f and not to g. The design is deliberately simple rather than economical to make clear the op-eration. For simplicity in following the signal changes assume the gates with no delay and the feedback loops respond in synchronism with one unit delay. The signals at each node are shown at times t_0 to t_4 (see flow table Figure 9.15) with the circuit starting at t_0 in state ① and input T going to 1 at time t_1 and remaining there. The two 2 unit delays suffice to delay the input change from affecting the f response relative to its path to g just long enough to cause malfunctioning from one essential hazard.

The significance of the essential hazard, besides the fact that it cannot logically be removed is that its symptomatic flow table structure is inherent in all asynchronous binary triggers, shift registers, rings, and counters; in short most of the sequential circuits normally used in a computer. How-ever, circuits can be designed which are relatively insensitive to malfunc-tions from the essential hazard. Several of them are derived in the next chapter. Another much used technique, since most computers are syn-chronous systems designed from asynchronous sequential elements, is to use a clock pulse to give the effect of inserted delay.

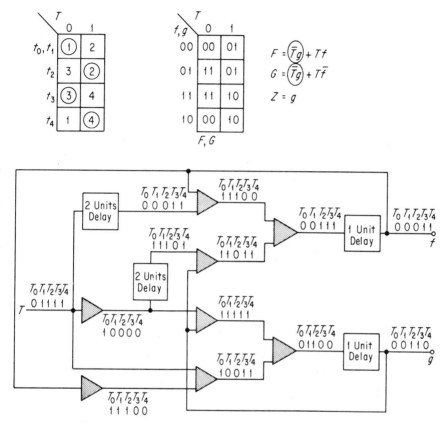

$$F = \left(\overline{Tg}\right) + Tf$$

$$G = \left(\overline{Tg}\right) + T\overline{f}$$

$$Z = g$$

Figure 9.15. The essential hazard illustrated in a binary trigger. (Gates assumed with zero delay and feedback loops respond in syncronism with one unit delay. Signals are shown for starting in state 1 at time T_0, and with T going to 1 at time T_1 and remaining there.)

Merging-Unmerging

So far we have approached merging with the idea that all redundant row states should be merged; that is, we should minimize memory. In terms of Huffman's original derivation, which was for relays, this was a reasonable rule, most, though not all of the time. Memory was represented by coils which were expensive; logic was represented by contacts which were inexpensive. Huffman realized nonetheless that although the cost ratio of memory to logic was high, there were still cases where minimizing memory was overly expensive in logic.

In transistor switching circuits the cost ratio is only two to one. A bi-stable circuit (memory without logic) costs generally only two logic blocks. Thus if adding a memory element saves more than two gates it pays to have the redundant memory where it often does not pay to minimize memory. A typical case in which this is very often true for both relays and transistors is the ring. (There are exceptions, especially for very short rings.)

Example I: This is a circuit which has a train of clock pulses (usually) for an input and has one output go up alone for the first pulse, another for the second and so on until the last output after which we start over. For a 15 stage ring there are one input and 15 outputs, only one of the outputs being up at a time.

For speed and economy usually the driving oscillator is run at half required frequency and the timing pulses are counted both on the rise of the oscillator and on the fall. Thus, we need only 16 rows in the flow table, 8 in the column when the oscillator is up and 8 when it is down. The flow table is shown in Figure 9.16. This example will further explain how a practical problem is carried out from start to finish. A reasonable cyclic coding is shown also. This primitive table contains no equivalencies or mergeable rows so it represents the minimal memory requirement for the problem, four feedback loops. Excitation matrix and equations are shown in Figure

$f_1 f_2 f_3 f_4$	Clock 0	1	Z_1	Z_2	Z_3	Z_4	Z_5	Z_6	Z_7	Z_8	Z_9	Z_{10}	Z_{11}	Z_{12}	Z_{13}	Z_{14}	Z_{15}	Z_{16}
0 0 0 0	(1)	2	1	0	0	0	0	0	0	0	0	0	0	0	0	0	0	0
0 0 0 1	3	(2)	0	1	0	0	0	0	0	0	0	0	0	0	0	0	0	0
0 0 1 1	(3)	4	0	0	1	0	0	0	0	–	–	–	–	–	–	–	0	0
0 0 1 0	5	(4)	0	0	0	1	0	0	0	0	–	–	–	–	–	–	0	0
0 1 1 0	(5)	6	0	0	0	0	1	0	0	0	0	–	–	–	–	–	0	0
0 1 1 1	7	(6)	0	–	–	–	–	1	–	–	–	–	–	–	–	–	0	0
0 1 0 1	(7)	8	0	–	–	–	–	–	1	–	–	–	–	–	–	–	0	0
0 1 0 0	9	(8)	0	–	–	–	–	–	–	1	–	–	–	–	–	–	0	0
1 1 0 0	(9)	10	0	–	–	–	–	–	–	–	1	–	–	–	–	–	0	0
1 1 0 1	11	(10)	0	–	–	–	–	–	–	–	–	1	–	–	–	–	0	0
1 1 1 1	(11)	12	0	–	–	–	–	–	–	–	–	–	1	–	–	–	0	0
1 1 1 0	13	(12)	0	–	–	–	–	–	–	–	–	–	–	1	–	–	0	0
1 0 1 0	(13)	14	0	–	–	–	–	–	–	–	–	–	–	–	1	–	0	0
1 0 1 1	15	(14)	0	–	–	–	–	–	–	–	–	–	–	–	–	1	0	0
1 0 0 1	(15)	16	0	–	–	–	–	–	–	–	–	–	–	–	–	–	1	0
1 0 0 0	1	(16)	0	–	–	–	–	–	–	–	–	–	–	–	–	–	0	1

Figure 9.16. Flow table for sixteen-output counter.

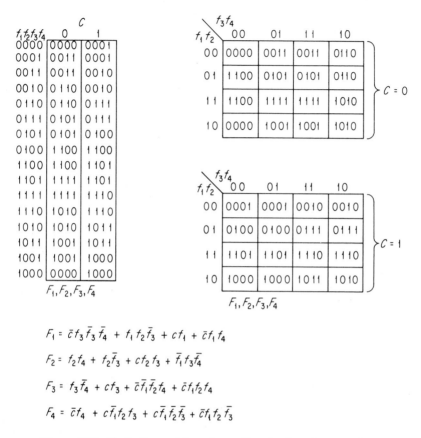

Figure 9.17. Excitation matrix and equations for four-stage counter.

9.17. Since this circuit is usually run fairly fast, we cannot go beyond 3 stages of gating which when including the output decoder means only two stages of gating. To this circuit of the counter, we must add a four bit binary decoder to the base 16. Since the speed requirements (and economy often as well) requires one level of gating in the decoder we need 16 four input "and" gates for the outputs.

The equations of Figure 9.17 together with the decoder have for the total circuit:

30 terms (including inverters as a term)
127 literals (maximum number of literals to a term: 4)
f_1 drives 14 loads f_1 drives 12 loads
f_2 drives 17 loads f_2 drives 10 loads
f_3 drives 14 loads f_3 drives 13 loads

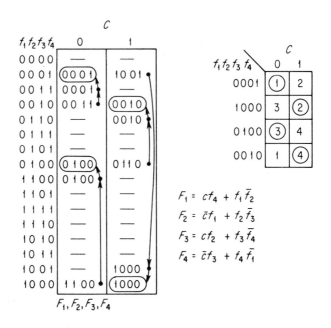

Figure 9.18. One solution to the ring problem.

f_4 drives 14 loads f_4 drives 11 loads
(including output matrix—each drives 8 there)
c drives 4 $\bar{c}$ drives 6

We might, however, have traded logic for memory or feedback. One can always trade off between memory and logic just as we can between time and logic as in a parallel versus a serial machine. The relationships among time, memory and logic is not sufficiently understood, but they are of great significance to the logical designer.

In this case we could have taken what would appear here a rather extreme step and follow in the steps of the pragmatic rule: always try to eliminate the output matrix. This would require assigning one feedback loop for each row of the table such that only one memory element would be on at a time corresponding to the output required at that time. These 16 feedback loops leave us with a 17 variable problem.

It is an orderly one, however, it is in fact iterative.

This, coupled with tremendous redundancy in the feedbacks, makes it easy to handle. Let us take just a fair output ring to simplify the problem although only two are sufficient. Note at this point that guessing the iterative nature of this solution has saved us from a 17 variable problem.

In Figure 9.18, using the flow table and its assumed codings as we decided, the circled excitations are given as out stable states. The remaining boxes must still be filled in for the transitions. There are many possibilities but in a source of timing signals we cannot afford any false outputs so only the presently activated feedback loop and the activated one can go up. This almost implies the transitions in the non-stable excitations of Figure 9.18; this also yields a circuit with many desirable properties. Implementations are shown in Figure 9.19. It should be obvious that this circuit may be extended to any number of stages and in particular to 16. Notice the range of output requirements it satisfies using but three $NANDs$. Each bit position has three outputs. Outputs 1 in Figure 9.19 are outputs gated from the clock pulse. If these are used we get non-overlapping timing pulses out. This is sometimes a requirement. The 2 and 3 are outputs complementary to each other and give reliably over-lapping timing pulses, i.e., or overlapping between successive stages. This may equally as well be the requirement or all outputs could be used mixed.

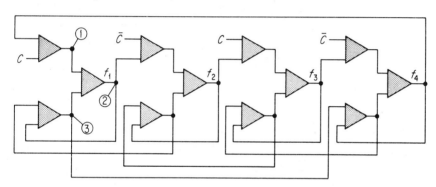

Figure 9.19. Implementation of equations from Fig. 9.18.

The circuit is very reliable because of the asynchronous feedback loops feeding back from each stage to the previous one. This essentially tells the preceding stage that the information is latched so it is all right to reset the old information. Thus, the circuit operates reliably for widely varying circuit delays within some bounds set by the clock frequency used.

One other point, in the final computer packages, the two clock pulses or shift signals "C and $\bar{C}$," supposed to be complements of each other but they may get shipped some distance or go through gating skewing them in time. Thus, it is possible both C and $\bar{C}$ might be up at the same time for short durations or they might both be down. The reader may see for himself this will not change the expected circuit action providing of course the sequence of pulses and minimum pulse width considerations are not lost.

Before leaving the 16 feedback loop approach, it might be instructive to consider one other choice for the transitions of Figure 9.18. They are shown in Figure 9.20.

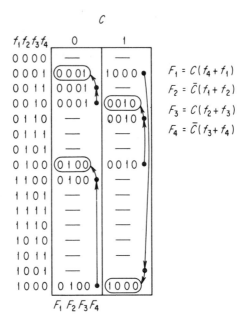

Figure 9.20. Second solution to the ring problem.

Here we've chosen to give excitations requiring double changes of variable to simplifying the logic, but keeping in mind, not a race, but a delay on the output of each feedback in the ring. Thus, for example, when we move from stable state (0001) in Figure 9.20 to the $C = 1$ column, the logis is different than that of Figure 9.18, but because of the delay in the fall of f_4, the excitation we see is (1001) even though the logic says (1000). Since we move through this state fairly fast this is all we need ask the delay. In Figure 9.21, transistors were used for the delay, but a delay

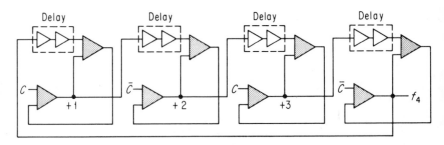

Figure 9.21. Implementation of the equations of Fig. 9.20.

time would do as well. There delay was used to simplify the circuit almost trivially. The reader will have noticed that there is delay only between every other stage. This is because the C pulse usually must be inverted to get $\overline{C}$ so $\overline{C}$ is always later than C giving us the effect of delay between every other stage.

This last circuit lacks many of the advantages of the first; it has but one non-overlapping output. If the inserted delay is too short, the circuit may lose the pulse; if too long, it will show the frequency it may be operated at. It requires a definite timed relation between C and $\overline{C}$. Nonetheless, this circuit has been used successfully on many occasions.

Now we may return to our comparison of the first timing counter using minimum memory of four feedback loops and that of Figures 9.18 and 9.19 of 16 feedback loops. The latter uses three terms and six literals per stage. A comparison table tells a story which is independent for a broad category of circuit costs:

4 feedbacks	16 feedbacks
30 terms	48 terms
127 literals	96 literals
13 average loading outputs	2 average output loading
17 maximum output loading	2 maximum output loading
4 loads for C	8 loads for C
6 loads for $\overline{C}$	8 loads for $\overline{C}$

We may draw several conclusions from this table; for the 4 feedback solution either the circuits must have very great drive or one will have to resort to drivers, an added cost. Also most logic blocks require five inputs. The other circuit outputs never drive more than two inputs.

In conclusion, the main advantages of the redundant feedback approach would appear to be, less requirements on the fan in and out of the blocks and not the least elimination of the output gating.

This last statement calls to mind our consistent insistence on trying to eliminate the output matrix. In the last chapter, we tried to do this with minimum feedback, but now even that restriction is released. There is more to be gained of course than just the output gates eliminated.

Let us try a small problem now to show this characteristic is not unique with large problems.

Example II: A circuit is to have a "Set" and a "Reset" line as inputs. The single output Z is to reset (go to, or stay at, zero) when the Reset line is lowered. Releasing the "Reset" does not affect the output. Lowering "Set" however, should not affect the memory unless or until "Reset" is also lowered and the output was previously a zero. The output however, when

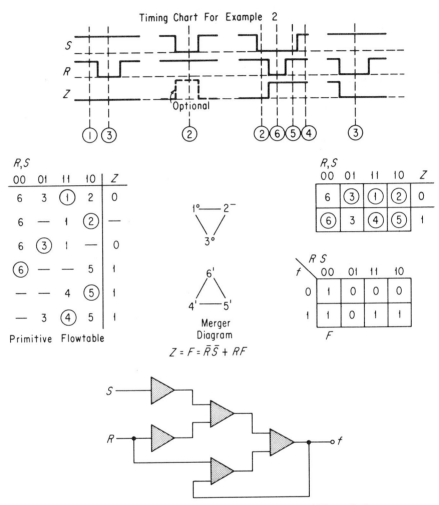

Figure 9.22. Straight forward implementation of Example 2.

$B = 1$, $S = 0$ is optional. With both inputs down the output changes to one; it is set. If both R and S are down, R will always go up first. Raising S next should not affect the output. (See the timing chart and step by step solution in Figure 9.22.) We assume no double changes of variables.

The assumption mode, of course, was to completely merge minimizing feedback loops. Rather, let us try merging rows 4, 5 and 6, but not 1, 2 and 3, giving us four rows and two feedback loops. This partial merger will be our starting point. See Figure 9.23.

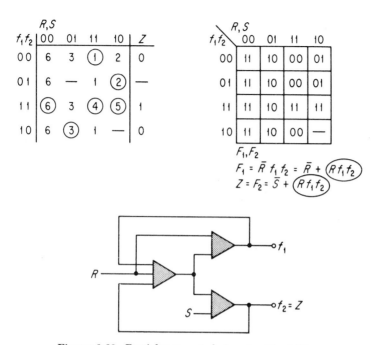

$f_1 f_2$ \ R,S	00	01	11	10	Z
00	6	3	(1)	2	0
01	6	—	1	(2)	—
11	(6)	3	(4)	(5)	1
10	6	(3)	1	—	0

$f_1 f_2$ \ R,S	00	01	11	10
00	11	10	00	01
01	11	10	00	01
11	11	10	11	11
10	11	10	00	—

F_1, F_2

$$F_1 = \bar{R} f_1 f_2 = \bar{R} + (R f_1 f_2)$$
$$Z = F_2 = \bar{S} + (R f_1 f_2)$$

Figure 9.23. Partial merger technique for Fig. 9.22.

Here you will note that by only partial merging, using redundant feedback, we were able even in a small problem to reduce the transistor count from 5 to 3 or 40% as well as to speed up the circuit by deleting some gating delay.

Example III: Let us take the flow table of problem 3 in the introduction. Now, leaving the table merged, let us add one feedback loop so we can identify the outputs with the feedback eliminating the output gating. The result is Figures 9.24 and 9.25.

A_1, A_2, A_3

000	001	010	100	$Z_1 Z_2 Z_3$
(1)	5	6	7	0 0 0
(2)	(5)	6	7	0 0 1
(3)	5	(6)	7	0 1 0
(4)	5	6	(7)	1 0 0

Figure 9.24. Merged table of Problem 3. "Don't care" columns omitted.

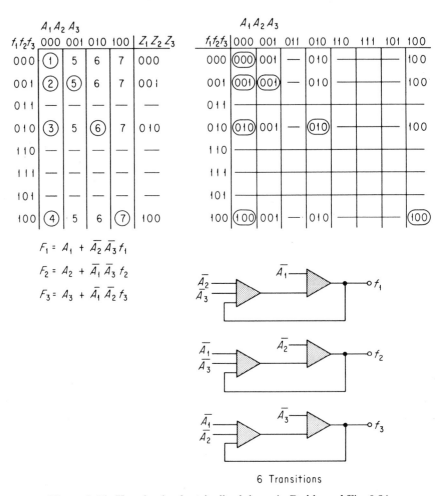

$$F_1 = A_1 + \bar{A_2}\,\bar{A_3}\,f_1$$

$$F_2 = A_2 + \bar{A_1}\,\bar{A_3}\,f_2$$

$$F_3 = A_3 + \bar{A_1}\,\bar{A_2}\,f_3$$

6 Transitions

Figure 9.25. Use of redundant feedback loops in Problem of Fig. 9.24.

Complemented Feedback Loops

A problem that continually crops up in implementing excitation equations is obtaining complements of the feedback loops. When using the $NAND$ and NOR functions, we have found that in combinational problems, the complement of a block may be obtained by going back to the inputs. This can require several wires to represent the complement which can easily exceed the fan in of the block it is going to, possibly negating the savings made.

In sequential circuits, we are in a somewhat better position. Figure 9.26 illustrates the basic situation. When $R = 1$, f_2 alone may be usable

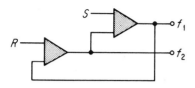

Figure 9.26. Complemented feedback loop.

as $\bar{f}_1$. However, if $S = R = 0$, f_1 and f_2 are not complements. Whether f_2 may be used as $\bar{f}_1$ or not must be determined from the excitation matrix. It may be and very often is, not required to be the complement during these input conditions.

A good example is the binary trigger designed in the last chapter. The excitation equations

$$F_1 = \bar{x}f_2 + xf_1$$
$$F_2 = \bar{x}f_2 + x\bar{f}_1$$

require the complement of f_1. Suppose in Figure 9.27a we try using node 1 for $\bar{f}_1$ as in Figure 9.27b

$$\bar{x}f_2 + x\text{①} = \bar{x}f_2 + x(\bar{x} + \bar{f}_1) = \bar{x}f_2 + x\bar{f}_1 = F_2$$

This works out well and we have saved a transistor.

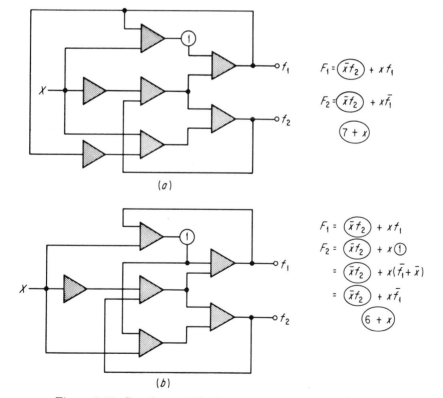

Figure 9.27. Complemented feedback loop in the binary trigger.

The Use of Critical Races, Logical Malfunctions and Delays

2 Delay Dependent and Delay Independent Transitions: One of the most powerful logical tools available to the logical designer of sequential circuits is controlled delay. With it, critical races and deliberate design errors may be used to significantly improve circuits, in speed, reliability or cost. Not all these will always result but the prime motivation will be cost savings. Trading three transistors for a capacitor represents sequential design on a level of sophistication well above the expectations of the original theory. Speed and reliability can, in certain cases, be side benefits as compared to the alternative circuit.

The techniques of this section, gleaned from the experience of the authors, gives no claims to rigor; we here but point the reader in a direction with but scanty signposts as aid. The authors feel the power of a method or the practicality of a trick are justification enough.

Since there are some who may question whether such trouble to save a few transistors is worth it, one or two preliminaries are in order though this is not meant as complete case for minimization which can be carried too far:

1. Redundant logic blocks slow the machine speeds since each are delays.

2. Redundant logic increase the probability of component failure.

3. In iterative circuits, they can represent substantial cost savings. The authors had occasion to redesign one sequential circuit for a machine from four to three transistors. Because of the wide use of this circuit in the machine, this resulted in a 16% savings in transistors for the whole computer.

4. Redundant logic can force the computer to expand to another frame for which alone a price tag of several thousand dollars may be attached.

The more obvious reasons we leave to the reader.

Example I: The register latch of Figure 9.28 must be done as cheaply as possible.

Note that:

$$F_1 = \bar{s} + \bar{f}_2 + Df_1 \qquad \text{and}$$
$$F_2 = \bar{s} + \bar{f}_1 + \overline{D}f_2 = \bar{s} + \bar{f}_1 f_2 + \overline{D}f_2 = \bar{s} + f_2(\bar{f}_1 + \overline{D})$$

from the excitation matrix. Now the new term $(\bar{f}_1 + \overline{D})$ in F_2 is generated

f_1f_2 \ S_1D	00	01	11	10
00	—	—	—	—
01	1	2	⑤	④
11	①	②	3	4
10	1	2	③	⑥

f_1f_2 \ S_1D	00	01	11	10
00	—	—	—	—
01	11	11	01	01
11	11	11	10	01
10	11	11	10	10

$$F_1F_2$$

$$F_1 = \bar{S} + \bar{f}_2 + Df_1$$
$$F_2 = \bar{S} + \bar{f}_1 + \bar{D}f_2$$

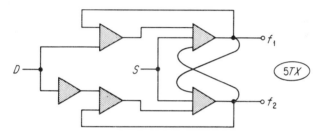

Figure 9.28. First solution to Example 1, $-5tx$.

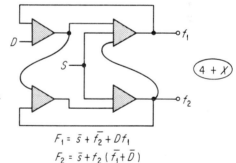

Figure 9.29. Second solution to Example 1, $-4tx$.

$$F_1 = \bar{S} + \bar{f}_2 + Df_1$$
$$F_2 = \bar{S} + f_2\,(\bar{f}_1 + \bar{D})$$

free in the $NAND$ function from its complement Df_1 in F_1. So we may save a transistor giving us the circuit of Figure 9.29.

Since we require this circuit to be as economical in transistors as possible, we must try all the alternatives we can think of that we had along the way. We may try unmerging, different codings, writing the excitations from the zeros and combinations of these—we may even go back and see if we can't change the problem where it originated so as to help the solution.

All these are powerful tools. Yet they do not seem to help this example, although the reader is invited to try. Indeed we have no assurance of a better solution. But let us try a new trick.

In the next excitation matrix and equations which are reproduced in Figure 9.30, we note that the excitation circled with label a is the only thing requiring the $\overline{D} \cdot f_2$ term in F_2 which would otherwise be quite simple. Since no double change of input variables occur, this excitation provides for the transition between stable states 1 and 4 in the flow table (Figure 9.30). In

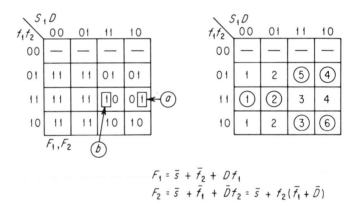

$$F_1 = \overline{s} + \overline{f}_2 + D f_1$$
$$F_2 = \overline{s} + \overline{f}_1 + \overline{D} f_2 = \overline{s} + f_2 (\overline{f}_1 + \overline{D})$$

Figure 9.30. Excitation and flow table of Example 1, showing ones to be removed.

this transition F_2 starts out as a one (in 1), stays a one in non-stable 4 to insure the proper transition and then goes to zero in 4. Suppose we change the a excitation of F_2 in non-stable state 4 to a zero as in Figure 9.30, introducing a critical race because of the double change of variables f_1 and f_2. Using this critical race may have simplified our solution but operation is now unreliable. But all we have to do is insure that f_1 always wins the race against f_2 and gets to zero first. Then the *effect* will be that the excitation a Figure 9.30 is a one even though the logic tells us it is a zero.

Insuring that f_2 wins the race may be accomplished in many ways.

Showing the fall of f_2 with capacitive loading, putting a faster transistor in the output f_1 or a slower one in the output f_2 or any of the several methods

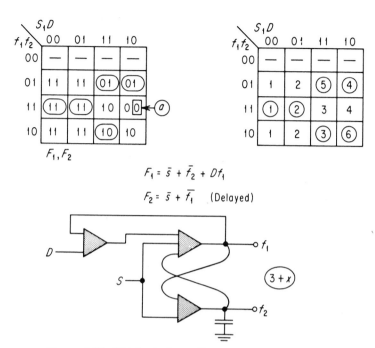

$$F_1 = \bar{s} + \bar{f}_2 + Df_1$$

$$F_2 = \bar{s} + \bar{f}_1 \quad \text{(Delayed)}$$

Figure 9.31. Third solution to Example 1, $-3tx$. Use of a delay dependent critical race.

mentioned in the first chapter. However, for whichever method used, the effect of the particular characteristics of this delay must be tested in all other transitions in the flow table to see if we haven't created another problem in solving this one.

In this case, one may easily see in the excitation matrix that slowing just the turn off of f_2 or both the turn on *and* turn off of f_2 will not impair any other transition. So the method of achieving delay is arbitrary over the methods mentioned in Chapter I.

We will call transition 4 of Figure 9.30 *delay dependent* and all other transitions of the table *delay independent* in this example.

Figure 9.31 shows our solution in three transitions. Thus, through the use of controlled delay we have saved 40% in transitions over the original five transistor circuit (Figure 9.28). In Figure 9.31, we show the delay achieved through capacitive loading. The capacitor here and throughout this book is to be construed only as indicating the minimum type of delay needed (f_1's fall delayed) and not necessarily as the circuit element to be used in achieving it.

An analysis of the circuit of Figure 9.31 shows f_1 must be delayed by about the turn off time of f_1 or f_1 speeded up by about the turn off time of f_2. Thus, the delay necessary to add is equivalent to the delay of the transistor that was removed (in Figure 9.30) from the circuit of Figure 9.31. Thus we have lost no speed advantage by inserting the delay.

The student may wish to try an alternative solution as an exercise. Excitation b of F_1 in Figure 9.30 may be removed instead of by a similar procedure. Working through this alternative, the student should arrive at a circuit symmetrically equivalent to the one in Figure 9.31.

One assumption was made throughout the previous example, that delay is cheap relative to the cost of a *NOR* function circuit. Here it had to be less than a *NOR* function circuit, but we can save more than a transistor or single *NOR* element at times (see set-dominate flip-flop of later chapter, e.g.) with a single delay.

There are sometimes side benefits, however, which can override economy. Sometimes we can gain in the switching speed or frequency response of a circuit or we may eliminate static and essential hazards. The logical elimination of hazards can be very expensive at times. (Compare the 10 *tx B.T.* and the 4 *tx* one.)

10

The following chapter is devoted exclusively to work examples. The problems worked in this chapter commonly appear in almost every computer. All circuits are static hazard free and are in actual use.

So as to make this chapter more usable as a handbook as well as a learning tool, a table of contents follows.

Table of Contents

Problem 1—Removing the Electrical Noise from a Mechanical Switch: Some mechanical hardware is always involved in the Input-Output area of a computer. This equipment usually contains a large number of mechanical switches that feed information to the main control section. Most inexpensive switches have the unfortunate characteristic of bouncing open during the time the switch is being closed. These same switches may be equipped

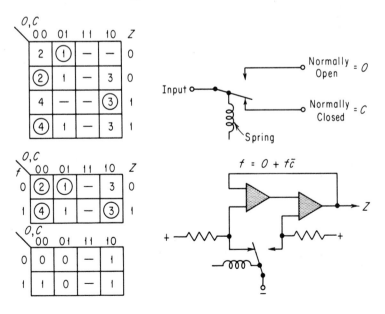

with a normal open point as well as a normal close point to aid in removal of this bounce; signal interruption, by the use of a logic configuration. The Figure above illustrates the construction of such a switch. This switch is constructed in such a fashion that both contacts cannot be closed at the same time. The bouncing is not severe enough to return the center contact to its starting point. In other words, the contact that is opening will not be closed again by the bouncing center contact once it has touched the opposite contact. The sequential circuit involved here has two inputs since both contacts may be open at the same time.

There are, of course, many resistor and voltage combinations that could be used with the switch to generate $\bar{o}$ and $\bar{c}$ as required by the logic configuration.

Problem 2—Gated Latch: (no reset line required) Within a computer data are often transferred from one register to another. It is sometimes desirable to use a gated latch which requires no reset line as the receiving element. Such a latch would have two input lines; a data line and a gate line. When the gate line is raised to a "1" the latch should be set to the value of the data line whether it is a "0" or a "1". The latch should be insensitive to the value of the data line as long as the gate line is a "0". It is assumed that the data line will not change when the gate line is a "1" or that both inputs will change at the same time.

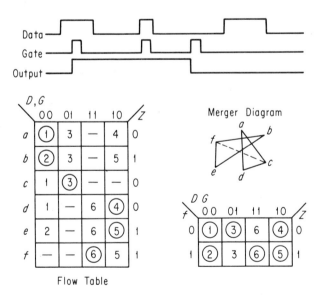

Flow Table

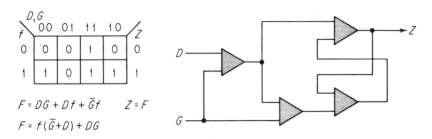

$$F = DG + Df + \bar{G}f \qquad Z = F$$

$$F = f(\bar{G}+D) + DG$$

Problem 3—Sampling Gate: The problem here is that of sampling an information line under the control of a gate signal. The output of this circuit should be down whenever the gate line is down. When the gate line is up, the output should remain stable at the level the information line was at when the gate line was going up. In other words, we wish to sample the information line only during the time the gate line is going up.

If both inputs go up at the same time or if the information line is going down while the gate is going up, the output is undeterminable and will be considered a "don't care" condition.

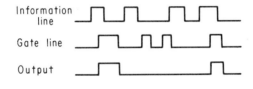

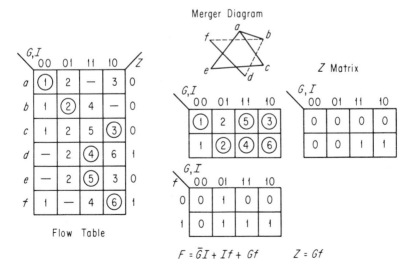

Merger Diagram

Flow Table

Z Matrix

$$F = \bar{G}I + If + Gf \qquad Z = Gf$$

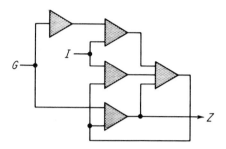

The merged flow table of this problem is exactly the same as the merged flow table of the "gated oscillator" which means that the same logic configuration may be used for both problems. The input lines must be relabeled to correspond to the new problem. It is interesting to note that the word statement of these two is entirely different and yet the resulting circuitry is the same with the exception of an interchange of inputs.

Problem 4—Gated Oscillation: Within a large computer time is metered out by the use of a crystal controlled oscillation. The output of this oscillation is amplified and clipped until a square wave is produced. This square wave is then gated to the control section of the computer and then distributed to many sections of the machine. The gating of this square wave requires

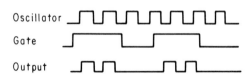

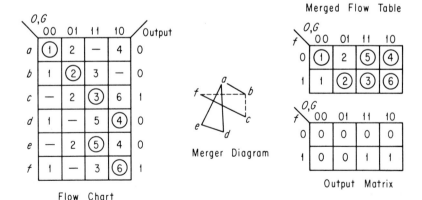

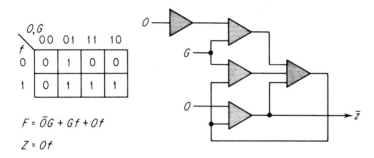

$$F = \bar{O}G + Gf + Of$$

$$Z = Of$$

a sequential circuit since the gate may be opened or closed at any time and it is important to pass only full width pulses to the control section.

If the gate line is raised in the middle of an oscillation pulse, the output does not appear until the next pulse. If the gate is lowered in the middle of an oscillation pulse, then the output must still be a full width pulse. A "don't care" condition occurs if both line change levels at the same time but under no conditions will an output pulse shorter than an oscillation pulse be permitted.

Problem 5—Single Pulse Generator: When a repairman is trouble-shooting a computer, it is important that he have the ability to step the main timing source one pulse at a time. For this reason a circuit must be designed that

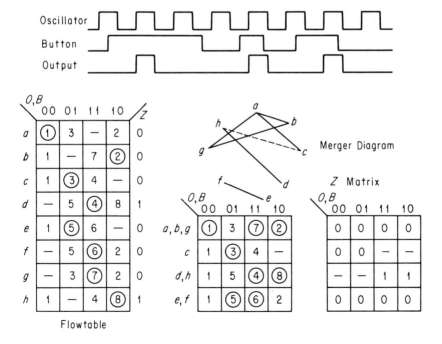

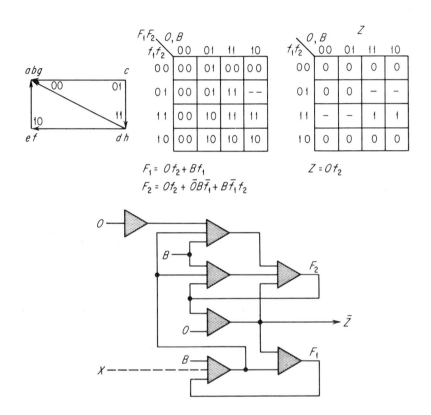

$$F_1 = 0f_2 + Bf_1$$
$$F_2 = 0f_2 + \bar{0}B\bar{f}_1 + B\bar{f}_1 f_2$$

$$Z = 0f_2$$

will pass one and only one pulse from the main square wave oscillator when a button is depressed. We will assume the signal from the button has been made noise-free by the method used in problem one of this chapter. The problem is best defined by using the timing chart given on the preceding page. It is permissible to miss a pulse if the button is depressed for too short a time but no half width pulses are permitted.

From the obtained circuit diagram, it is interesting to note that if a third input is inserted in the lower left hand block, the function of the configuration may be changed from a "Single Pulse Generator" to a "gated oscillator". If input X is up, the circuit will behave as a Single Pulse Generator while if this input is down, the circuit will act as a gated oscillator. This addition makes the circuit extremely useful since it allows a computer to be single-pulsed or run it in normal mode.

Problem 6—Binary Compare Circuitry: The ability to compare two binary numbers is very important to any binary computer. This comparison may be accomplished in parallel (all bits at one time) by a rather large combinational circuit or it may be performed serially (one bit from each number at a time) by using a sequential circuit. It is the design of this sequential circuit which interests us at this time.

The two binary numbers will be sent to the Comparer, High order first, one bit from each of the numbers at a time. Our circuitry will therefore have two inputs for the data, oně for each word which will arrive serially. A clock signal will be used to tell when the data are present at the inputs and the data will not change while the clock signal is present. When the clock

f_1f_2 \ A,B,C	000	010	110	100	001	011	111	101	$a\ b$
00	①	④	⑦	11	⑫	15	⑰	⑳	00
01	②	⑤	⑧	⑩	⑬	⑮	⑱	㉑	0 1
10	③	⑥	⑨	⑪	⑭	⑯	⑲	㉒	1 0

C = 0

f_1f_2 \ ABC	00	01	11	10
00	00	00	00	00
01	01	01	01	01
11	--	--	--	--
10	10	10	10	10

C = 1

f_1f_2 \ ABC	00	01	11	10
00	00	10	00	01
01	01	01	01	01
11	--	--	--	--
10	10	10	10	10

$$F_1 = f_1\bar{f}_2 + \bar{A}B\bar{f}_2C = \bar{f}_2(f_1 + \bar{A}BC)$$
$$F_2 = \bar{f}_1f_2 + A\bar{B}\bar{f}_1C = \bar{f}_1(f_2 + A\bar{B}C)$$

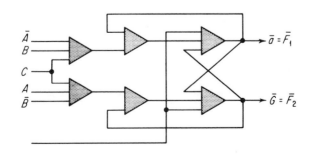

signal is not present, the data lines may change in any fashion but should have no effect upon the circuitry. The circuitry should have two outputs. One output should indicate that number A is larger than number B. This output should come up as soon as it is possible to determine this fact and should remain up through the rest of the operation. This condition will remain until a reset sign is applied. Output B will indicate that number B is larger than number A and will be reset by the same signal used by output A. Both outputs will never be up at the same time but both will be down when the two numbers are equal. When reset, the output will indicate that both numbers are equal.

To simplify the design of this circuitry the reset line will not be used in our flow table but will be included later in the circuitry. This means that the flow table will show no possible method of returning to the starting point. This method of leaving off a required input is very useful in reducing the problem to manageable size but is rather a dangerous procedure that is often used. The primitive flow is not shown because of its rather large size. Merging in this case was rather straightforward.

The "don't care" conditions in the map were used as zeros in this case to aid in factoring the resulting equations. The outputs are in complement form and it was assumed that the complements of the inputs are available. The reset line was inserted by a trial and error procedure.

Problem 7—Simultaneous Set-Reset Binary Trigger: In vacuum tube pulse circuit technology there is a flip-flop with a Set and a Reset line such that if both are pulsed simultaneously, the flip-flop acts like a binary trigger, changing to the opposite state. For DC level-type circuits we must modify

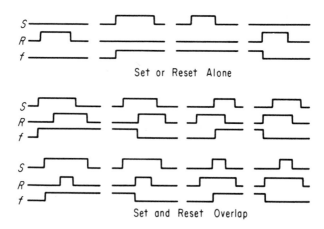

Set or Reset Alone

Set and Reset Overlap

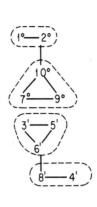

	S,R			Z
00	01	11	10	
①	2	5	3	0
1	②	5	–	0
4	–	5	③	1
④	7	9	8	1
4	6	⑤	3	1
4	⑥	–	–	1
1	⑦	9	–	0
4	–	9	⑧	1
1	7	⑨	10	0
1	–	–	⑩	0

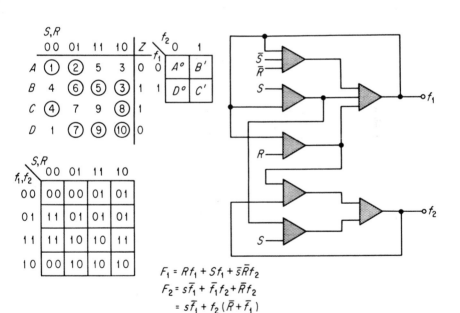

	S,R				Z
	00	01	11	10	
A	①	②	5	3	0
B	4	⑥	⑤	③	1
C	④	7	9	⑧	1
D	1	⑦	⑨	⑩	0

f_1 \\ f_2	0	1
0	$A°$	B'
1	$D°$	C'

f_1,f_2 \\	S,R			
	00	01	11	10
00	00	00	01	01
01	11	01	01	01
11	11	10	10	11
10	00	10	10	10

$$F_1 = Rf_1 + Sf_1 + \bar{s}\bar{R}f_2$$
$$F_2 = s\bar{f}_1 + \bar{f}_1 f_2 + \bar{R}f_2$$
$$= s\bar{f}_1 + f_2(\bar{R}+\bar{f}_1)$$

the problem somewhat since it must trigger reliably independent of any
skew in the two signals. This is illustrated by the desired operation shown
in the timing chart. Thus for Set and Reset alone, it acts as a normal Set-
Reset flip-flop. If Set and Reset signals overlap in any (minimum) way, it
acts like a binary trigger.

Problem 8—Reliable Binary Trigger (6 tx.): The binary trigger derived in the first chapter on Sequential Circuits was done before we studied hazards and has two important static hazards which render it unreliable and even inoperative in other than some alloy junction circuits even with capacitors for delay to prevent the hazard. For reliable DC operation, relatively insensitive to variations in transistor circuit parameters, transistor types, and distributed or lumped delays in the circuit, we require the addition of the redundant hazard eliminating terms for smooth, reliable operation. However, one would prefer not to use any more transistors in this oft used circuit. The hazardous circuit requires six transistors. The interesting thing is that after adding two hazard terms (below), we factor to a solution which, while hazard free, uses no more transistors than before. This, curiously, holds true in many cases; that the hazard terms are just the redundant terms necessary for economical factoring of the equation, and in many of our important circuits, hazard-free operation costs no more than hazardous operation.

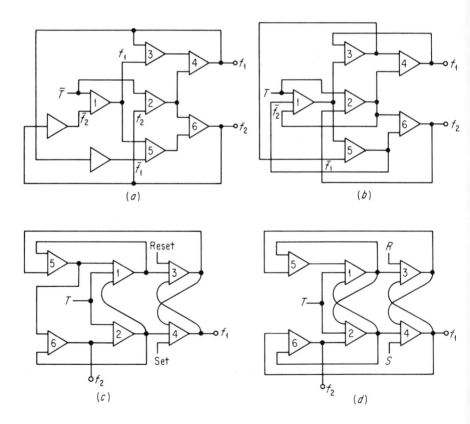

(a)   (b)

(c)   (d)

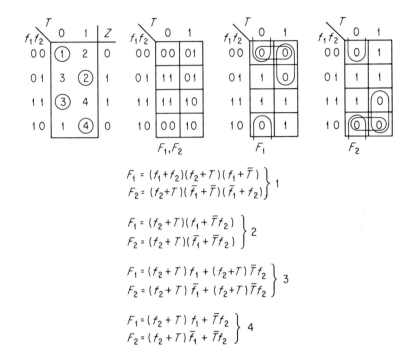

$$F_1 = (f_1 + f_2)(f_2 + T)(f_1 + \bar{T})$$
$$F_2 = (f_2 + T)(\bar{f}_1 + \bar{T})(\bar{f}_1 + f_2) \Bigg\}\ 1$$

$$F_1 = (f_2 + T)(f_1 + \bar{T}f_2)$$
$$F_2 = (f_2 + T)(\bar{f}_1 + \bar{T}f_2) \Bigg\}\ 2$$

$$F_1 = (f_2 + T)f_1 + (f_2 + T)\bar{T}f_2$$
$$F_2 = (f_2 + T)\bar{f}_1 + (f_2 + T)\bar{T}f_2 \Bigg\}\ 3$$

$$F_1 = (f_2 + T)f_1 + \bar{T}f_2$$
$$F_2 = (f_2 + T)\bar{f}_1 + \bar{T}f_2 \Bigg\}\ 4$$

We chose this time to write from the zeros (since we plan to factor one level); we include the hazard terms and factor as shown in the Karnaugh Maps and equations 1, 2, 3, 4 (above). The step from equations 1 to equations 2 is straightforward factoring leaving the common terms alone. The step to equations 3 although not entirely straightforward, is to get the equations in the proper form for implementing in the stroke function.

Direct implementation of the equations yields the circuit (a) below. Getting the complements of the feedback loops off the inputs to the outputs yields the circuit (b). Notice we have also dropped the complement on T since the binary trigger is invariant to complementation of the input variable (as can be seen in the flow table). The feedback loops are all interlaced so we unwrap them, a mere change in geometry, circuit c.
But

$$5 = \bar{3} + \bar{1} = f_1 \cdot 1 + \bar{1} = f_1$$

so

$$6 = \bar{5} + \bar{2} = \bar{f}_1 + \bar{2}$$

This gives us the circuit (d). Both (c) and (d) are equivalently good circuits. Notice that we had to replace the term $(T + f_2)$ in equation 3 in going to (d).

Set and Reset lines can be added in obvious places now as in (c) and (d). By leaving them out of the problem we greatly reduced it and Set and Reset lines can usually be inserted in a solution in a fairly obvious manner.

Problem 9—Binary Counter: One of the most frequently encountered sequential circuits is the binary counter. There are many variations to the counter problem, but we shall limit our discussion to a basic configuration. Furthermore, we will design a counter capable of counting from zero to

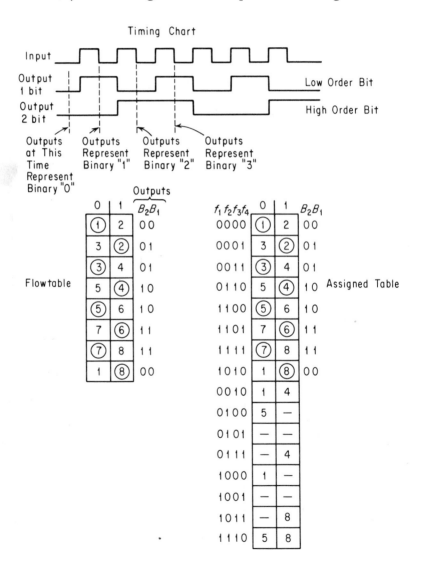

I

| 0 | | | | | 1 | | | |

I = 0

$f_1 f_2$ \ $f_3 f_4$	00	01	11	10
00	0000	0011	0011	0000
01	1100	—	—	1100
11	1100	1111	1111	1100
10	0000	—	—	0000

I = 1

$f_1 f_2$ \ $f_3 f_4$	00	01	11	10
00	0001	0001	0110	0110
01	—	—	0110	0110
11	1101	1101	1010	1010
10	—	—	1010	1010

$$F_4 = f_4 \bar{I} + \bar{f_3} I$$
$$F_3 = f_4 \bar{I} + f_3 I$$
$$F_2 = f_2 \bar{f_3} + f_2 \bar{I} + \bar{f_1} f_3 I = f_2 (\bar{f_3} + \bar{I}) + \bar{f_1} (f_3 I)$$
$$F_1 = f_2 \bar{f_3} + f_2 \bar{I} + f_1 f_3 I = f_2 (\bar{f_3} + \bar{I}) + f_1 (f_3 I)$$

three in binary and then extend the general principles to counters of greater capabilities. With these restrictions the problem has been narrowed to one input and two outputs. The two outputs are required to represent the binary numbers two and three. A Timing Chart of the desired operation is given above. When the circuit is pulsed after the count has reached three it should return to zero and continue to cycle through the count again. The flow table for the counter is given above. Since the flow table contains eight rows it would appear that three feedbacks would be sufficient. But with three feedback lines it is impossible to assign them in such a fashion as to let two of them serve as outputs and yet have no critical races. It is possible to assign feedback conditions to the rows so as to obtain no critical races but now a "Z" matrix will be required. This will slow down the outputs from the circuitry, and yet will not insure a minimum component count. Counters like "adders" are usually required to operate at a high rate of speed therefore we shall rule out the use of a "Z" matrix. With this thought in mind we are now forced to use at least four feedback lines. The race conditions still exist but it is possible now to make them non-critical races as shown on page 268. With this assignment f_2 may be used as output B_2 while f_4 serves as output B_1. The outputs may be wrong during the non-critical race period and therefore these outputs should not be used during the transition time. This is no real restriction since there are times when both outputs must change and no matter how the circuit is designed, this difficulty will arise.

The flow table is now converted to a four output five variable Karnaugh map as shown on page 269. Looking at the expressions for F_3 and F_4 it is clear that the first section of this circuitry is a binary trigger which has been designed earlier in this chapter. The input to this trigger will be "I". The expressions for F_1 and F_2 after some factoring also appear to form a binary trigger. In this case, the input to the trigger will be f_2I. When implemented with Stroke or Dagger functions the "and" gate may be inte-

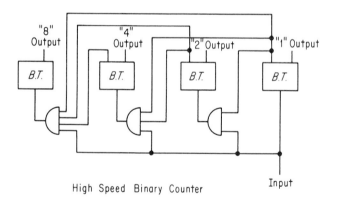

High Speed Binary Counter

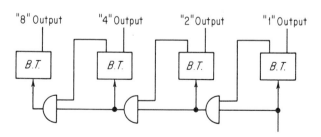

Binary Counter

grated into the second trigger if the "fan-in" and "fan-out" characteristic will permit. In many applications further gating is required on this line especially when dealing with large counters.

This same principle of connecting binary triggers together to form a binary counter may be extended in two different ways. A mixture of the two methods shown may be used to obtain the desired speed-cost relationship desired.

Problem 10—Shift Register: A shift register is an iteration of identical shift cells with the following property. It has two inputs, I, the output, f, of the preceding cell, and S, the signal to shift the bit in each cell into the cell whose input is connected to this cell's output.

Operation: When S goes up, the cell maintains the value of the bit stored on the output f so the next stage may be sampling it as input. When S goes down, f takes on the value that I had when S was just up.

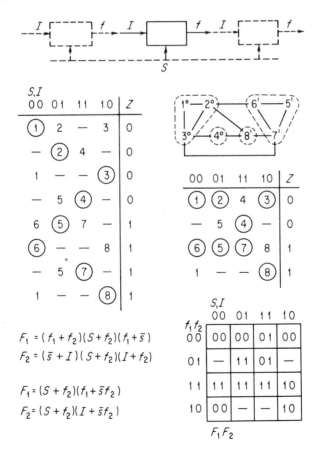

S,I

	00	01	11	10	Z
①	2	—	3	0
—	②	4	—	0
1	—	—	③	0
—	5	④	—	0
6	⑤	7	—	1
⑥	—	—	8	1
—	5	⑦	—	1
1	—	—	⑧	1

	00	01	11	10	Z
①	②	4	③	0
—	5	④	—	0
⑥	⑤	⑦	8	1
1	—	—	⑧	1

$F_1 = (f_1 + f_2)(S + f_2)(f_1 + \bar{S})$

$F_2 = (\bar{S} + I)(S + f_2)(I + f_2)$

$F_1 = (S + f_2)(f_1 + \bar{S}f_2)$

$F_2 = (S + f_2)(I + \bar{S}f_2)$

S,I

$f_1 f_2$	00	01	11	10
00	00	00	01	00
01	—	11	01	—
11	11	11	11	10
10	00	—	—	10

$F_1 F_2$

$$1 \begin{cases} F_1 = (f_1 + f_2)(S + f_2)(f_1 + \bar{S}) \\ F_2 = (\bar{S} + I)(S + f_2)(I + f_2) \end{cases}$$

$$2 \begin{cases} F_1 = (S + f_2)(f_1 + \bar{S} f_2) \\ F_2 = (S + f_2)(I + \bar{S} f_2) \end{cases}$$

$$3 \begin{cases} F_1 = (S + f_2) f_1 + \bar{S} f_2 \\ F_2 = (S + f_2) I + \bar{S} f_2 \end{cases}$$

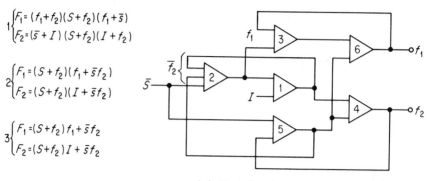

(a) First Solution From Equations (3)

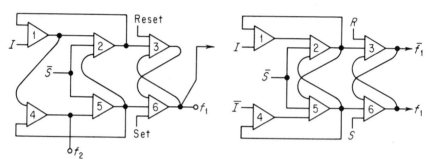

(b) Shift Register Solution ((a) In
A Different Geometry)

(c) An Alternative Solution Which
Drives Both Set and Reset Lines

Problem 11—Single Shot: We require a single circuit that will act as both a pulse shortener and a pulse extender. It has one input and one output. The output gives out a pulse of fixed width for every input pulse regardless of the input pulse width.

When we try to write the flow table for this, however, we find we need another signal to tell us when the fixed pulse width duration is over.

$$I$$

	0	1	
	①	2	0
	1	②	1

Essentially we require this signal some fixed time after the beginning of the input pulse. One way of doing this is to bring in another input I', delayed behind I the time duration of the required output pulse width.

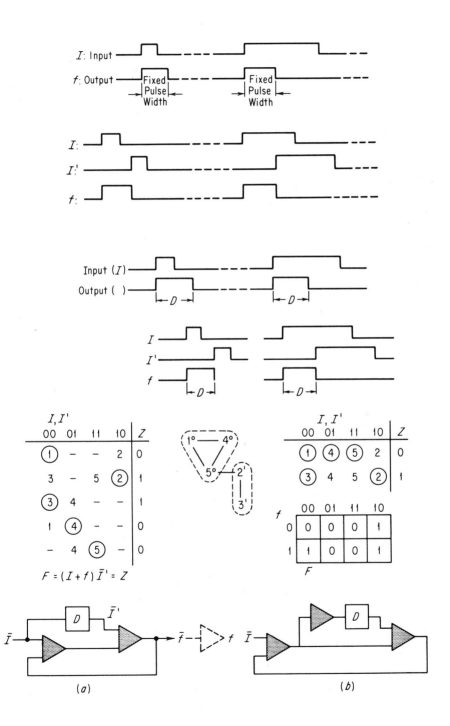

$$F = (I + f)\, \bar{I}' = Z$$

Problem 12—Set Dominant Flip-Flop: In using the familiar Set-Reset flip-flop (two crosscoupled *NOR*s), we usually must avoid pulsing both inputs at the same time because the result would be indeterminate due to skew between the signals. If Set and Reset lines both went down, whichever happens to go up last would determine which state the circuit would go to.

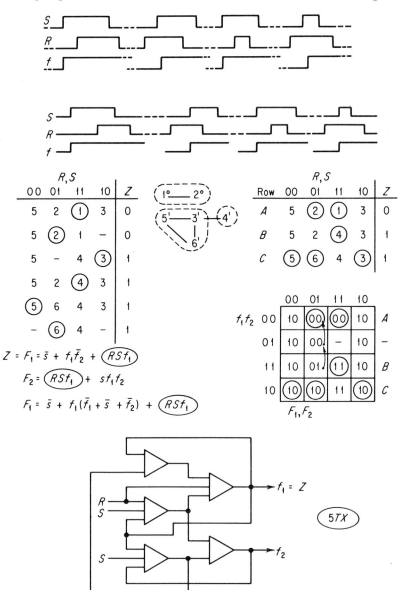

$$Z = F_1 = \bar{s} + f_1\bar{f}_2 + \boxed{RSf_1}$$

$$F_2 = \boxed{RSf_1} + sf_1f_2$$

$$F_1 = \bar{s} + f_1(\bar{f}_1 + \bar{s} + \bar{f}_2) + \boxed{RSf_1}$$

$$\boxed{5TX}$$

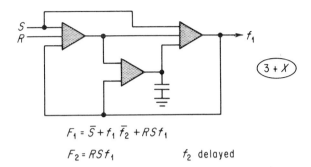

$$F_1 = \bar{S} + f_1\,\bar{f_2} + RSf_1$$

$$F_2 = RSf_1 \qquad\qquad f_2 \text{ delayed}$$

Some pulsed-circuit flip-flops allow simultaneous pulsing of Set and Reset (if they are synced with a clock and thus with each other) with one input dominant over the other. We are to design a DC reliably set dominant flip-flop which goes to one if Set alone is pulsed, to zero if Reset alone is pulsed, and goes to one if Set and Reset overlap, regardless of skew. What is meant by *reliable* set-dominance is indicated in the timing chart.

Since the *NOR* function flip-flop requires inputs to be normally up we start in that column to avoid complements in the result. The reason for merging 3 with 5 and 6 in the flow table, rather than with 4 (at least on the first pass) is that 3, 5, and 6 are all similar "on the way to 4" states. A straightforward 5 *tx.* solution is shown in the figure.

This flip-flop is general enough so that we might use it quite often, thus we want it as economical as possible. Note that if the Sf_1f_2 term in F_2 could be eliminated, $\bar{F_2} = \overline{RS}f_1$ and this is free since it can be gotten from F_1. Note also that F_2 is not used in any of the equations except in this term, Sf_1f_2, so if this is eliminated only $\bar{f_2}$ would be needed.

Note that if the fall of f_2 were delayed, the $f_1f_2\overline{R}S$ one in the excitation matrix would not be needed and we could drop the Sf_1f_2 term. Since f_2 is not now needed, we must insert the delay such as to have the effect of delaying the *rise* of $\bar{f_2}$. But since this is shared, the delay must be inserted further on. The final three transistor (one capacitor) circuit shown illustrates the placing of the capacitor. Notice we have reduced a three row table to one feedback loop and replaced two transistors by a capacitor.

Problem 13—(4 *tx.*) Binary Trigger with Controlled Delay: We can apply the principle of controlled delay to many practical circuits. Here we have a sophisticated use of it in a binary trigger, reducing the cost to but four *NOR* transistors. This can be synthesized directly from a minimum row flow table but its derivation is a bit messy. Rather, we'll start with the three feedback circuit (c) of the RELIABLE BINARY TRIGGER (6 *tx.*). Writing the excitation equations for nodes 1, 2, 3, 4, as g_1, g_2, g_3, g_4, respectively:

T

$g_1\ g_2\ g_3\ g_4$	0	1	
0 0 0 0	↑ ↑ ↑ ↑	↑ ↑ ↑ ↑	
0 0 0 1	↑ ↑ ↑ ↑	↑ ↑ ↑ ↑	
0 0 1 1	↑ ↑ ↑ ↑	↑ ↑ ↑ ↑	
0 0 1 0	↑ ↑ ↑ ↑	↑ ↑ ↑ ↑	
0 1 1 0	↑ ↑ ↑ 0	(0 1 1 0) ②	
0 1 1 1	↑ ↑ ↑ 0	0 1 1 0 (2a)	$G_1 = g_1 g_3 + \bar{T} + \bar{g}_2$
0 1 0 1	↑ ↑ ↑ ↑	0 1 1 ↑	$G_2 = g_2 g_4 + \bar{T} + \bar{g}_1$
0 1 0 0	↑ ↑ ↑ ↑	0 1 1 ↑	$G_3 = \bar{g}_1 + \bar{g}_4$
1 1 0 0	↑ ↑ ↑ ↑	0 0 1 ↑	$G_4 = \bar{g}_2 + \bar{g}_3$
1 1 0 1	(↑ ↑ 0 ↑) ①	0(d) 1(*) 0 ↑	
1 1 1 1	↑ ↑ 0(b) 0	↑ ↑ 0 0	
1 1 1 0	(↑ ↑ ↑ 0) ③	1(c) 0 1 0	
1 0 1 0	↑ ↑ ↑ ↑	↑ 0 1 ↑	
1 0 1 1	↑ ↑ 0 ↑	↑ 0 0 ↑	
1 0 0 1	↑ ↑ 0 ↑	(1 0 0 1) ④	
1 0 0 0	↑ ↑ ↑ ↑	↑ 0 1 ↑	

$$G_1, \ G_2, \ G_3, \ G_4$$

$$G_1 = g_1 g_3 + \bar{T} + \bar{g}_2$$
$$G_2 = g_2 g_4 + \bar{T} + \bar{g}_1$$
$$G_3 = \bar{g}_1 + \bar{g}_4$$
$$G_4 = \bar{g}_2 + \bar{g}_3$$

Note that in the excitation matrix, written with these equations, the starred one is replaced by delaying the fall of g_2 removing the $g_2 g_4$ term in G_2. This delay does not affect the other transitions.

Next we might be tempted to remove $g_1 g_3$ from G_1 by delaying the fall of g_1 removing the one marked c in the matrix. But this would mean delaying the fall of G_1 in the transition to the 0 marked d and the two delays of g_1 and g_2 would be racing critically against each other.

But we could replace the $g_1 g_3$ term in G_1 by $\overline{g_4}$ saving another transistor except for state 2. If we do this anyhow, and also make

$$G_4 = \overline{g_1} + \overline{g_2} + \overline{g_3}$$

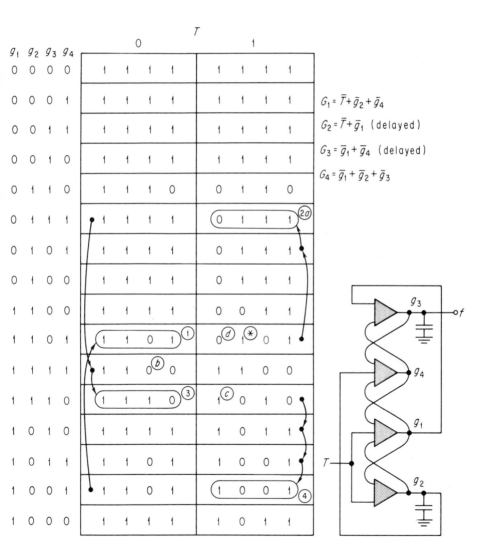

$G_1 = \overline{T} + \overline{g}_2 + \overline{g}_4$

$G_2 = \overline{T} + \overline{g}_1$ (delayed)

$G_3 = \overline{g}_1 + \overline{g}_4$ (delayed)

$G_4 = \overline{g}_1 + \overline{g}_2 + \overline{g}_3$

the stable state 2 now moves to 2a. We now get the revised matrix following. We find a critical race in the box marked b but if we delay the fall of g_3 the race is fixed in our favor and no other transitions are affected. These revised equations reduce (with two capacitors) to the four transistor circuit shown. This is the most economical DC binary trigger yet devised.

SELF-TIMING ASYNCHRONOUS CIRCUITRY

11

Introduction

Each operation in a computer designed around the synchronous mode is allotted a specific amount of time. As a result of using specific delay times, it is possible that machines of this type are operating at a fraction of their potential speed. On the other hand, each operation in a computer designed around the asynchronous mode is started by a signal from a finish signal from the previous operation. Thus each operation here requires only enough time to complete its prescribed function.

Synchronous Mode

To gain an understanding of asynchronous operations in a computer, it is necessary to first define the synchronous mode of operation. If a computer is designed around the synchronous mode, then each operation is allotted a specific amount of time. (Time is often metered out by a crystal controlled oscillator.) Thus, a four bit adder may be allotted two microseconds to complete the sum, while a shift register may be allotted one microsecond to shift all bits right or left one position. This would be adequate if it were economical to construct functional blocks that would require the same response regardless of input conditions. Unfortunately, the most economical functional blocks are produced by rather ingenious factoring and this factoring results in functional blocks that have different path lengths for different input conductions. This means that the functional block will require a varying amount of time to complete its operation.

An example is the parallel adder in a binary computer. The addition of 0001 to 0000 will require a much shorter interval of time than the addition of 0001 to 0111 as the latter involves carries. The designer of the synchronous machine is therefore forced to construct the adder in such a way that the longest carry will be complete within the prescribed interval of time. He may choose to do this by using logic connectives which have the speed capabilities necessary for the longest carry to be complete within the allotted time. But it must be remembered that the averaged addition problem does not require a full length carry. The adder will therefore, on the average, finish its operation long before the answer is used. The synchronous machine will not speed up to take advantage of this situation.

Another solution open to the designer is that of reducing all paths through a functional block to a minimum number of levels. This method becomes increasingly expensive as the path length is reduced. To build a thirty-six bit parallel adder with a carry path of only four blocks for the highest order bit is almost completely out of the question, yet it is possible to shorten the longest path to some extent.

Either of the above solutions, or combinations thereof, might be adequate if it were not for the following complication. It is almost impossible to predict the exact time delay of a signal passing through a series of logic connectives since no two blocks have identical characteristics and furthermore these characteristics will change with time. At present, an assembly line produced "*NOR* Circuit," may have a five to one variation in delay when placed in a machine. This variation is not completely accounted for by variations in components or power supplies, but by variables in loading and wave shape of input. When logic connectives with delays in the mil-micro-second range are used, even the wire lengths must be used in calculating the delays. At present, most designers of synchronous machines use a rather specified delay time for each logic connective. If the chain of logic is rather long, more than four blocks in series, it is customary to use an average time delay per block. But if the chain of logic is short, then worst case time delays must be used which may be rather long compared with actual speed. This condition will occur in such simple circuits as the "Latch." Thus, by designing in this fashion, it is possible that machines are being operated at far less than their potential speed.

Asynchronous Operations

When a computer is designed around the asynchronous mode, each operation is started by a signal from the previous operation stating it has finished. With this method, each operation requires only enough time to complete the prescribed function. The four bit adder used as an example previously would produce a signal when it had completed the addition operation. This signal would appear very quickly when numbers were being added that involved no carries, and comparatively slower when it is necessary to propagate a carry. The designer, in this case, would be relieved of the detailed specifications of each block, but would be concerned only with the overall average speed of the functional block being designed.

A machine designed around the asynchronous mode of operation might have some interesting characteristics. If germanium transistors, whose speed is a function of temperature, were used in the construction of a machine, then such a machine might run slower on warm days than on cool days. This is as would be expected since an asynchronous machine will always operate as fast as the switching can be accomplished. The theory of asynchronous machines is based on the premise that functional blocks can be designed to emit a signal when the input signals have been processed. Functional blocks may be as simple as an *"OR"* circuit feeding an *"AND"* circuit. A line must now be produced that will indicate, even in this case, when the input signals have passed through the blocks. This is easy when the output is going to be a one. A shift in the output level will indicate that the output has arrived. But what if the output is going to be zero? The output line will remain at zero and there will be no indication. The problem here is centered around the fact that zero and nothing, that is no signal, are both assigned the same voltage level. It is therefore impossible to distinguish between the two. The obvious answer to this problem is to use three levels, each one being assigned one of the values, zero, nothing, or one. To the author's knowledge, no computer has ever been built using this principle, but for a better understanding of what has been built, it is useful to explore this method. With three levels available on a wire, we must now examine our previous logic connectives.

Three Level Logic

The truth table for the three level, two input "AND" circuit is given in Figure 11.1. This truth table may differ somewhat from what the reader expected. It would pay at this point to look at each of the nine squares in the table. With both inputs at zero; the upper left-hand square should, of course, have an output of one with both inputs at one. With a zero on one leg and a one on the other leg, the output should be a zero as a normal *AND* would have. The output of a zero when a zero signal is applied to one

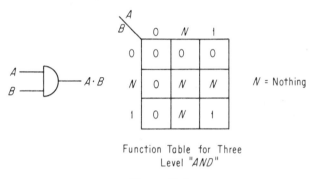

Function Table for Three
Level "*AND*"

Figure 11.1

leg and a nothing to the other leg requires a short explanation. The input conditions in this case state that one leg has received a signal, namely a zero, and the signal to the other leg has yet to arrive. But there is no need to wait for this delayed input to arrive since the output must be a zero when it does arrive. This one condition should substantially increase the average speed of the functional blocks produced.

It is necessary at this point to define the relationship between the voltage levels and the signals to make possible the hardware design of this connective. The obvious method is to assign "nothing" a voltage level located half way between a "zero" and a "one." Such an assignment might yield voltage outputs as shown in Figure 11.2. By examination of the truth table, it can be noticed that the output should be the more negative of the two input signals. This is fortunate since our conventional diode *AND* circuit does precisely this. In other words, the diode *AND* will operate equally as well with three levels as with two levels. The truth table for a two input, three level "OR" is given in Figure 11.3. The truth table in this case will yield an output of "one" as soon as either of the legs reaches the "one" level, regardless of the other leg. The output in this case is always the more positive of the input signals. This, of course, is nothing more than the diode "OR" circuit used now with three levels.

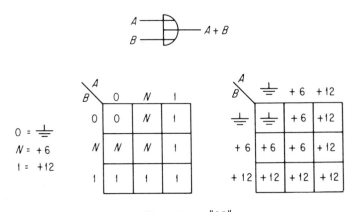

Voltage Output for Three Level "AND"

Figure 11.2

Three Level "OR"

Figure 11.3

The inverter circuit is one of the most obvious reasons why this asynchronous method has not been used. This circuit should put out a "one", a $+12$ in this case, when the input is at ground, and a ground signal when the input is $+12$ and the most difficult: a $+6$ out when the input is $+6$. It must be remembered that the inverter should supply power at all of these levels. A detector circuit would also be needed with this system. This detector is rather difficult to design since it should produce an output level that is the same with an input of $+12$ or ground and a different level if the input is $+6$. The detector block will be used to detect if information has arrived at the output of a functional block. Since, at this time, no completely satisfactory inverter of detector has been designed, we are forced to resort to another method normally referred to as double rail.

Double Rail

This method involves the use of two lines to carry one bit of information. The two lines in this case will each have only one of two levels. This will yield four signals, 00, 01, 10, and 11; when actually only three are needed. In most cases one of these signals, namely the 11, is not allowed to occur and only by a failure of a component will it appear. The most commonly used assignment for these four signals is listed below.

$$00 = \text{nothing}$$
$$01 = \text{zero}$$
$$10 = \text{one}$$
$$11 = \text{error}$$

In order to identify a bit of information one must look at two wires, referred to as a "pair." When the information carried by them is unknown, a capitalized variable will be used for the left-hand bit while the right-hand line will be given the same small case variable. Again it will be necessary to redesign all logic connectives previously used. The truth table for a two-input asynchronous AND circuit is given in Figure 11.4. This block will have two pairs of input leads and one pair of output lines.

The 11 row and the 11 column are completely filled with "don't cares," since these input conductions will never occur. If both inputs to the asynchronous AND are nothing, that is 00, then the output should be nothing.

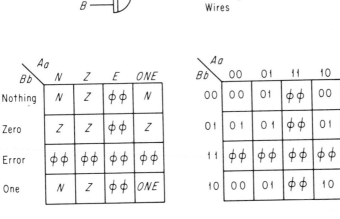

Double Rail "AND"

Figure 11.4

If both inputs are one, that is 10, then the output should be 10. Let us now look at the output when one leg is zero, 01, and the other is nothing, 00. The output under these input conditions is zero, 01, as explained previously in the three level method. This table may now be converted into two boolean equations: one equation for F, which is the left-hand bits in all the square, and another for f which is the right-hand bits. It is important to take full advantage of the "don't care" conditions in this truth table as illustrated in Figure 11.5.

Bb \ Aa	00	01	11	10
00	00	01	01	00
01	01	01	01	01
11	01	01	11	11
10	00	01	11	10

Function Table for Double Rail "AND"

Figure 11.5

This reduces to the following equations:

$$F = AB$$
$$f = a + b$$

The asynchronous double rail AND may now be constructed of conventional hardware in the following manner. (Figure 11.6.) To expand this AND circuit to more than two pairs of inputs is a rather simple matter and will reduce to an "n" way conventional AND circuit and an "n" way conventional OR circuit. Capitalized lines will all feed the conventional AND while all small case variables will feed the conventional OR.

The truth table for the two input asynchronous OR circuit is given in Figure 11.7. The asynchronous inverter is very simple and is actually no circuit at all. By simply crossing the two leads we obtain inversion. A zero will become a one and a one will become a zero. The nothing, 00, will remain unchanged (Figure 11.8). It is now possible to detect that information has passed through a series of logic connectives. This is accomplished by feeding the pair of output lines from the last block in the chain of

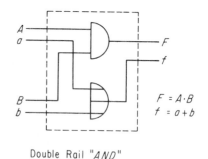

Double Rail "AND"

Figure 11.6

logic into a conventional OR circuit. The output of this OR circuit will be up only when information, either a zero or a one, is present at the last logic connective. It is important to mention at this point that the entire chain of logic must be cleared to nothing before starting information

Aa Bb	00	01	11	10
00	00	00	φφ	10
01	00	01	φφ	10
11	φφ	φφ	φφ	φφ
10	10	10	φφ	10

Aa Bb	00	01	11	10
00	00	00	10	10
01	00	01	11	10
11	10	11	11	10
10	10	10	10	10

$F = A + B$

$f = ab$

Double Rail "OR" Function Table

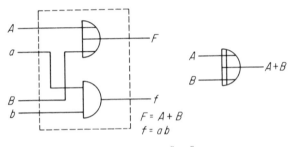

Double Rail "OR" Circuit

Figure 11.7

A Prime Is Used To Indicate
Double Rail Inversion

Double Rail Inverter

Figure 11.8

through. This is to prevent false indications of information arrival at the output. The system designer must lay out the entire machine in such a fashion that the clearing of the circuitry does not reduce the overall speed. This is possible since one functional block may be clearing while another functional block is operating.

Implementation: It should be possible at this point to design any combinational logic desired. A fully asynchronous exclusive OR circuit is shown

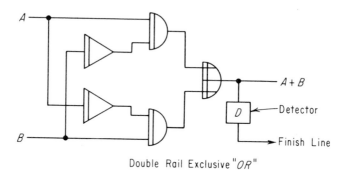

Double Rail Exclusive "OR"

Figure 11.9

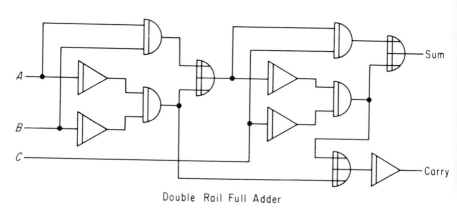

Double Rail Full Adder

Figure 11.10

in Figure 11.9. When using the double rail asynchronous circuitry, the designer should remember that the complement of a signal is always available by simply crossing wires. Logic diagrams may show many inverters in an effort to minimize the number of AND and OR connectives.

An asynchronous full adder circuit constructed of diode logic is shown in Figure 11.10. A number of these full adder circuits may now be connected together to form a functional adder of "n" binary digits. Such an arrangement is shown in Figure 11.11. The Finish Line in a function adder will come up only when an asynchronous zero or one is available at all of the output lines. This finish line will thus indicate that the adder has finished its operations.

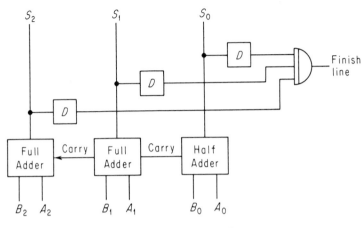

Double Rail Functional Adder

Figure 11.11

Sequential Circuitry

Since the output of combinatory logic may feed into a sequential circuit, the designer may wish to produce the finish line after the information has been stored in the sequential circuitry. In most cases the sequential circuitry will be a latch of some type. To be a completely asynchronous latch, the device should have three stable conditions with at least three input lines. Two of these lines, "S" and "s" will be used to set the latch to a zero or to a one. If a one is carried on this pair of inputs, the latch should be set to a zero. The third line "R" will be used to reset the latch to nothing and will override the input conditions. This latch should supply double rail outputs to make it compatible with the entire system. The flow table of such a latch is shown in Figure 11.12.

Since there are many "don't care" conditions and many ways to make use of non-circuital races in Figure 11.12, there will be countless equations that may be used for implementation. One of the better implementations, obtained by a cut and try solution, is illustrated in Figure 11.13. Implementation is given in Figure 11.14. The latch of Figure 11.13 has an interesting and useful output for the logic designer. The output is labeled "nothing stored." This line will be positive when nothing is being stored in the latch and negative when either a one or a zero is stored. The output from this line will therefore serve as a finish line.

Function Arrangements: It would be well to look at a rather large section of logic to be designed in the asynchronous mode. The problem of

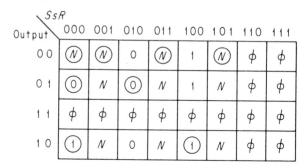

Flow Table for Double Rail Latch

Figure 11.12

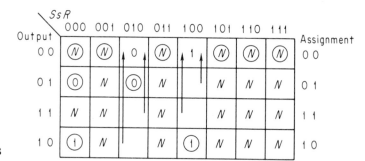

Assigned Flow Table

Figure 11.13

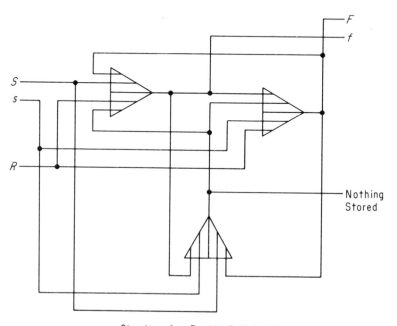

Circuitry for Double Rail Latch

Figure 11.14

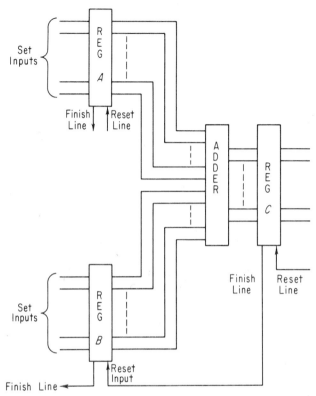

Functional Arrangement of Adder and Registers

Figure 11.15

taking two full binary numbers from two sets of latches and adding them together results in the sum which will be placed in a third set of latches (Figure 11.15). Binary number in Register A is added to binary number in Register B with sum appearing in Register C. The interesting point in the above diagram is the use of the finish line from Register C. This line will be up when every latch in Register C contains either a one or a zero. This finish line may be used to reset Register B, thereby clearing the adder outputs to nothing. When the number in Register C has been used, this register will then be reset.

Error Detecting

As computers grow larger, it becomes more important to detect the failure of a component. It has been suggested that the double rail method with its redundant signal, "11" may be used to detect errors. If error detecting is being designed into a machine, then the previous maps should be examined to determine what output signal will be generated when an error signal is present on the inputs. Let us first examine the double rail AND circuit. If both sets of input lines carry error signals "11", the output will also be an error signal. This propagation of an error is a desirable feature since error detecting circuitry placed at several points in the machine will inform the operator of the presence of an error. Unfortunately, an error on only one set of inputs will not always propagate an error signal. The double rail AND circuit will propagate a zero signal "01" when an error is present on one set of inputs while zero signal is present on the other set of inputs. This at first appears to be undesirable, but on second thought the circuit has actually connected an error. Since one set of input lines is a zero, "01", the output should be zero, "01" no matter what appears on the other set of input lines. If one input is an error signal and the other input a one "10," an error signal will be propagated as desired. Unfortunately, when an error signal is present on one input set and nothing "00" is present on the other set, a zero will be propagated. This situation and a similar one in the double rail OR circuit rule out most of the error detection ability of the double rail method.

Partial Asynchronous

To construct a machine of completely asynchronous circuitry will require about twice as much hardware as the synchronous method. This increase may be justified by the increase in overall operating speed of the resulting machine, but to double the hardware in a computer is a decision that has not been completely accepted. The more normal approach is to construct only parts of a machine in the asynchronous method and other sections in the synchronous mode. The asynchronous method is used in sections of the machine where an increase in hardware will result in a large increase in average speed. A parallel adder with its associate ripple carry would be such an example. It is possible to further economize by constructing only the carry circuit of double rail. The finish line in this case will produce an output when the carry has finished propagating. Such a circuit is shown in Figure 11.16.

Since a two-block delay is encountered in producing the finish line and a two-block delay is needed after the carry is complete to produce the sum, then the sum should be completed when the finish line goes up. Before the two numbers being added are gated to the adder, both carry lines should be down. To accomplish this, an AND is inserted in the "no carry" line from the first adder position. This gate should not be opened until the

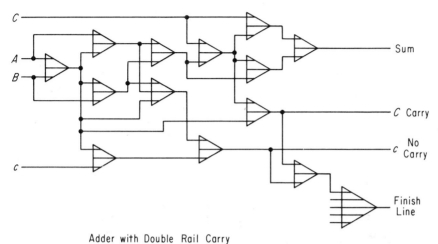

Adder with Double Rail Carry

Figure 11.16

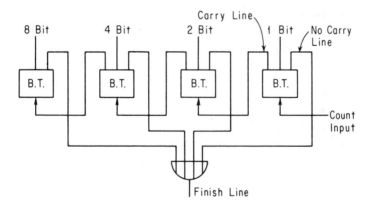

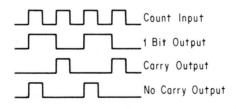

Asynchronous   Counter

Figure 11.17

second adder stage is ready to interact with the carry or no carry signal. If this gate is opened too soon, a false "no carry" signal may propagate and bring up the finish line. Even this small amount of double-unit circuitry will considerably increase the average speed of a parallel adder. As Burks, Goldstein and Von Neuman pointed out: a forty-bit binary adder will have an average carry of four-point six position. Some types of functional blocks lend themselves to this type of asynchronous approach. The binary counter illustrated in Figure 11.17 is an example. It is constructed of three binary triggers connected in series. The binary trigger produces, at no increase in components, an output that goes negative when an input is applied and the trigger is going to a one output. Since the second trigger only receives a plus-going pulse when the first trigger is going to a zero output state, then the first output line is actually the double rail complement of the signal going to the second trigger. This line then will tell us when the second trigger is not going to change. Furthermore, if the second trigger is not going to change, then no trigger further down the line will change. If these output lines, from all the triggers in the counter, are fed into a stroke function, then the output of this block will go positive only after all the triggers that are going to change have changed. An infinite number of ingenious circuits are possible by combining the best of synchronous theory with the best of asynchronous.

Reference

J. Sims and H. Gray, "Design Criteria for Autosynchronous Circuits", Eastern Joint Computer Conference, Dec. 1958.

APPENDICES

Decimal to binary conversion table

Decimal number	Binary number	Number of "1's" in binary number
0	0	0
1	1	1
2	10	1
3	11	2
4	100	1
5	101	2
6	110	2
7	111	3
8	1000	1
9	1001	2
10	1010	2
11	1011	3
12	1100	2
13	1101	3
14	1110	3
15	1111	4
16	10000	1
17	10001	2
18	10010	2
19	10011	3
20	10100	2
21	10101	3
22	10110	3
23	10111	4
24	11000	2
25	11001	3
26	11010	3
27	11011	4
28	11100	3
29	11101	4
30	11110	4
31	11111	5
32	100000	1
33	100001	2
34	100010	2
35	100011	3
36	100100	2

Decimal to binary conversion table

Decimal number	Binary number	Number of "1's" in binary number
37	100101	3
38	100110	3
39	100111	4
40	101000	2
41	101001	3
42	101010	3
43	101011	4
44	101100	3
45	101101	4
46	101110	4
47	101111	5
48	110000	2
49	110001	3
50	110010	3
51	110011	4
52	110100	3
53	110101	4
54	110110	4
55	110111	5
56	111000	3
57	111001	4
58	111010	4
59	111011	5
60	111100	4
61	111101	5
62	111110	5
63	111111	6
64	1000000	1
65	1000001	2
66	1000010	2
67	1000011	3
68	1000100	2
69	1000101	3
70	1000110	3
71	1000111	4
72	1001000	2
73	1001001	3
74	1001010	3
75	1001011	4
76	1001100	3
77	1001101	4

Decimal to binary conversion table

Decimal number	Binary number	Number of "1's" in binary number
78	1001110	4
79	1001111	5
80	1010000	2
81	1010001	3
82	1010010	3
83	1010011	4
84	1010100	3
85	1010101	4
86	1010110	4
87	1010111	5
88	1011000	3
89	1011001	4
90	1011010	4
91	1011011	5
92	1011100	4
93	1011101	5
94	1011110	5
95	1011111	6
96	1100000	2
97	1100001	3
98	1100010	3
99	1100011	4
100	1100100	3

Appendix 2

Decimal table grouped according to number of "1's" in binary representation: Table from 1 to 127

ONE "1"	THREE "1's"	FOUR "1's"
1	7	
2	11	15
4	13	23
8	14	27
16	19	29
32	21	30
64	22	39
	25	43
TWO "1's"	26	45
	28	46
3	35	51
5	37	53
6	38	54

TWO "1's"	THREE "1's"	FOUR "1's"
9	41	57
10	42	58
12	44	60
17	49	71
18	50	75
20	52	77
24	56	78
33	67	83
34	69	85
36	70	86
40	73	89
48	74	90
65	76	92
66	81	99
68	82	101
72	84	102
80	88	105
96	97	106
	98	108
	100	113
	104	114
	112	116
		120

FIVE "1's"	SIX "1's"	SEVEN "1's"
31	63	127
47	95	
55	111	
59	119	
61	123	
62	125	
79	126	
87		
91		
93		
94		
103		
107		
109		
110		
115		
117		
118		
121		
122		
124		

Appendix 3

TABLE of POWERS of 2

2^{+n}	n	2^{-n}
1	0	1
2	1	.5
4	2	.25
8	3	.125
16	4	.0625
32	5	.03125
64	6	.015625
128	7	.0078125
256	8	.00390625
512	9	.001953125
1024	10	.0009765625
2048	11	.00048828125
4096	12	.000244140625
8192	13	.0001220703125
16384	14	.00006103515625
32768	15	.000030517578125
65536	16	.0000152587890625
131072	17	.00000762939453125
262144	18	.000003814697265625
524288	19	.0000019073486328125
1048576	20	.00000095367431640625

Appendix 4

Switching Functions of Three Variables

The following list gives "$NAND$" implementations for each of the 254 non-trivial three variable functions. Under permutation of input variables and assuming complements of inputs are not available, the list of 254 functions reduces to 78 circuit configurations.

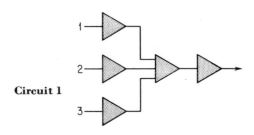

Circuit 1

The functions are listed by their decimal number representations derived by labeling the *"K"* map in the following manner.

$(A = 4, B = 2, C = 1)$

AB \ C	0	1
00	0	1
01	2	3
11	6	7
10	4	5

The functions are grouped by *"M"* numbers where *"M"* stands for the number of *"1's"* in the *"K"* map. The 78 circuits have inputs labeled 1, 2, 3 and the table of functions indicates how these inputs should be relabeled to correspond to the given *"K"* map.

With the exception of circuit number 49, all implementations have been proved minimum by Dr. Leo Hellerman of the IBM Corporation. Minimality in this case is defined by the following rules.

1. All *"NAND"* blocks are restricted to at most 3 inputs and any block may feed up to three other blocks.
2. The circuits are minimal first by total number of blocks and second by total number of inputs. Only one minimal solution is shown for each case.

Circuit 49 has been proved minimal for a *"NAND"* block count but not from a total input count. Furthermore, circuit 49 requires that one block drive four other blocks. Eight transistors would be required if the restriction of driving capability of three was enforced.

$$\text{``}M\text{''} = 1$$

Function number	Function	Inputs 1 2 3	Circuit number
1	0	A B C	1
2	1	A B C	2
3	2	A C B	2
4	3	A B C	3
5	4	B C A	2
6	5	B A C	3
7	6	C A B	3
8	7	A B C	4

"M" = 2

Function number	Function	Inputs 1 2 3	Circuit number
9	0, 1	A B	5
10	0, 2	A C	5
11	0, 3	B C A	8
12	0, 4	B C	5
13	0, 5	A C B	8
14	0, 6	A B C	8
15	0, 7	A B C	12
16	1, 2	B C A	9
17	1, 3	A C	6
18	1, 4	C A B	9
19	1, 5	B C	6
20	1, 6	B C A	13
21	1, 7	A C B	10
22	2, 3	A B	6
23	2, 4	A B C	9
24	2, 5	A B C	13
25	2, 6	C B	6
26	2, 7	A B C	10
27	3, 4	C A B	13
28	3, 5	C B A	11
29	3, 6	B A C	11
30	3, 7	B C	7
31	4, 5	B A	6
32	4, 6	C A	6
33	4, 7	B A C	10
34	5, 6	A B C	11
35	5, 7	A C	7
36	6, 7	A B	7

"M" = 3

Function number	Function	Inputs 1 2 3	Circuit number
37	0, 1, 2	C B A	14
38	0, 1, 3	A C B	15
39	0, 1, 4	A C B	14
40	0, 1, 5	B C A	15
41	0, 1, 6	A B C	20
42	0, 1, 7	A B C	21
43	0, 2, 3	A B C	15
44	0, 2, 4	A B C	14
45	0, 2, 5	C A B	20
46	0, 2, 6	C B A	15
47	0, 2, 7	A C B	21

48	0, 3, 4	B C A	20
49	0, 3, 5	C B A	26
50	0, 3, 6	B A C	26
51	0, 3, 7	B C A	24
52	0, 4, 5	B A C	15
53	0, 4, 6	C A B	15
54	0, 4, 7	C B A	21
55	0, 5, 6	A B C	26
56	0, 5, 7	A C B	24
57	0, 6, 7	A B C	24
58	1, 2, 3	B A C	16
59	1, 2, 4	A B C	27
60	1, 2, 5	C B A	22
61	1, 2, 6	B C A	22
62	1, 2, 7	B A C	28
63	1, 3, 4	C A B	22
64	1, 3, 5	C B A	17
65	1, 3, 6	C A B	23
66	1, 3, 7	C A B	18
67	1, 4, 5	A B C	16
68	1, 4, 6	A C B	22
69	1, 4, 7	A B C	28
70	1, 5, 6	B C A	23
71	1, 5, 7	C B A	18
72	1, 6, 7	A B C	25
73	2, 3, 4	B A C	22
74	2, 3, 5	B A C	23
75	2, 3, 6	B A C	17
76	2, 3, 7	B A C	18
77	2, 4, 5	A B C	22
78	2, 4, 6	A C B	16
79	2, 4, 7	B C A	28
80	2, 5, 6	B C A	23
81	2, 5, 7	A C B	25
82	2, 6, 7	B C A	18
83	3, 4, 5	A B C	23
84	3, 4, 6	A C B	23
85	3, 4, 7	C B A	25
86	3, 5, 6	A B C	29
87	3, 5, 7	A C B	19
88	3, 6, 7	A B C	19
89	4, 5, 6	A B C	17
90	4, 5, 7	A B C	18
91	4, 6, 7	A C B	18
92	5, 6, 7	B A C	19
93			

$$``M" = 4$$

Function number	Function	Inputs 1 2 3	Circuit number
93	0, 1, 2, 3	A	30
94	0, 1, 2, 4	A B C	32
95	0, 1, 2, 5	B C A	36
96	0, 1, 2, 6	C B A	36
97	0, 1, 2, 7	A B C	40
98	0, 1, 3, 4	A C B	36
99	0, 1, 3, 5	A B C	33
100	0, 1, 3, 6	A B C	41
101	0, 1, 3, 7	A B C	37
102	0, 1, 4, 5	B	30
103	0, 1, 4, 6	C A B	36
104	0, 1, 4, 7	B A C	40
105	0, 1, 5, 6	B A C	41
106	0, 1, 5, 7	B A C	37
107	0, 1, 6, 7	A B	46
108	0, 2, 3, 4	A B C	36
109	0, 2, 3, 5	A C B	41
110	0, 2, 3, 6	C A B	33
111	0, 2, 3, 7	A C B	37
112	0, 2, 4, 5	B A C	36
113	0, 2, 4, 6	C	30
114	0, 2, 4, 7	C B A	40
115	0, 2, 5, 6	C A B	41
116	0, 2, 5, 7	A C	46
117	0, 2, 6, 7	C A B	37
118	0, 3, 4, 5	B C A	41
119	0, 3, 4, 6	C B A	41
120	0, 3, 4, 7	B C	46
121	0, 3, 5, 6	A B C	48
122	0, 3, 5, 7	C B A	45
123	0, 3, 6, 7	B A C	45
124	0, 4, 5, 6	B C A	33
125	0, 4, 5, 7	B C A	37
126	0, 4, 6, 7	C B A	37
127	0, 5, 6, 7	A B C	45
128	1, 2, 3, 4	C A B	42
129	1, 2, 3, 5	B A C	38
130	1, 2, 3, 6	C A B	38
131	1, 2, 3, 7	B C A	34
132	1, 2, 4, 5	A B C	42
133	1, 2, 4, 6	B C A	42
134	1, 2, 4, 7	A B C	49
135	1, 2, 5, 6	B C	47

136	1, 2, 5, 7	C B A	44
137	1, 2, 6, 7	B C A	44
138	1, 3, 4, 5	A B C	38
139	1, 3, 4, 6	A C	47
140	1, 3, 4, 7	C A B	44
141	1, 3, 5, 6	C B A	43
142	1, 3, 5, 7	C	31
143	1, 3, 6, 7	C A B	39
144	1, 4, 5, 6	C B A	38
145	1, 4, 5, 7	C A B	34
146	1, 4, 6, 7	A C B	44
147	1, 5, 6, 7	C B A	39
148	2, 3, 4, 5	A B	47
149	2, 3, 4, 6	A C B	38
150	2, 3, 4, 7	B A C	44
151	2, 3, 5, 6	B A C	43
152	2, 3, 5, 7	B A C	39
153	2, 3, 6, 7	B	31
154	2, 4, 5, 6	B C A	38
155	2, 4, 5, 7	A B C	44
156	2, 4, 6, 7	A B C	34
157	2, 5, 6, 7	B C A	39
158	3, 4, 5, 6	A B C	43
159	3, 4, 5, 7	A B C	39
160	3, 4, 6, 7	A C B	39
161	3, 5, 6, 7	A B C	35
162	4, 5, 6, 7	A	31

$$"M" = 5$$

Function number	Function	Inputs 1 2 3	Circuit number
163	0, 1, 2, 3, 4	A B C	50
164	0, 1, 2, 3, 5	A B C	51
165	0, 1, 2, 3, 6	A C B	51
166	0, 1, 2, 3, 7	A B C	52
167	0, 1, 2, 4, 5	B A C	50
168	0, 1, 2, 4, 6	C B A	50
169	0, 1, 2, 4, 7	A B C	56
170	0, 1, 2, 5, 6	B A C	60
171	0, 1, 2, 5, 7	A C B	61
172	0, 1, 2, 6, 7	A B C	61
173	0, 1, 3, 4, 5	B C A	51
174	0, 1, 3, 4, 6	A B C	60
175	0, 1, 3, 4, 7	B C A	61
176	0, 1, 3, 5, 6	C B A	57
177	0, 1, 3, 5, 7	C B A	53

178	0, 1, 3, 6, 7	$A \ B \ C$	64
179	0, 1, 4, 5, 6	$B \ C \ A$	51
180	0, 1, 4, 5, 7	$B \ A \ C$	52
181	0, 1, 4, 6, 7	$B \ A \ C$	61
182	0, 1, 5, 6, 7	$B \ A \ C$	64
183	0, 2, 3, 4, 5	$A \ C \ B$	60
184	0, 2, 3, 4, 6	$C \ A \ B$	51
185	0, 2, 3, 4, 7	$C \ B \ A$	61
186	0, 2, 3, 5, 6	$B \ A \ C$	57
187	0, 2, 3, 5, 7	$A \ C \ B$	64
188	0, 2, 3, 6, 7	$B \ C \ A$	53
189	0, 2, 4, 5, 6	$C \ B \ A$	51
190	0, 2, 4, 5, 7	$C \ A \ B$	61
191	0, 2, 4, 6, 7	$C \ B \ A$	52
192	0, 2, 5, 6, 7	$C \ A \ B$	64
193	0, 3, 4, 5, 6	$A \ B \ C$	57
194	0, 3, 4, 5, 7	$B \ C \ A$	64
195	0, 3, 4, 6, 7	$C \ B \ A$	64
196	0, 3, 5, 6, 7	$A \ B \ C$	59
197	0, 4, 5, 6, 7	$A \ B \ C$	53
198	1, 2, 3, 4, 5	$C \ B \ A$	63
199	1, 2, 3, 4, 6	$B \ A \ C$	63
200	1, 2, 3, 4, 7	$B \ A \ C$	58
201	1, 2, 3, 5, 6	$B \ A \ C$	62
202	1, 2, 3, 5, 7	$C \ A \ B$	54
203	1, 2, 3, 6, 7	$B \ A \ C$	54
204	1, 2, 4, 5, 6	$A \ B \ C$	63
205	1, 2, 4, 5, 7	$A \ B \ C$	58
206	1, 2, 4, 6, 7	$B \ C \ A$	58
207	1, 2, 5, 6, 7	$B \ C \ A$	65
208	1, 3, 4, 5, 6	$A \ B \ C$	62
209	1, 3, 4, 5, 7	$C \ B \ A$	54
210	1, 3, 4, 6, 7	$C \ A \ B$	65
211	1, 3, 5, 6, 7	$C \ B \ A$	55
212	1, 4, 5, 6, 7	$A \ B \ C$	54
213	2, 3, 4, 5, 6	$A \ C \ B$	62
214	2, 3, 4, 5, 7	$A \ B \ C$	65
215	2, 3, 4, 6, 7	$B \ C \ A$	54
216	2, 3, 5, 6, 7	$B \ A \ C$	55
217	2, 4, 5, 6, 7	$A \ C \ B$	54
218	3, 4, 5, 6, 7	$A \ B \ C$	55

$$"M" = 6$$

Function number	Function	Inputs 1 2 3	Circuit number
219	0, 1, 2, 3, 4, 5	$A \ B$	66
220	0, 1, 2, 3, 4, 6	$A \ C$	66

221	0, 1, 2, 3, 4, 7	*C B A*	69
222	0, 1, 2, 3, 5, 6	*C B A*	70
223	0, 1, 2, 3, 5, 7	*A C*	67
224	0, 1, 2, 3, 6, 7	*A B*	67
225	0, 1, 2, 4, 5, 6	*B C*	66
226	0, 1, 2, 4, 5, 7	*A C B*	69
227	0, 1, 2, 4, 6, 7	*A B C*	69
228	0, 1, 2, 5, 6, 7	*B A C*	73
229	0, 1, 3, 4, 5, 6	*A C B*	70
230	0, 1, 3, 4, 5, 7	*B C*	67
231	0, 1, 3, 4, 6, 7	*A B C*	73
232	0, 1, 3, 5, 6, 7	*A B C*	71
233	0, 1, 4, 5, 6, 7	*B A*	67
234	0, 2, 3, 4, 5, 6	*A B C*	70
235	0, 2, 3, 4, 5, 7	*A C B*	73
236	0, 2, 3, 4, 6, 7	*C B*	67
237	0, 2, 3, 5, 6, 7	*A C B*	71
238	0, 2, 4, 5, 6, 7	*C A*	67
239	0, 3, 4, 5, 6, 7	*C B A*	71
240	1, 2, 3, 4, 5, 6	*A B C*	74
241	1, 2, 3, 4, 5, 7	*A B C*	72
242	1, 2, 3, 4, 6, 7	*A C B*	72
243	1, 2, 3, 5, 6, 7	*B C*	68
244	1, 2, 4, 5, 6, 7	*C B A*	72
245	1, 3, 4, 5, 6, 7	*A C*	68
246	2, 3, 4, 5, 6, 7	*A B*	68

$$"M" = 7$$

Function number	Function	Inputs 1 2 3	Circuit number
247	0, 1, 2, 3, 4, 5, 6	*A B C*	75
248	0, 1, 2, 3, 4, 5, 7	*A C B*	76
249	0, 1, 2, 3, 4, 6, 7	*A B C*	76
250	0, 1, 2, 3, 5, 6, 7	*C A B*	77
251	0, 1, 2, 4, 5, 6, 7	*B A C*	76
252	0, 1, 3, 4, 5, 6, 7	*A B C*	77
253	0, 2, 3, 4, 5, 6, 7	*A C B*	77
254	1, 2, 3, 4, 5, 6, 7	*A B C*	78

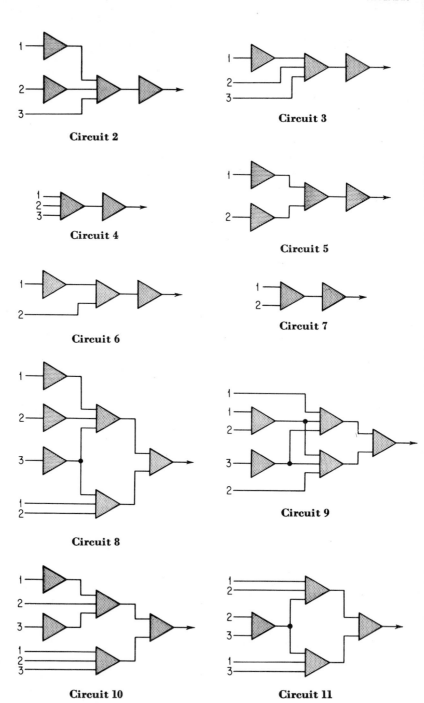

Circuit 2

Circuit 3

Circuit 4

Circuit 5

Circuit 6

Circuit 7

Circuit 8

Circuit 9

Circuit 10

Circuit 11

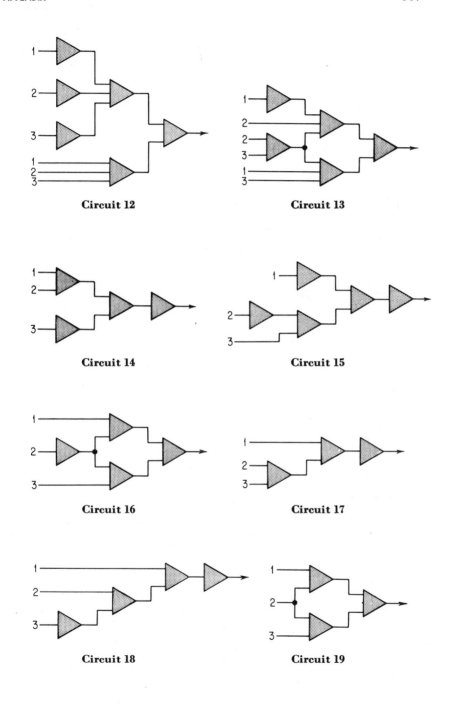

Circuit 12

Circuit 13

Circuit 14

Circuit 15

Circuit 16

Circuit 17

Circuit 18

Circuit 19

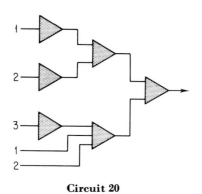

Circuit 20

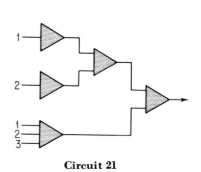

Circuit 21

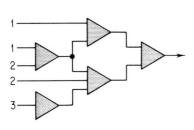

Circuit 22

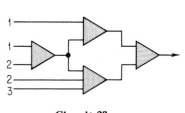

Circuit 23

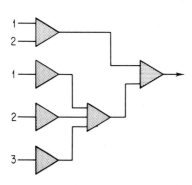

Circuit 24

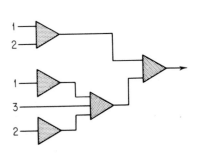

Circuit 25

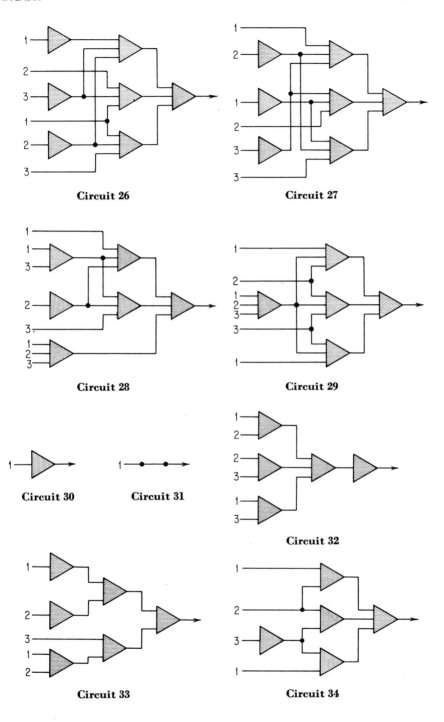

Circuit 26

Circuit 27

Circuit 28

Circuit 29

Circuit 30

Circuit 31

Circuit 32

Circuit 33

Circuit 34

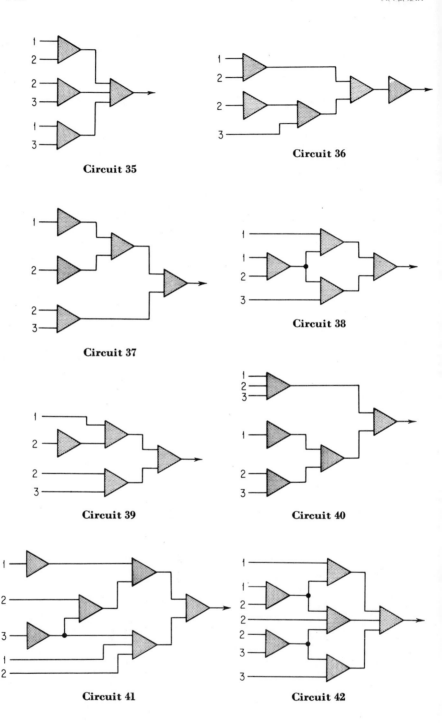

Circuit 35

Circuit 36

Circuit 37

Circuit 38

Circuit 39

Circuit 40

Circuit 41

Circuit 42

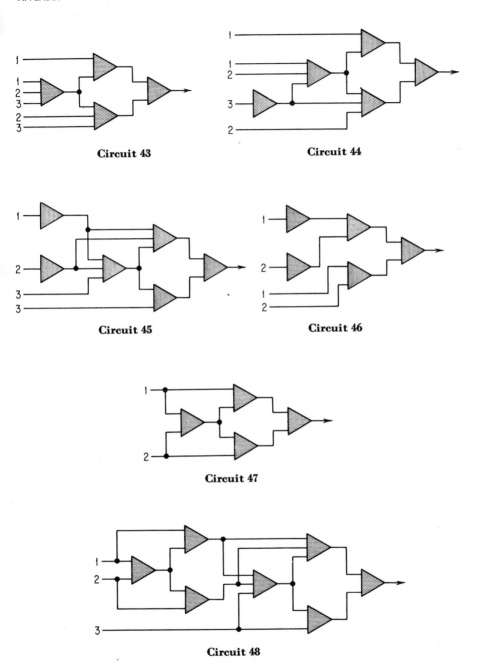

Circuit 43

Circuit 44

Circuit 45

Circuit 46

Circuit 47

Circuit 48

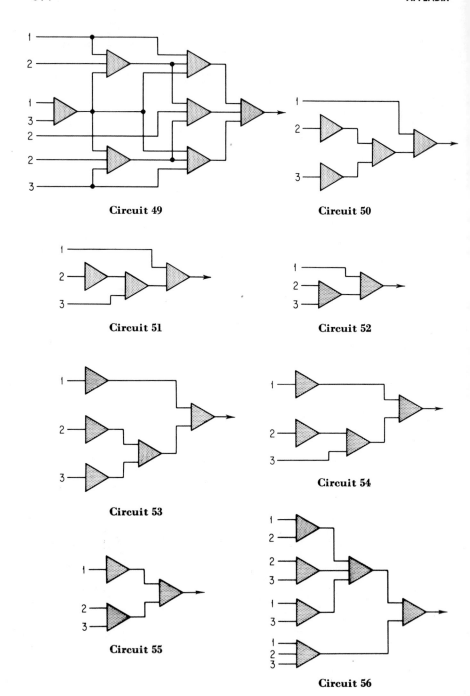

Circuit 49

Circuit 50

Circuit 51

Circuit 52

Circuit 53

Circuit 54

Circuit 55

Circuit 56

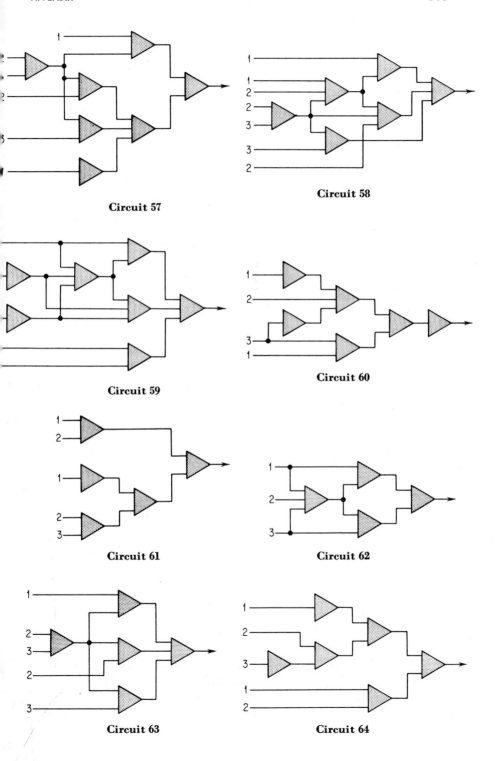

Circuit 57

Circuit 58

Circuit 59

Circuit 60

Circuit 61

Circuit 62

Circuit 63

Circuit 64

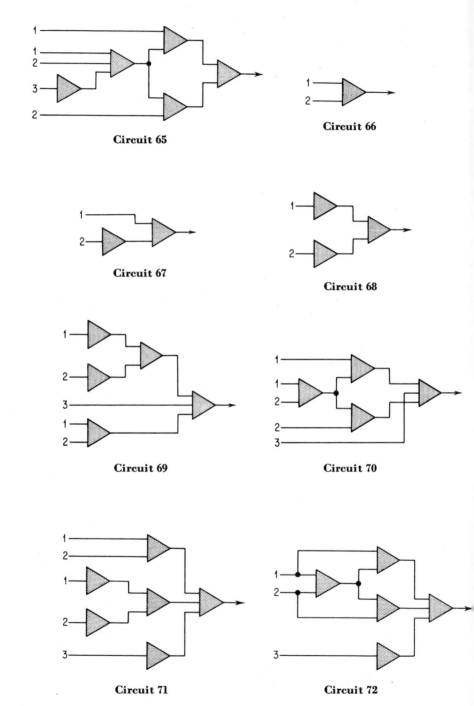

Circuit 65

Circuit 66

Circuit 67

Circuit 68

Circuit 69

Circuit 70

Circuit 71

Circuit 72

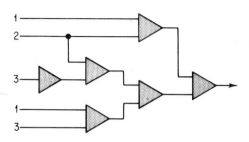

Circuit 73

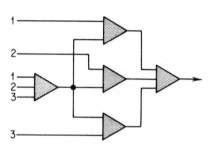

Circuit 74

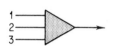

Circuit 75

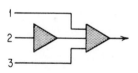

Circuit 76

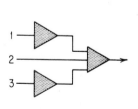

Circuit 77

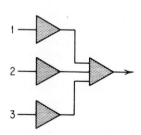

Circuit 78

INDEX